Introduction

A single volume on the history of unbuilt American bomber aircraft would, if it tried to be even remotely comprehensive, be vast and unwieldy. So instead, here is a modest attempt at telling a brief history of one corner of that topic: supersonic bombers. Even by narrowing the focus to this relatively small subset of bomber aircraft, the topic is large enough that several volumes are planned.

The definition of a 'bomber' is itself sometimes a little vague. For the purposes of this work, a 'bomber' is a flying vehicle designed primarily to deliver bombs or missiles to stationary ground targets. The aircraft need not be manned, but it should be designed to be reusable. These limits exclude aircraft that would normally be considered 'ground-attack' aircraft that go after tanks and other mobile surface targets, and they exclude cruise missiles, ICBMs and other single-use surface attack vehicles. A history of those would be interesting, of course, but is beyond the current scope.

This first volume covers the evolution and derivatives of aircraft concepts that progressed far enough in the political process to be granted 'B-for-bomber' numbers. Most of these aircraft were actually built, and most of those entered service; as there are any number of good books out there that describe these aircraft in detail, the actual flown aircraft will not be covered in great depth here. The designs that led to these well-known aircraft, and proposals derived from them… those will be covered as best as can be with available resources.

The second volume will cover designs that did not get as far politically or technically, but sometimes went much further imaginatively: hypersonic designs, VTOL concepts, nuclear powered designs.

Scott Lowther
aerospaceprojectsreview.com

Contents

Author/illustrator: Scott Lowther
Cover art: Rob Parthoens
Publisher: Steve O'Hara
Published by:
Mortons Media Group Ltd,
Media Centre, Morton Way, Horncastle,
Lincolnshire LN9 6JR, Tel. 01507 529529

Typeset by: Druck Media Pvt. Ltd.
Printed by: William Gibbons and Sons, Wolverhampton

Acknowledgements: This book could not have been completed without the assistance of a number of authors and historians, including but not limited to: Dennis Jenkins, Tony Landis, Tony Buttler, Tommy Thomason and Phillip Moore. Their assistance and contributions are greatly appreciated.

ISBN: 978-1-911703-03-7

1 CHAPTER Convair B-58

The Convair B-58 was the first American bomber aircraft designed to fly supersonically for a substantial portion of its mission. Being the first of its kind, its development was long and unusual, with many concepts and diversions that look strange to modern eyes. It began life when a supersonic bomber was far beyond the state of the art, so numerous unconventional tricks were felt needed in order to make it work.

Near the end of the Second World War, Consolidated Vultee began studying a ramjet powered interceptor designated the XP-92. As the war in Europe ended, American military and civilian engineers and scientists began to sift through the aeronautical leavings of the Third Reich, often with experts poking through German factories while fighting continued to rage nearby. Knowledge gleaned from studying captured records, wind tunnel models and personnel indicated that swept and delta wings showed great promise for supersonic flight.

As initially designed, the XP-92 was to be modestly supersonic with rocket boosters and a single large ramjet engine, supported by swept wings. But the swept wings soon gave way to delta wings, showing great potential for high speed performance and solid structural design without the need for additional stabilizers. The XP-92 was wind tunnel tested in 1946 and a mockup was inspected in early 1947, with high hopes that a production contract would follow.

The aircraft was seemingly simple in layout… a fat cylindrical fuselage composed largely of the single ramjet engine (the cockpit being situated within the fixed inlet spike) with two 60° swept delta wings and one large delta vertical stabilizer. The wings were aerodynamically simple with full-span elevons and an all-moving vertical tail. This simplicity was appealing at the time, but in the course of development to an operational aircraft it would transition to some considerable complexity.

The ramjet and the associated booster rockets needed to get the aircraft up to speed were competing against early turbojets. While the ramjet's performance looked good compared to 1945-vintage turbojets, by 1948 turbojets had greatly improved, with much further improvement foreseen. The ramjet would, at best, work well for a point defence interceptor, but the USAF was looking for more wide-ranging fighters. Additionally, the ramjet engine, while theoretically simple compared to the turbojet, was presenting some difficulty to develop. So in August of 1948 the XP-92 programme was terminated.

The idea of the delta wings did not die however; a turbojet powered derivative of the XP-92, the XF-92A, flew in September of 1948. This used essentially the same wings and tail as the XP-92, mated to a slimmer fuselage with a nose inlet feeding a turbojet located internally and to the rear, with a conventional raised cockpit up front. This, the first true delta winged manned aircraft to fly under its own power, was purely a test aircraft despite the F-designation, and was only capable of breaking the sound barrier in a dive. Still, it demonstrated that a delta winged aircraft would be capable of well-controlled powered flight, and supersonic flight at that.

Even as they were working on the XP-92, Consolidated Vultee's designers were also studying the concept of a supersonic bomber of somewhat similar configuration. The vast GEBO ('Generalized Bomber') study project at Consolidated Vultee began in 1946 and resulted in reportedly 10,000 configurations studied for strategic bombers.

The final reports for GEBO were completed in 1949, though these largely remain unavailable. A number of different designs were examined over the next two years or so, but one concept that was looked at in some depth was a supersonic jet bomber equipped with a large bomb/fuel pod carried aloft by a B-36 or B-36 derivative. At that time this made sense; turbojets of the day could stuff an aircraft past the sound barrier, but those engines would burn through fuel incredibly quickly. Jet aircraft had woefully short ranges and supersonic flight only made the problem far worse. But if a large, slow, propeller-driven aircraft carried the smaller supersonic bomber most of the way to the target (or at least across an ocean), it could then release the bomber to fly to the target under its own power at high speed.

In 1948 Consolidated Vultee – now Convair – produced a design that was proposed both to the US Air Force and to the US Navy. More information is available on the Navy variant, proposed in response to BuAer Outline Specification 115 (OS-115), released in late August 1948. However, the Air Force and Navy variants are, from available information, virtually

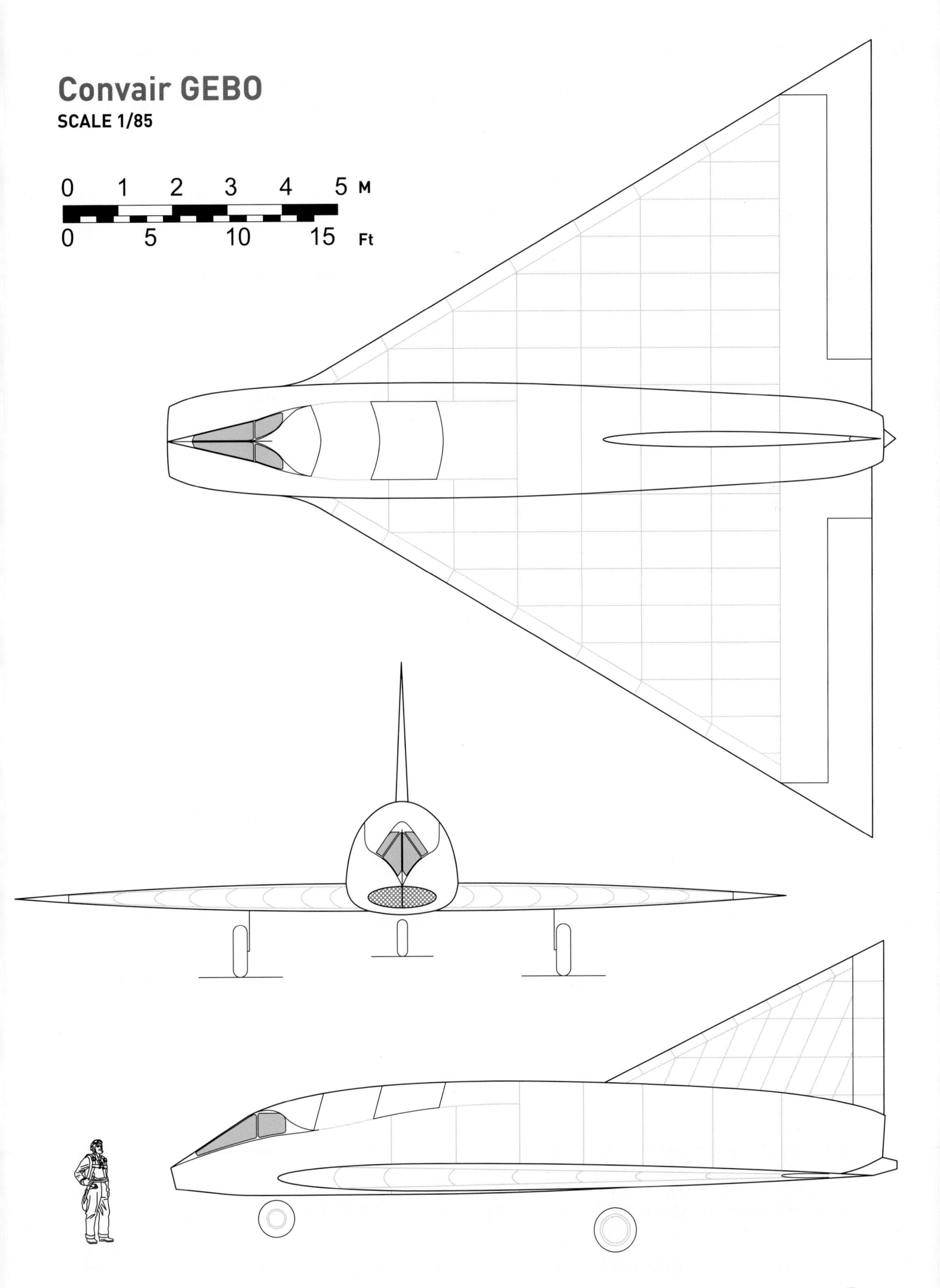
Convair GEBO
SCALE 1/85
0 1 2 3 4 5 M
0 5 10 15 Ft

identical apart from means of launch. OS-115 called for a technologically aggressive aircraft capable of reaching at least Mach 1.2 during the cruise to the target, which was to be at no less than 40,000ft and no less than 1,700 nautical miles from the launch point. The aircraft was to weigh no more than 100,000lb and carry a 10,000lb 'special' bomb. In this context, 'special' refers to atomic weaponry; 10,000lb was a standard weight target for atomic bombs based on the Fat Man-type of implosion bomb. An aircraft as complex as this design would be wasted dropping anything less 'special' than a few dozen kilotons of canned sunshine.

The bomber was a two-component aircraft… a manned bomber with two crew, a single afterburner-equipped turbojet and 3,125lb of fuel and an expendable pod containing three additional turbojets, 5,208lb of fuel, bomb directing radar and the atomic bomb itself. The bomb would be dropped from a bay in the middle of the pod, using radar in the nose of the pod for bomb-aiming. After the bomb was dropped, the pod itself would be jettisoned, left to simply tumble unguided and unpowered from the sky. The pod had no control surfaces nor thrust vectoring, so it could not have been used as a stand-off weapon.

The manned component was clearly a relative of the XP-92, featuring very similar wings and vertical tail (though that had a separate rudder, rather than being all-moving). The fuselage was quite a bit different, though. Rather than being a fat cylinder, it was somewhat squashed with a roughly triangular cross-section. The turbojet in the tail of the aircraft was fed through a nose inlet that bifurcated around the tandem two-seat cockpit. Aerodynamics was justified by supersonic wind tunnel testing and actual flight testing of the XF-92A. The pod's three turbojets were in a triangular cluster in the tail, each fed from a separate inlet. The rest of the pod was a straightforward body of rotation with a flattened top that mated to the flat bottom of the bomber aircraft.

The Navy and Air Force versions were more or less identical in appearance, but not in operation. The Navy version would be launched directly from the deck of an aircraft carrier, flying the entire mission under its own power. In this case, the carrier was expected to be the CVA 'USS *United States*' class supercarrier. To aid in launch from the deck of a carrier the pod would be fitted with both jettisonable landing gear and RATO bottles. The landing gear had fairly long legs and a nose-down attitude; presumably

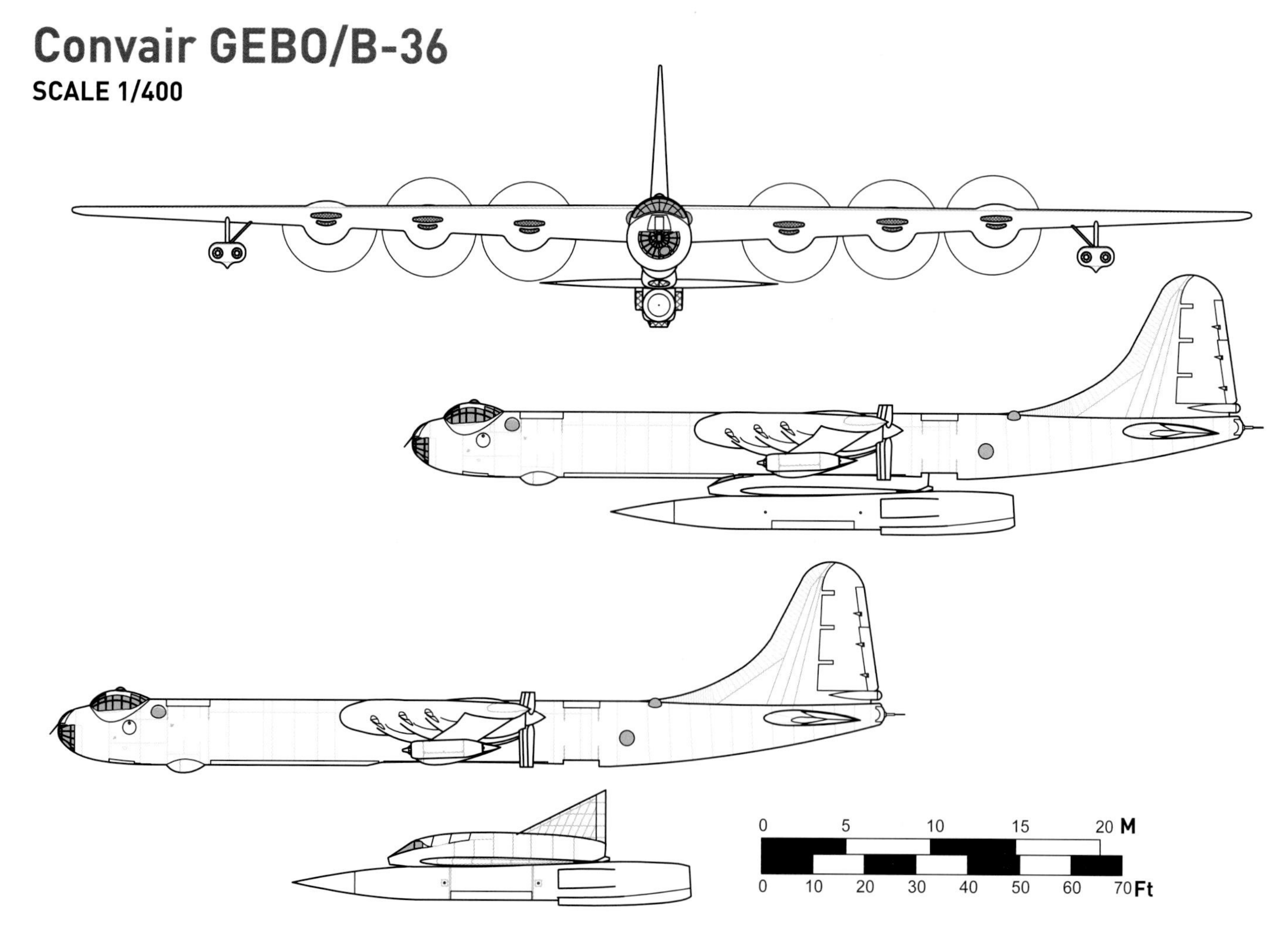

this helped in keeping the rocket exhaust from tearing up the carrier's deck.

The Air Force version would be carried underneath a B-36. This would allow the bomber to get closer to the enemy and launch from high altitude; less fuel would be burned just getting to cruising altitude and the mission would have a much greater radius. As with the Navy version, the pod did not have retractable landing gear; unlike the Navy version, it was not fitted with jettisonable gear either since it would take off attached to the bomb bay of a B-36. Once underway the Navy and Air Force aircraft would perform much the same mission. The B-36 could carry the supersonic bomber 2,000 miles from a base; from the B-36 launch point, the bomber would fly 2,000 miles to the target and fly 4,000 miles back to base.

The composite bomber, using the pod's three turbojets as well as the manned component's one turbojet, would cruise at the then-impressive speed of Mach 1.3 (with a maximum speed before release of the pod of Mach 1.6); but after separation, the single engined manned component would only be able to cruise at Mach 0.9 at 50,000ft altitude. The bomber had no defensive systems because in 1948 an aircraft flying at one and a half times the speed of sound seemed like it would be too fast to intercept. There were no surface-to-air missiles of any consequence, and the jet interceptors of the day were quite incapable of reaching that speed. That, of course, was the entire point of the exercise: supersonic flight made a bomber invulnerable to Soviet air defences.

The composite aircraft could not land with the pod still attached. This would make normal training flights amazingly expensive, so Convair proposed a special trainer variant that did away with the pod's radar, warhead and much of the fuel in favour of a retractable tricycle landing gear. This would allow the composite aircraft to land, though obviously the landing characteristics would be notably different from those of the return component alone. Controls for the aircraft should have been simple as there were only three control surfaces, two elevons and one rudder.

Douglas Model 1186A

Competing against the unusual Convair GEBO design for the role of supersonic bomber based on the USS

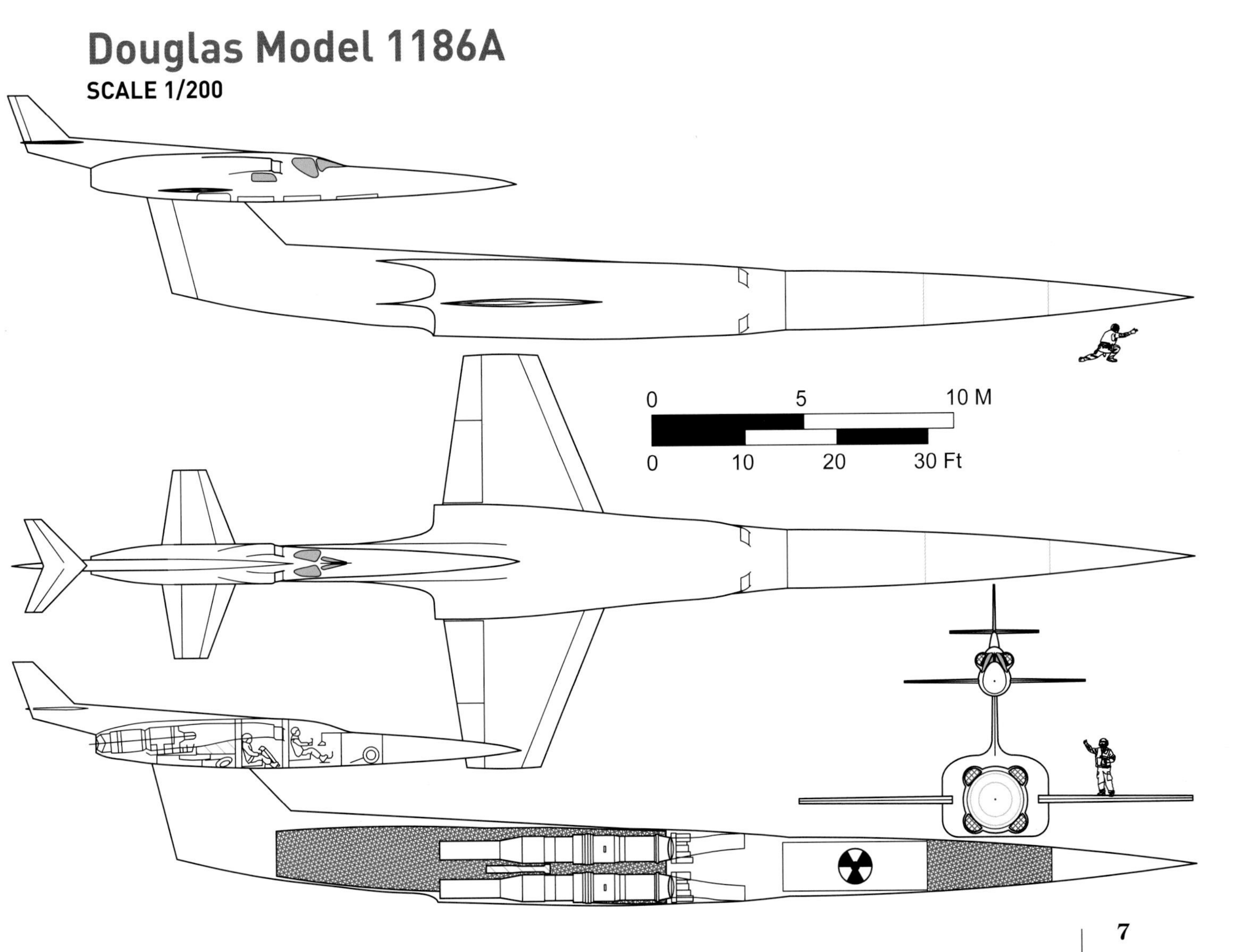

United States was the even more unconventional Douglas Model 1186. A long series of designs made up Model 1186, but they shared the same basic concept: a small manned aircraft carried well above a much larger unmanned carrier aircraft. All of the designs look quite bizarre, almost more science fiction (of the Flash Gordon variety) than aeronautical engineering; but like the Convair concept, they were an engineer's way of attaining performance goals with jet engines that were still basically in their infancy.

The Model 1186 was a product of the Santa Monica division of Douglas. The El Segundo division produced their own take on the same basic idea with the Model 594. The general 'small manned aircraft atop a large expendable aircraft' concept was shared, but where the Model 594 included either a somewhat generic looking 'supersonic fighter' for the manned aircraft or one which took inspiration from the Douglas F4D Skyray, the Model 1186 used the Douglas X-3 Stiletto as its basis.

When the Model 1186 was submitted in October of 1948, the X-3 was not yet even properly designed. The goal of the X-3, which first flew in 1952, was to achieve 2,000mph using a narrow pointed configuration that lived up to its nickname. But while the aerodynamics of the Stiletto seemed tailor-made for incredible speed, the reality, made all too real by underperforming turbojet engines, was that the aircraft could not shove itself past the speed of sound.

But in 1948, this disappointing result was not yet known. So the Stiletto configuration (not yet the X-3, but the MX-656) was selected as the manned aircraft. Unlike the Convair design, which closely mated a fuel/bomb pod directly to the aircraft which had the bulk of the wing area of the composite aircraft, the Douglas Model 1186A mounted the manned aircraft well above a much larger expendable aircraft with much larger wings. The expendable portion was more than a pod, being in fact an aircraft in its own right, several times larger and much heavier than the manned component.

Most of the Model 1186 designs, much like the Model 594, sat the manned component atop a pylon well above the expendable aircraft. The Model 1186A differed from its siblings in that the pylon in this case was the expendable aircraft's vertical stabilizer. The expendable portion was configured much like the Stiletto as well, only more so, with a very long, thin and pointed nose. The wings of both stages were short, unswept, low aspect ratio razor blades, setting the stage for the successfully supersonic Lockheed F-104 Starfighter which would arrive some years later.

With the manned aircraft atop the vertical fin, its wings served as the horizontal stabilizers of the composite aircraft until separation. Which raises an obvious issue: without those stabilizers, what would happen to the unmanned component after separation? Without stabilizers it seems likely that it would tumble. Details on the nuclear weapon and its employment are vague, but the diagrams refer to it being contained within a 'bomb bay' rather than a 'compartment' or similar descriptor. This suggests that the composite aircraft would actually drop the bomb, as Convair originally planned for its vehicle. After dropping the bomb, if the expendable component tumbled out of control after separation it would hardly matter so long as the manned component had successfully separated. The expendable component may have been intended to break apart, the nose separating from the rest to dart in a controlled and predictable path towards the ground.

The expendable component had four large turbojets, the manned aircraft only one. It would carry a crew of two. It was expected to use catapults to take off from the aircraft carrier deck, using JATO assist and droppable dollies rather than retractable landing gear. Training flights seem likely to have been expensive – with hair-raising landings. Most of the cruise to and from the target would be at Mach 0.85, with a Mach 2.0 dash on the bombing run.

GEBO II

The GEBO studies ended and were promptly followed by GEBO II studies which focused on the composite aircraft concept. As with GEBO, GEBO II resulted in a wide array of designs ranging from minor mathematical abstractions to concepts with considerable amounts of engineering design work. One such design, originating from late 1949 but finished in February of 1951 and reported on in June of 1951, is shown here. This is recognizable as a mid point between the earlier GEBO/Class VA design and the eventual B-58. As with the earlier concept, it was composed of a manned return aircraft and a turbojet-equipped expendable fuel/bomb pod, all carried to altitude by a conventional bomber. The design was refined considerably from the earlier version; the fuselage is much finer and the delta wings have given way to slimmer swept-back wings of the 'arrow' variety.

There was a reversal in the number of jet engines. The composite aircraft still had four, but they were located differently. The fuel/bomb pod had only a single jet engine (used to counteract the drag of the pod) while the manned aircraft itself was equipped with three turbojets, one in the tail and two in individual – and seemingly very large – underwing pods.

Unlike the podded engines of the B-58, the two podded engines in this design were sacrificial: after turning tail to flee the now rather more radioactive enemy territory, the bomber would drop the podded engines and continue home at slower speed with the single remaining engine. Consequently, a single flight

Convair GEBO II Arrow wing configuration

SCALE 1/144

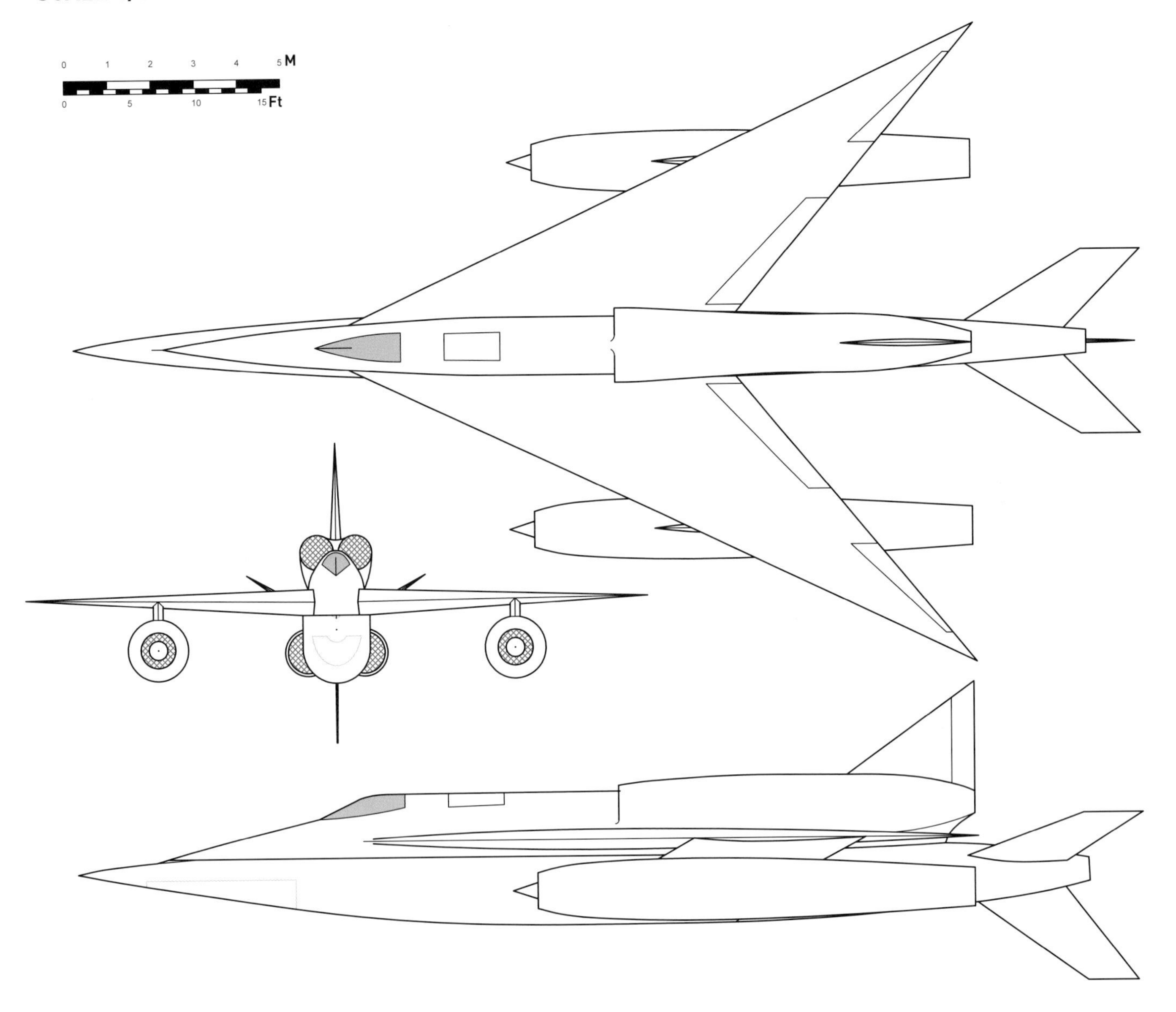

of this aircraft would still expend a large amount of costly hardware… the pod and everything in it as well as two of the engines originally attached to the manned aircraft. But as this aircraft was intended to carry nuclear weapons, the probability was that it would only need to fly a single operational mission. After that mission was done, the crew could rest easy and watch the colourful and only somewhat horrifyingly radioactive sunsets.

The bomb/fuel pod was substantially larger than the fuselage of the aircraft, and contained not only the turbojet, bomb (weighing 6,000lb) and fuel, but also radar. As originally envisioned it would simply drop ballistically as a free-fall bomb after release, using the onboard bomb aiming equipment to improve accuracy. But it was soon decided that once separated from the aircraft it would continue on under power for a short distance as a standoff weapon, continuing to use the turbojet in the tail. For control it had a trio of tail fins; the ventral one could fold to the side to provide ground clearance for takeoff. Presumably at least part of the explanation for the drop from 10,000lb to 6,000lb for the 'special' warhead was, since the bomb was not to be dropped but to remain within the pod, fins, outer casing, radar fusing and the like would have been removed.

This design was considerably sleeker than the earlier concept, being accurately described as "pointy". The flat underside of the aircraft mated flush with the flat topside of the pod, creating a fairly low drag body. The vertical stabilizer projecting above the rear fuselage of the aircraft was substantially smaller than the prior design, due to the bigger moment arm of the longer fuselage. The manned aircraft's internal turbojet was fed from two inlets located to each side of the upper fuselage; pressure recovery for these inlets may have been a concern, especially at high angles of attack such as during landing.

For the carrier aircraft, the GEBO II design shown here would use not the B-36 but the B-36G, later redesignated the B-60. The B-60 added swept wings to the B-36 and removed the piston engines, replacing them with four individually podded turboprops (see *Boeing B-47 Stratojet & B-52 Stratofortress: Origins and Evolution* for more on the B-60). The GEBO II bomber would take off equipped with eight engines but return with only one, having separated from four of them and thrown away three more. Where GEBO reportedly analyzed 10,000 configurations, GEBO II upped that number to 100,000.

Following the GEBO II studies, Convair refined its work. The updated Convair design, first shown to the USAF in late January of 1951, was generally similar to the earlier studies: a relatively small aircraft with highly swept delta wings, an underslung bomb/fuel pod larger than the aircraft's fuselage, carried to altitude and range underneath a swept-wing turboprop-powered B-60. The Air Force assigned this new configuration the MX-1626 programme designator in mid-February 1951. The MX-1626 was

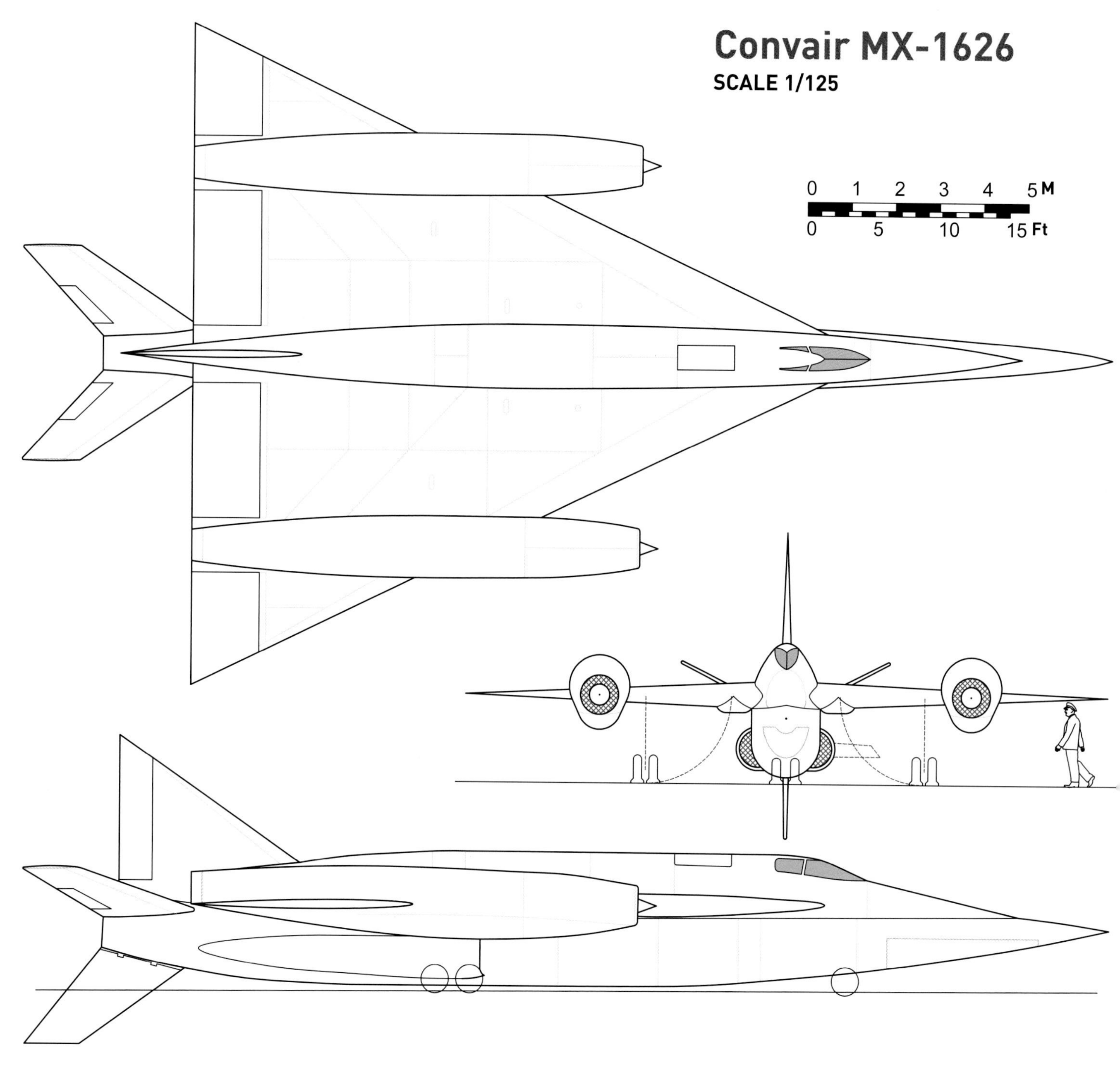

intended from the outset to be configurable as either a bomber or a recon platform.

It would not have been simply dropped from the B-60's bomb bay; instead a trapeze system would deploy the supersonic bomber well below the carrier aircraft prior to release. This would have placed the bomber outside of the turbulent airflow that was closely associated with the underside of the B-60, a lesson learned during the development of the McDonnell XF-85 Goblin parasite fighter. Unlike the Goblin, inflight recovery of the MX-1626 does not seem to have been contemplated, nor does it seem likely to have been a feasible – not to mention sensible – proposition.

The pod contained one turbojet, the fuel for the outbound leg and either the nuclear weapon or reconnaissance equipment, along with navigation radar in the nose. The pod also had three tail fins for stabilization; the lower fin could fold to provide ground clearance while stowed within the carrier aircraft's modified bomb bay. For reconnaissance variants, the data recorded during the flight would be stored within the manned aircraft on tape and/or film; the recon equipment itself, such as cameras, would be expended. The nose of the pod had an empty space that would be used as a passageway for the nosegear… the gear retracting into the nose of the aircraft, with a separate set of doors on the lower surface of the pod. The composite aircraft would have little ground clearance, but the manned aircraft alone would have a tall stance.

The manned aircraft had two turbojet engines mounted roughly at mid-span in long nacelles, the nacelles buried within the wing rather than located above or below. This would have complicated maintenance and increased the weight of the spars that would have to encircle the engines, but the overall drag would have been somewhat reduced compared to a design with engines suspended from pylons. Mounting the engines that far out put them outside of the carrier aircraft's bomb bay, allowing them to operate cleanly while the MX-1626 was still retracted into the carrier.

Perhaps oddly, the pod was meant to fall ballistically after separation from the aircraft; it does not seem that it was intended to use its own turbojet to increase delivery range. As with the previous supersonic bomber configurations, the upper surface of the pod was flat, mating to a flat undersurface of the aircraft fuselage (which had a distinctly triangular cross-section). This would reduce drag while the pod was attached to the aircraft: while the frontal area was greater than if the pod and the aircraft fuselage were discrete, separate structures, the turbulent interference between two closely coupled cylinders would have created far more drag.

The wings themselves were 65° delta wings with a simple symmetrical airfoil, similar to the first supersonic bomber configuration. The aircraft did not have the area ruling that would give the F-106 its distinctive 'wasp waist', as the area ruling concept for supersonic drag reduction was being tested at that time, but was not yet well characterised. The overall configuration of the MX-1626 was quite reminiscent of the later Lockheed A-12, though substantially less refined and elegant. It was an interesting case of convergent evolution in action. Considerable effort and expense went into testing the MX-1626 configuration, using not only Air Force wind tunnels but NACA and Navy tunnels as well. Further, metal models of the configuration were built and launched skywards by solid-propellant sounding rockets to test stability at supersonic speeds.

The MX-1626 was capable of launching itself from a runway without the use of a carrier aircraft. This would come with a substantial performance penalty, greatly reducing range. The composite aircraft would be fitted with jettisonable tricycle landing gear which would fall away immediately after liftoff, saving considerable weight. The landing gear was of distressingly low stance, giving almost no ground clearance; it would have been vital that the runways be kept in good working order as the smallest bump could have led to catastrophe. Whether self-launched or dropped from a carrier plane, the MX-1626 was incapable of landing with the belly pod still attached. Once airborne, the aircraft would need to expend the pod, destroying the expensive equipment on board.

And for all the effort, the performance of the MX-1626 was surprisingly modest, with a maximum speed of only Mach 1.5. That may have been respectable for 1951, but within relatively short order it would seem positively lacklustre. This was something of the end of an era in conceptual aircraft design. Up until this point 'staged' aircraft such as this, carried to distance by a larger, slower aircraft, were seen as the only way to achieve certain missions. But in the early 1950s air-to-air refuelling technology and techniques improved by leaps and bounds, and soon it was clear that it made far more sense to achieve great range via in-flight tanking. But staged aircraft were not *quite* done.

In December 1951 the design was refined in important ways. It was no longer to be a parasite aircraft; advances in in-flight refuelling meant that the B-36G/B-60 would change from a carrier aircraft to an aerial tanker. Additionally, the turbojet in the pod was deleted as unnecessary, considerably simplifying the design while lowering weight and cost of the expended components. The aircraft now had only two turbojet engines, none expendable. A third crew member was added for the first time to operate newly added defensive systems.

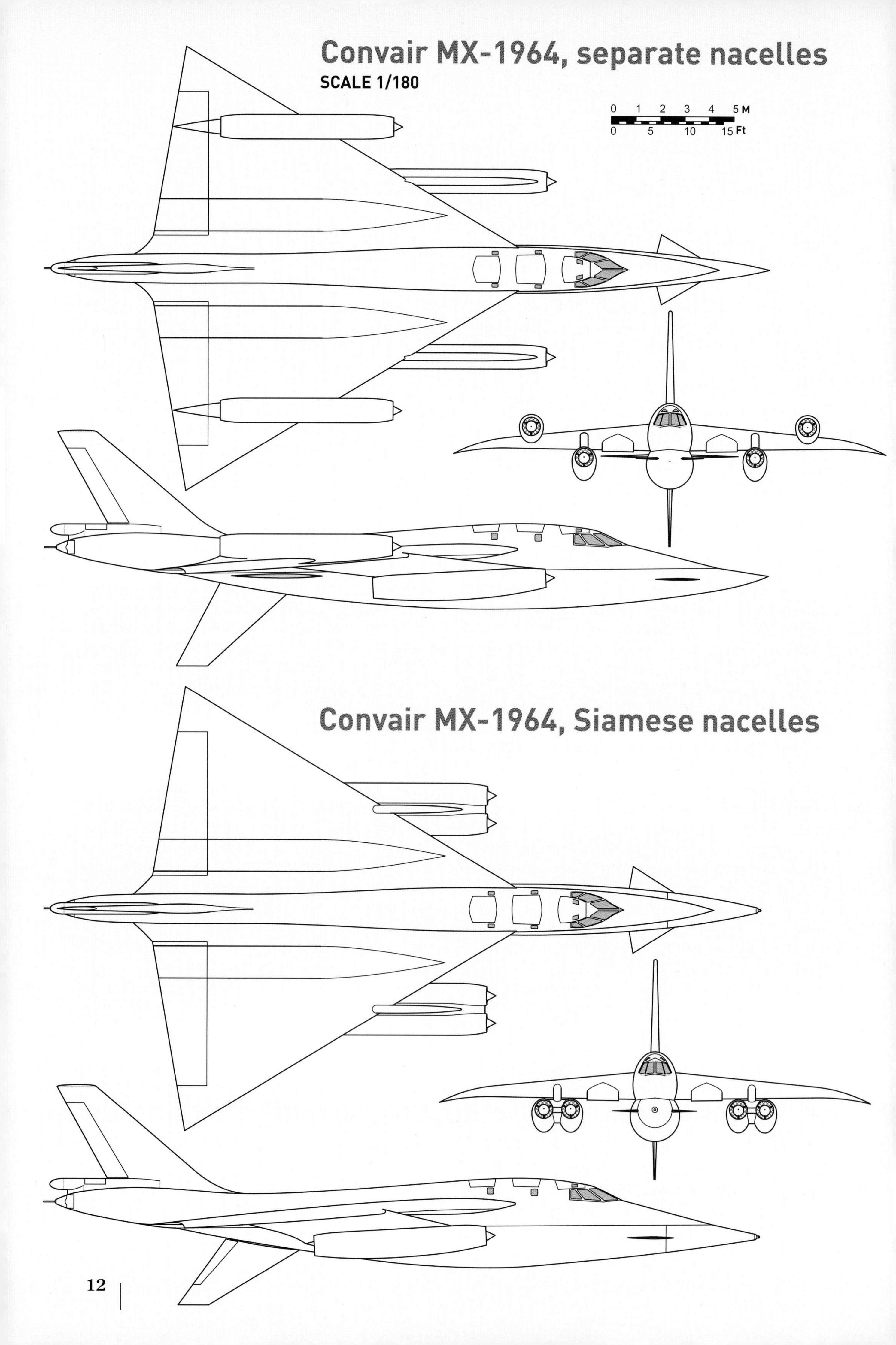
Convair MX-1964, separate nacelles
SCALE 1/180
0 1 2 3 4 5 M
0 5 10 15 Ft
Convair MX-1964, Siamese nacelles

In June to August 1952 a new configuration was produced to fulfill the Air Force's operational requirement, becoming designated MX-1964. The turbojets were lowered from mid-wing to underslung pylons, and were increased to four in number with two engines side-by-side in a 'Siamese' nacelle under each wing. The aircraft was generally increased in size and weight (gross weight was now 150,000lb) compared to the MX-1626, with wing sweep reduced slightly from 65° to 60° to improve altitude and range performance. Area ruling was fully incorporated, based on thousands of hours of wind tunnel and flight model testing, resulting in a coefficient of drag at supersonic speeds approximately half that of the MX-1626. The MX-1964 appears elegant in its refined aerodynamics – at last having transitioned from a somewhat brutalist dart into something beautiful.

The MX-1964 retained the same integral pod concept as the MX-1626. There was a noticeable change though: the pod had retractable nose gear, while directly above it, the aircraft too had its own nose gear, stowed within the forward fuselage of the aircraft. Directly ahead of the pod's nose gear was the main ground tracking and bomb aiming radar system; the aircraft itself had no radar, as dropping the pod meant that its job was done and the only task left to it was to get the hell out of Dodge and to a safe landing site. The pod had a large ventral fin that had to fold to the side while the aircraft was on the ground; when deployed, it was a good fraction of the size of the aircraft's vertical stabilizer.

As the aircraft was improved, so was the payload. The kiloton-yield bomb that the GEBO-era bombers would have employed was now to be replaced with a megaton-yield thermonuclear H-bomb. This meant not only heavier devices, but devices that needed to be gotten away from as soon as possible after release. The detonation of a megaton bomb posed a dire threat to even a high altitude bomber.

The aircraft impressed the Air Force enough that in December of 1952 it was designated the B-58.

As Convair continued to develop the delta wing, the geometry would become more complex. Early delta wing designs back to those of Alexander Lippisch in wartime Germany were thick and symmetrical: the contour of the upper surface was a mirror image of the contour of the lower surface. This worked well enough for low speeds, but testing at higher and higher airspeeds showed that this was not an optimal design for supersonic flight. Convair designs such as the XF-92A, the GEBO/GEBO II and MX-1626 all used symmetrical airfoils... thinner by far than the Lippisch wings, but still robust and draggy. But the late 1940s and early 1950s was an era of great advances in transonic and supersonic aerodynamics. For example, area ruling not only greatly reduced supersonic drag it also created elegant aircraft configurations that would have previously been only artistic interpretations. Similar advances were made in the aerodynamics of individual components such as wings.

The 'mean camber line' is a theoretical line running from the leading edge of a wing cross-section to the trailing edge, following a curve defined as the midpoint between the top and bottom surfaces. Thus for a symmetrical airfoil, the mean camber line would be perfectly straight. A post-war development was the idea of the 'conical camber' that produced a leading-edge suction at high speed, reducing drag while not adversely affecting lift. Studied in depth at the NACA-Ames Aeronautical Laboratory at Moffet Field, California, Convair designers soon adopted the concept on several of their ongoing projects.

The YF-102 prototypes for the Delta Dagger, however, were built with neither area rule nor conical camber – and flight testing showed abysmal transonic performance, with the aircraft incapable of pushing itself to supersonic speeds. The production F-102A aircraft had area ruled-refined fuselages and modest conical cambering to the wings, with the result that the F-102A could reach Mach 1.25. Still not spectacular, but it was a first-generation supersonic fighter. Area ruling and conical cambering were incorporated into the design of the follow-on F-106 Delta Dart from the beginning, helping to produce a fighter capable of Mach 2.3.

The conical camber of the B-58 wing, a feature first conceptually employed during the MX-1964 phase, resulted in a fairly flat mean camber line at the wing root, but a distinctly down-turned wingtip, with a rounded upper surface and a concave lower surface. This feature was quite distinctive of the B-58 and was visible in modified form on the Lockheed SR-71 and to an extent on the McDonnell-Douglas F-15. It greatly reduced the drag due to lift at high speed and contributed to the impressive performance of the aircraft. At this stage the wing of the MX-1964 was essentially that of the eventual B-58.

The design was revised in April 1953 with a major change in the position of the engines. The twin-engine nacelles were dispensed with. One engine on each wing remained underslung, the pylon attached in the same place as before, but the second engine was moved outboard and attached to the upper surface of the wing. With the above-wing engines located further aft, the below-wing engines were moved forward to counter the CG shift, and to conform to the needs of area ruling. This configuration would have had improved supersonic drag compared to the Siamese nacelle version. It would, however, have weighed about 1,000lb more and would have complicated maintenance, as well as posing some difficulties with the elevons since the exhaust of the upper engines would directly impinge on them when deflected upwards. The decision of which arrangement to use flipped back and forth; in July of 1953 the supersonic performance of the Siamese nacelles was judged sufficiently good that that arrangement was again set as the baseline, producing what was called Configuration II. This design could attain a speed of a little over Mach 1.7.

At this time, construction on full scale mockups was begun. Initially there were mockups of various components, but eventually a mockup of the complete aircraft was constructed.

Speed was no longer considered adequate to make the B-58 invincible. So along with electronic countermeasures, the bomber now sported a 30mm gun in the tail below a radar aiming unit. The gun was mounted in a low-drag turret capable of 60° of coverage. A total of 400 rounds were carried for the tail gun, enough for a thirty-second burst. Control of the tail gun was the responsibility of the recently added third crewman.

In October of 1953 a major change to the design was instituted. The pod was separated from the aircraft fuselage; instead of having a flat upper surface to mate directly with the flat lower surface of the aircraft, the pod was turned into a circular cross-section body of rotation. The aircraft fuselage was given a rounded underside, and the pod was connected to the aircraft with a stubby long-chord pylon. The pod was shortened and the separate nose gear deleted from the pod. The aircraft nose gear would now serve for takeoff duty as the shorter pod provided clearance. The radar formerly housed within the nose of the pod was moved to the nose of the aircraft, substantially changing the profile. This, now dubbed Configuration III, retained the Siamese nacelles and had the option of expendable fuel tanks mounted to the upper surfaces of the leading edges of the outboard wings.

Wind tunnels tests of the latest configuration continued, with a debate ongoing about the advantages of the Siamese over the split nacelle configurations. Refined studies showed that the Siamese nacelles created noticeable additional drag at higher Mach

Convair Early XB-58

SCALE 1/180

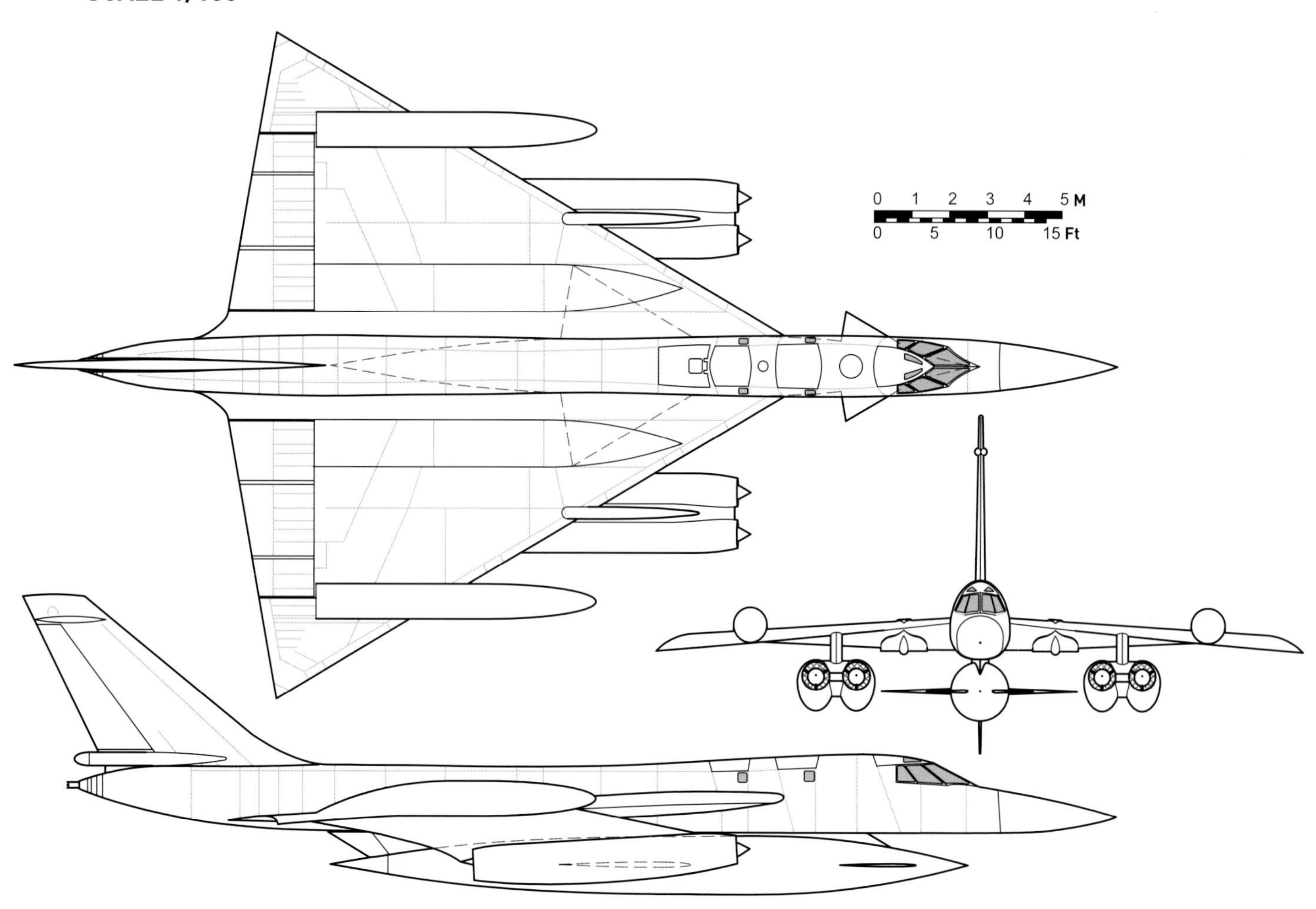

numbers – above Mach 1.6 – resulting in performance losses that offset the presumed maintenance benefits. By July 1954 the decision was made to go with a split nacelle configuration, but with the outboard engines located below the wings under short pylons. The 30mm cannon in the tail was replaced with a 20mm T-171, the original designation of the M61 Vulcan gatling gun. This, at last, was the basic configuration that would become the B-58A.

B-58A in brief

Despite advancements in propulsion and aerodynamics, by late 1954 the B-58 programme was running into some resistance in the US Air Force due to it not meeting hoped-for range goals. However, Convair remained optimistic that the normal course of refinement, along with future improvements in engines and the possible use of high energy fuels and possible redesign of important elements of the aircraft, could allow the aircraft to realise its full potential.

The design was expected to be fully capable of Mach 2 as a result of the decision to use the split nacelles, but that did not satisfy General Curtis LeMay, Chief of the Strategic Air Command. He wanted a bomber that had global range, like that of the B-52 or greater, and a substantial payload. The B-58 was never going to be that; it was designed to replace the B-47, not compete with the B-52 – a medium bomber with a single nuclear weapon, rather than a heavy bomber with a vast payload of conventional bombs or a number of nuclear weapons. But General LeMay wanted aircraft that could win wars practically unaided… a single B-52 could destroy virtually an entire nation in a single sortie, while a B-47 or its replacement the B-58 could merely destroy a single city or military installation. As a result, General LeMay did not want the B-58. Still, the programme forged ahead as much of the rest of the Strategic Air Command did want the shiny new bomber. Construction of the tooling needed to build the aircraft began.

The first B-58 prototype was completed in August of 1956. As is sadly traditional, the engines, General Electric YJ79-GE-1s, were taking longer to develop than anticipated; the first prototype had its four engines, but the second prototype did not. Taxi tests of the first prototype began in October, gradually building up ground speed. On November 11, 1956, the B-58 took to the air for the first time, successfully carrying out the test schedule planned for it… and revealing itself to the public for the first time. The B-58 went supersonic on the seventh test flight on December 30 1956; the MB-1 bomb/fuel pod was first flown in February 1957. While these flights showed that the aircraft could certainly fly, they confirmed that range would be marginal for Strategic Air Command goals.

The B-58 made extensive use of aluminium for structure and skin, with steel used sparingly for high temperature areas. Titanium was not available in sufficient quantity to be used on an aircraft like this in an important way. The structure made use of honeycomb reinforced panels, both phenolic resin fibreglass honeycomb bonded to aluminium skins and aluminium honeycomb brazed to aluminium skins were used. This proved a lightweight and strong approach, but with temperature limits. Still, the fibreglass and resin used could withstand temperatures in excess of 325°F.

The B-58 was an elegant-looking design, with a fuselage with a distinct 'wasp waist' or 'Coke bottle' shape to take advantage of the area rule principle. This, coupled with the mirror-like finish of the polished aluminium skin, made it, like the Boeing B-47 Stratojet before it, a distinctly aesthetically pleasing design, popular with the public if not General LeMay.

The crew of three consisted of the pilot, the navigator/bombardier and the defensive system operator. Each was in a separate compartment; the crew could not exchange positions in flight. Initially each crewman was equipped with an ejection seat, but testing – and the in-flight ejections from the first B-58 to be lost, in December 1958 – showed that the standard ejection seat of the time would not perform well at Mach 2. That first crew to eject did so at high speed and suffered injuries from buffeting.

As a result, Stanley Aviation was contracted to develop an ejection capsule. Development began in February of 1958 and resulted in a remarkable and successful device. The capsule was required not only to fully enclose and protect the crewman, but to fit within the cockpit space originally designed and built for the non-encapsulated conventional ejector seat and ride the same rails.

During normal operations, the capsule resembled a standard ejection seat with the addition of a large 'hood' over the crewman's head. Upon activation, within one second the mechanism retracted the crewman's feet and torso, adjusted the seat, and deployed three segmented doors from the hood. The doors slammed down and completely enclosed the occupant, sealing them into a leak-proof pressurized volume that could then be ejected into a high-speed, high dynamic pressure environment. Largely made out of forged aluminium, the pressure shell would stay closed throughout the descent, only opening after landing upon the occupant's command.

The aircraft's wings, sealed volumes serving as fuel tanks, were based on aluminium spars with honeycomb sandwich skins. Inflight refuelling was built into the design from the beginning. This was achieved through a receptacle located on the upper

Convair B-58A

SCALE 1/125

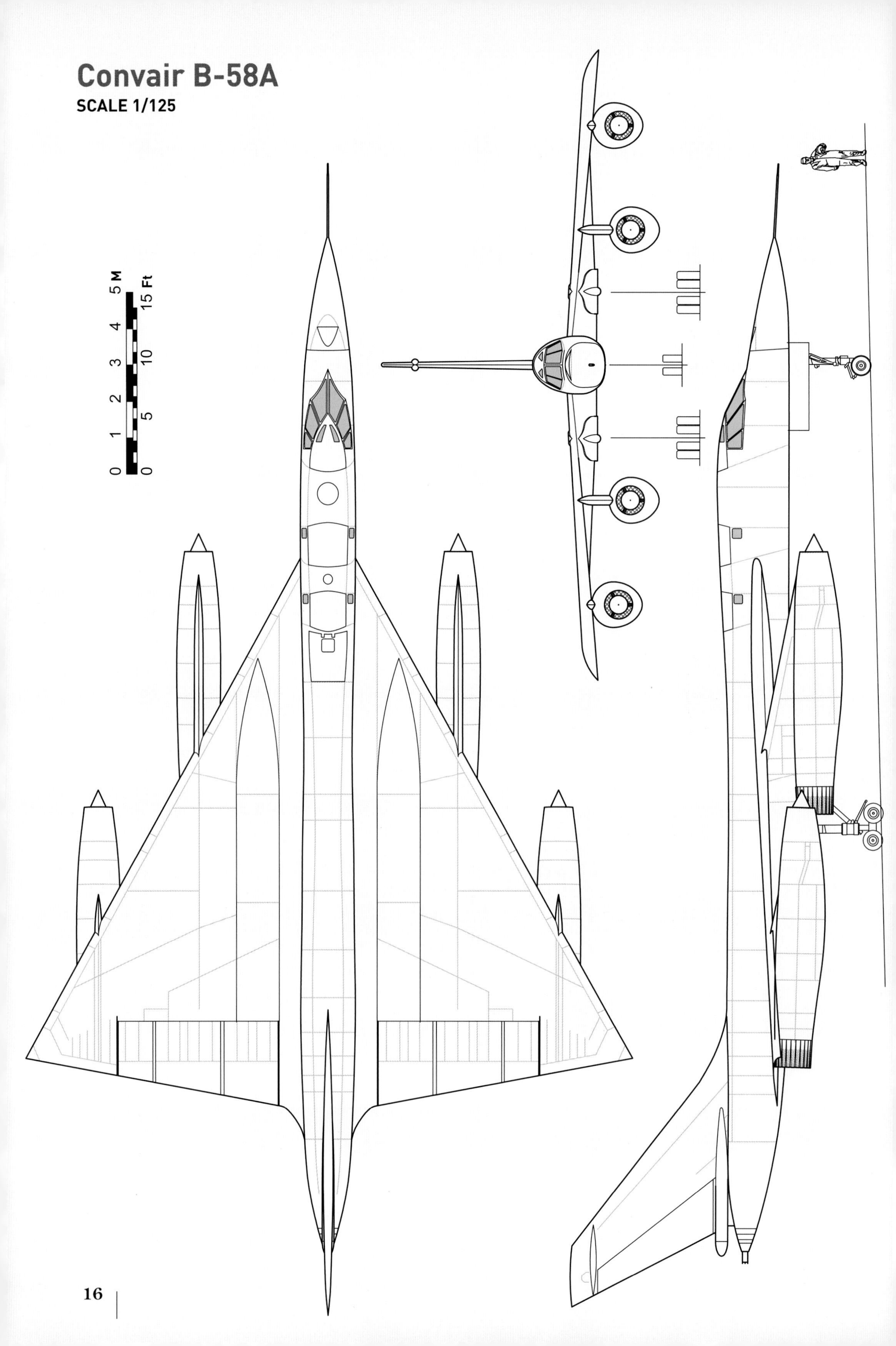

surface of the nose, along the centreline just aft of the radar, ahead of the canopy. The B-58 turned out to be a very stable platform while refuelling from a KC-135 tanker.

The feature that changed the most throughout the life of the B-58 was the bomb/fuel pod. For some time the pod of choice was the MA-1; this is often seen in early promotional art, mockups and models, as well as toys and model kits of the time. A large pod containing both fuel and a single thermonuclear weapon, it also featured small delta canards and somewhat larger delta wings. It did not need these surfaces while attached to the B-58 – they were to provide lift and control after release.

The MA-1 was more than simply a bomb with fuel in it: it would have also had a rocket engine. This was a Bell Aerospace LR81-BA-1, a derivative of the Agena engine. It would produce 15,000lb of thrust burning JP-4 with red fuming nitric acid; enough thrust to propel the winged pod forward as a standoff weapon. It had enough fuel to burn for about 65 seconds, giving it a range of about 160 miles. A Sperry navigational system would keep the missile on a simple trajectory towards the target, ending in a gliding descent. The MA-2 and MA-3 pods were similar, but included successively larger themonuclear warheads at the expense of less jet fuel. Detail is seemingly lacking on what warheads these pods would carry.

The MA-1 was ambitious, but the addition of the rocket engine, control systems, wings and propellants took up space and weight that could be devoted to fuel for the B-58. No MB-1 pod flew, either under its own power or carried beneath a B-58. Still, it was a striking feature of the early B-58, and was often depicted.

The MB-1 pod replaced the MA-1. It was much simpler – just fuel and a 3.8 megaton W39Y1-1 warhead. Four fins at the tail would provide post-release stability; once dropped it would fall unpowered and unguided, with a spin imparted by a slight twist in the fins. In essence it was a pair of fuel tanks fore and aft of a bomb, wrapped in an aerodynamic shell. Throughout its service life, though, it had an issue with fuel leaking into the bomb compartment. Additionally, the pod fuel would run out well before the bomb was to be dropped, with the result that the B-58 would need to continue hauling around a large empty draggy tank. As a consequence of these issues, a third type of pod was designed and delivered.

The replacement was known as the Two Component Pod because it had two components: a bomb pod, the diameter of which was sized specifically for the nine megaton B53 warhead; and a larger fuel-only pod. The bomb pod nested snugly into the fuel pod, with the result it had a 'double bubble' cross section. The bomb pod also contained smaller fuel tanks fore and aft of the warhead. As the fuel was drained from the lower, larger fuel pod, it could be jettisoned; this would eliminate a substantial amount of both weight and drag from the B-58. The BLU-2 bomb pod would deploy a stowed dorsal fin from its tail after being dropped.

Both the MB-1 and TCP pods were deployed operationally. The TCP was preferred due to the performance benefits, but the MB-1 pod could contain a substantially larger warhead.

The B-58A received a major upgrade in its capability during its operational lifetime. Modifications were made which allowed it to carry four additional nuclear weapons, the small and aerodynamic Mk-43 bomb. Two stubby pylons were added on either side of the lower wing, just outboard of the fuselage, flanking the centreline pod. This increased the number of nuclear weapons the B-58 could carry from one to five. The Mk-43 – later B43 – was a variable yield device capable of being set from 70 kilotons to one megaton. Even at full yield, all four Mk-43 bombs did not equal the firepower of the fully armed and operational B53 warhead in the Two Component Pod... but the ability to strike multiple targets with a one megaton bomb (frankly far more than enough canned sunshine for virtually any application) would have made the B-58 a far more versatile and deadly weapon.

A total of 116 B-58s were built and flown, with another built as a static test article. Unfortunately, a very high number – 26 – were lost. The B-58 turned out to be a troublesome aircraft, due largely to the fact that it was the first of its kind. Convair and the USAF were still learning how to design, build, fly and maintain Mach 2-capable aircraft. Any first aircraft of its kind is usually plagued with difficulties and the B-58 was no exception. Along with aircraft losses, a major problem for the B-58 was the sheer cost of the programme. Maintenance and fuel costs were very high and capability was, by the standards of the mid 1960s, beginning to look marginal.

Starting in 1961, two Strategic Air Command Bombardment Wings – the 43rd and 305th – operated the B-58. This time frame was unfortunate for the B-58, as it heralded the rise of two important enemies of American military aviation: the Soviet SA-2 Guideline surface-to-air missile which would prove problematic for American aircraft over North Vietnam, and Secretary of Defense Robert McNamara, who would prove problematic for American military aircraft in general. The new SAM showed the Strategic Air Command that flying high and fast was no longer the way to survive on the modern battlefield; instead, aircraft should fly low and fast, below the coverage of air defence radar.

The B-52 Stratofortress was able to make the transition, but the B-58 was never quite able to do

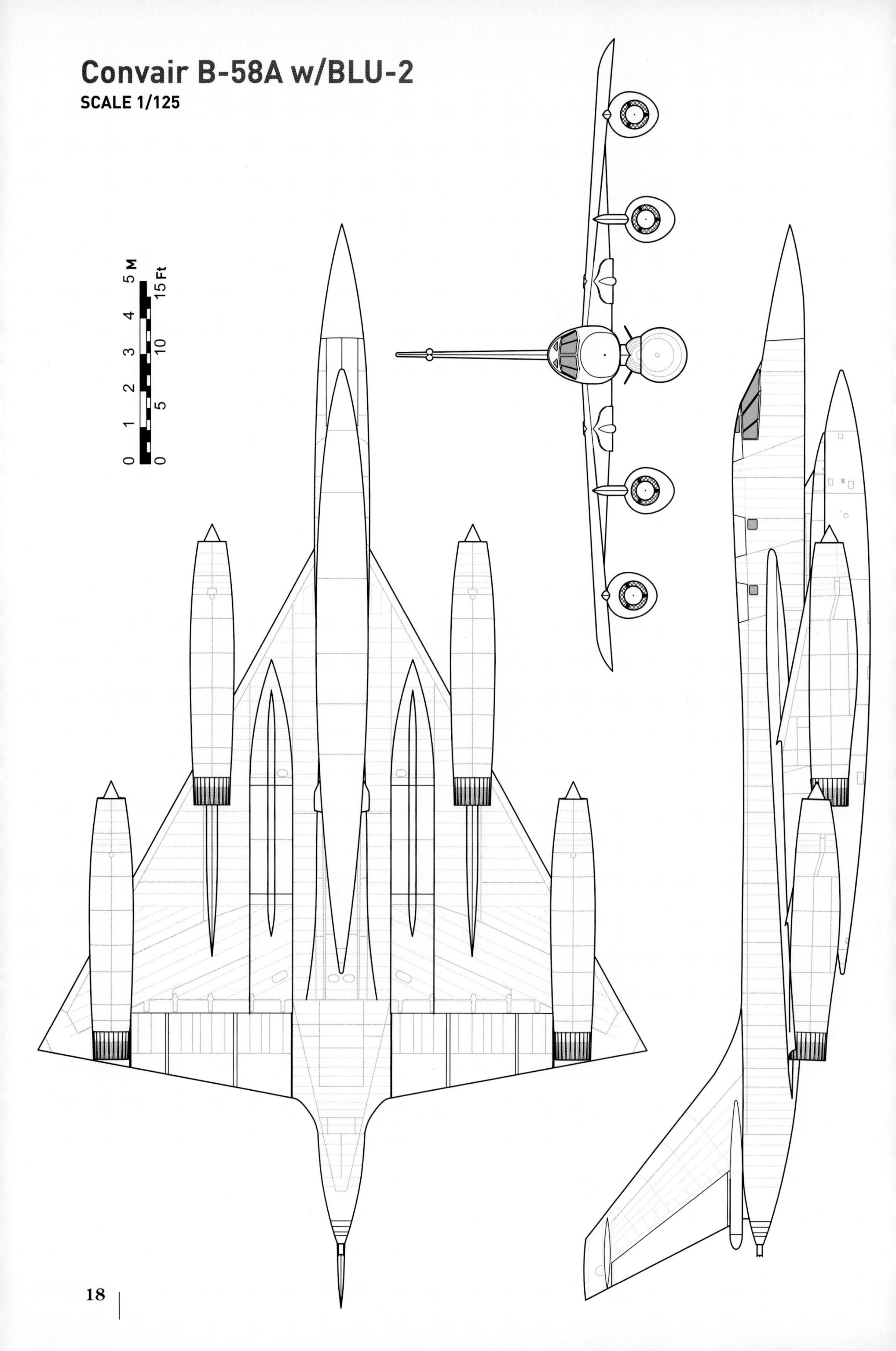
Convair B-58A w/BLU-2
SCALE 1/125
5 M
4
3
2
1
0
15 Ft
10
5
0

it. Low altitude flight meant not only dense air but highly disturbed dense air, consequently the airframe would take a hell of a beating just trying to fly a more or less straight line. The B-58 was unable to cruise supersonically at low altitude, negating its primary virtue; trying to slog through the thick air meant that its range, already marginal when flying at optimal design conditions, fell even further. In 1965 Secretary McNamara ordered that the B-58 be withdrawn from service by 1970. And by the end of that year the entire surviving fleet of B-58s were put into storage at Davis-Monthan Air Force Base; in 1977 the bulk of them were broken up for scrap.

As any good designer will, those responsible for the Convair B-58 attempted to sell customers on the idea of new missions, roles and airframes for the B-58. Some ideas involved modifications to existing aircraft; some involved new production lines. The B-58 generated a wide range of proposed derivatives, including various technology testbeds (made possible due to the designed-in ability to carry a large and heavy centreline pod), interceptors, satellite launchers and even passenger transports. Below are a number of the bomber variants that were proposed, some more unusual than others.

B-58B and B-58MI

Only a single model of B-58 entered service as a bomber. By default that was dubbed the B-58A, but plans were quickly afoot for improved versions, naturally to be called the 'B-58B'. However, while snippets of information have been seen about these improved versions, distressingly little hard data is currently available.

Several studies of "B-58 Model Improvement" were done, with several called 'B-58B', and several others not. However, the various designs are somewhat similar, and are lumped together here for convenience. The first known B-58B, apparently dating from 1958, was designed in part to serve as a carrier aircraft for the Convair 'FISH' reconnaissance aircraft (see *Lockheed SR-71 Blackbird: Origins and Evolution* for the story of the FISH and Kingfish Mach 4 aircraft), as well as a generally improved B-58 bomber. This B-58B was characterized by a 5ft fuselage extension added behind the third crew compartment, small canard 'linearizers' added to the sides of the fuselage just ahead of and above the leading edge roots of the wings, a slightly enlarged and strengthened vertical tail and the use of improved J79-9 turbojet engines. The landing gear would be enlarged and strengthened in order to accommodate the increased 186,000lb gross takeoff weight.

The design was soon refined somewhat. The revised B-58B was much the same, but replaced the separate canards with large leading edge root extensions and reverted to the standard tail. This version carried not only the two-component bomb/fuel pod, but two air launched ballistic missiles as well under the centre of the wing, one just on each side of the aircraft centreline. Convair also described the use of pylons located between the inboard and outboard engines as positions for the missiles. As depicted here, the missiles carried are Douglas GAM-87 Skybolt ALBMs, but shown alongside are two other air launched ballistic missiles that Convair looked at: the Convair/Lockheed High Virgo and Convair's 'Snap Shot Configuration 29C'.

High Virgo was a joint Lockheed and Convair project initiated in 1958 under WS-199 in order to quickly demonstrate the practicality of the B-58 as a carrier and launcher of stand-off ballistic missiles. The High Virgo missiles were developed by Lockheed (Convair was responsible for developing the pylon to connect the missile to a B-58) with a Thiokol TX-20 solid rocket motor for the first and only stage. The first test flight on September 5, 1958, launched at 40,300ft and Mach 0.995, failed shortly after launch when the control system malfunctioned. The second flight on December 19, 1958, made at 40,000ft and Mach 1.46, attained a range of 185 miles and was considered successful.

The third launch, on June 4, 1959, at 40,000ft and Mach 1.46, reached an apogee of 35 nautical miles and a range of 208 nautical miles, and was also considered successful. The fourth launch, on September 22, 1959, was aimed not at a ground target but the recently launched Discoverer V satellite. It carried a recoverable camera package in order to photograph the satellite, but communications with the missile were lost 19 seconds after launch and no hardware was ever recovered.

The Convair/Lockheed High Virgo was part of the WS-199 programme, which also resulted in the Bold Orion and Alpha Draco missiles. Alpha Draco was a two-stage ground-launched missile designed and built by McDonnell Aircraft, using a slim conical hypersonic aeroballistic 'glider' to extend range. The Martin Bold Orion was closer in concept to the High Virgo in that it was a single-stage vehicle launched from an aircraft, in this case the Boeing B-47 (see *Boeing B-47 Stratojet & Boeing B-52 Stratofortress: Origins and Evolution* for more on this programme). All three vehicles showed promise, but none were picked by the Air Force for further development, partly due to the fact that 200 miles range was not considered especially impressive. Instead, the USAF began project WS-138A in early 1959. This resulted in the Douglas GAM-87 Skybolt.

High Virgo was intended to be purely a research and demonstration programme, but Convair believed

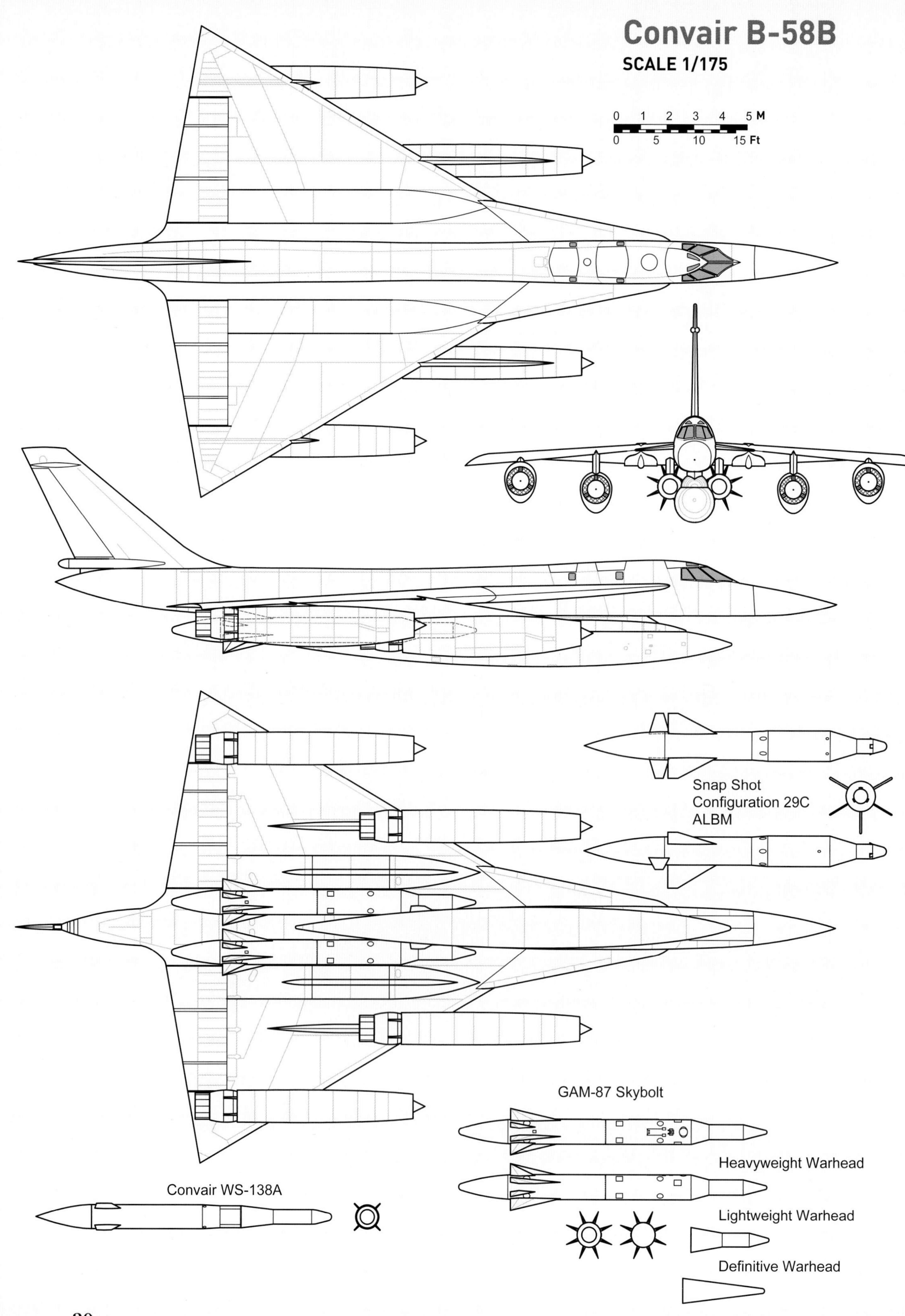
Convair B-58B
SCALE 1/175
0 1 2 3 4 5 M
0 5 10 15 Ft
Snap Shot
Configuration 29C
ALBM
GAM-87 Skybolt
Heavyweight Warhead
Lightweight Warhead
Definitive Warhead
Convair WS-138A

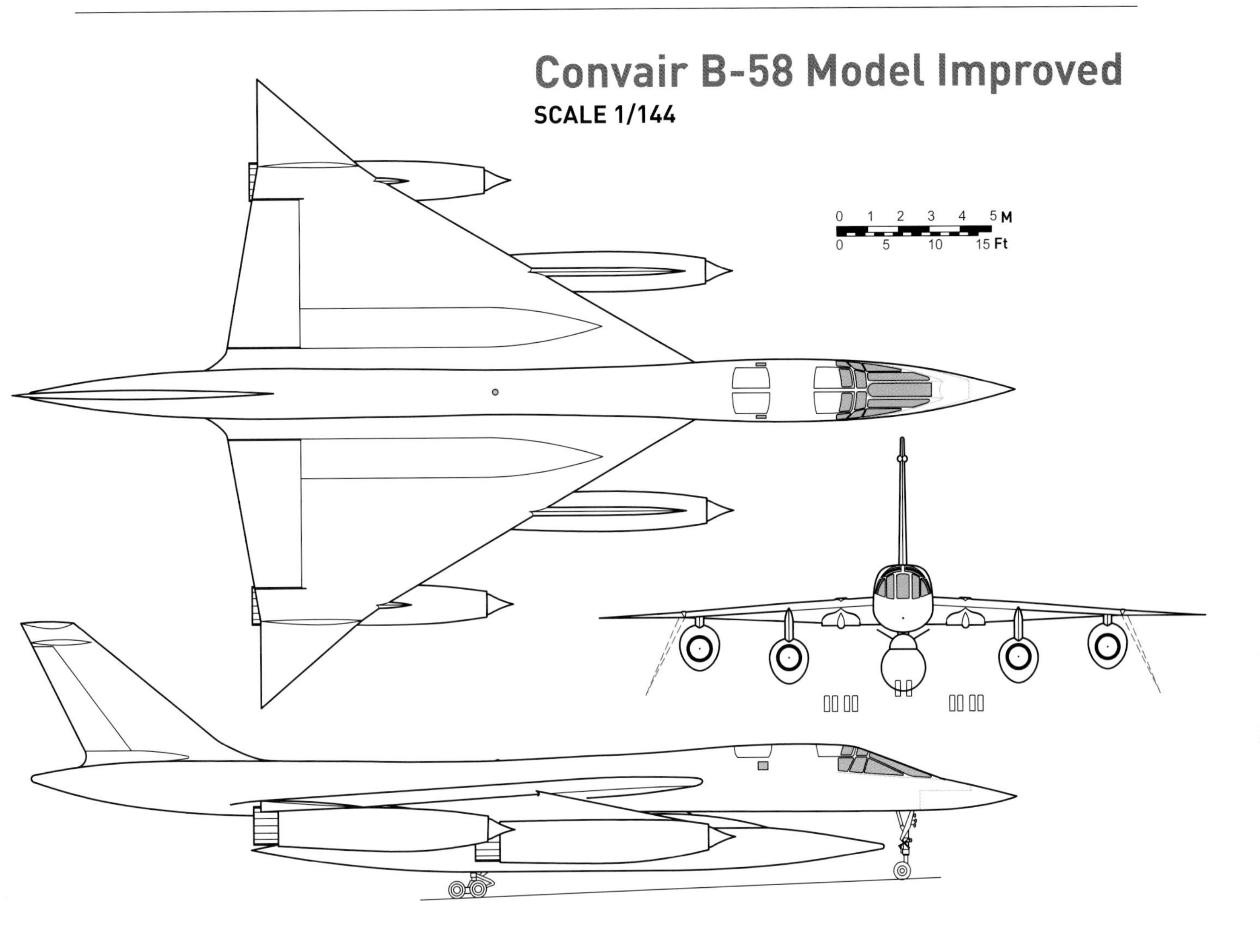

that the missile could be quickly converted into an operational nuclear-armed air launched ballistic missile. Prior to Douglas's submission winning the WS-138A programme, Convair proposed its own concept, an improvement upon the High Virgo design. Where High Virgo was a single stage vehicle with no nuclear warhead, the Convair WS-138A submission added a second stage motor, a Thiokol product to be designed specifically for this missile. A re-entry vehicle with a nuclear warhead would complete the vehicle. When launched from a B-58 at Mach 2.2/60,000ft, it was to have a range of 1,365 nautical miles.

Also shown is Convair's 'Snap Shot Configuration 29C' air launched ballistic missile, also dated 1959. This would have been a two stage vehicle using a modified Thiokol TX-172 for the first stage and a pair of Aerojet 10-41 motors for the second. Details, sadly, are lean for this design.

Along with carrying two ALBMs, one on each side of the centreline, the B-58B could carry a Two Component Pod, or a new 'bomb bay' pod. This pod, with more or less conventional bomb bay doors, could carry a variety of conventional and/or nuclear bombs. As an alternative to the ALBMs, the B-58 could carry two fuel tanks or four Class D (B43) nuclear bombs.

The B-58B was intended from the outset to be the prime carrier for the WS-138A ALBM. As it happened, only the B-52 ended up actually carrying and launching Skybolt missiles; the B-52 was a fallback option. This was necessitated due to the cancellation of the B-58B effort in late July 1959.

The known B-58B concepts were a part of the B-58 Model Improvement studies, the name of which should be fairly self-explanatory Details are again rather thin on the ground for the B-58MI studies, though it appears to have operated in two phases. B-58MI studies began in late 1954 and ran into late summer of 1955; and again from the middle of 1956 into August or so of 1957. Two B-58MI concepts are at least known, if fragmentarily. Both concepts share a unique feature: extended, lower-sweep wingtips that could droop. Presumably this feature was for the same reason as the drooping wingtips of the B-70: added high speed stability, reducing drag and increasing range and max speed. Photos show that wind tunnel models date from 1957 and were tested at the NACA Langley Aeronautical Laboratory, but unfortunately no reports have so far come to light on these wind tunnel tests.

Convair B-58 Model Improved (wind tunnel model)

SCALE 1/200

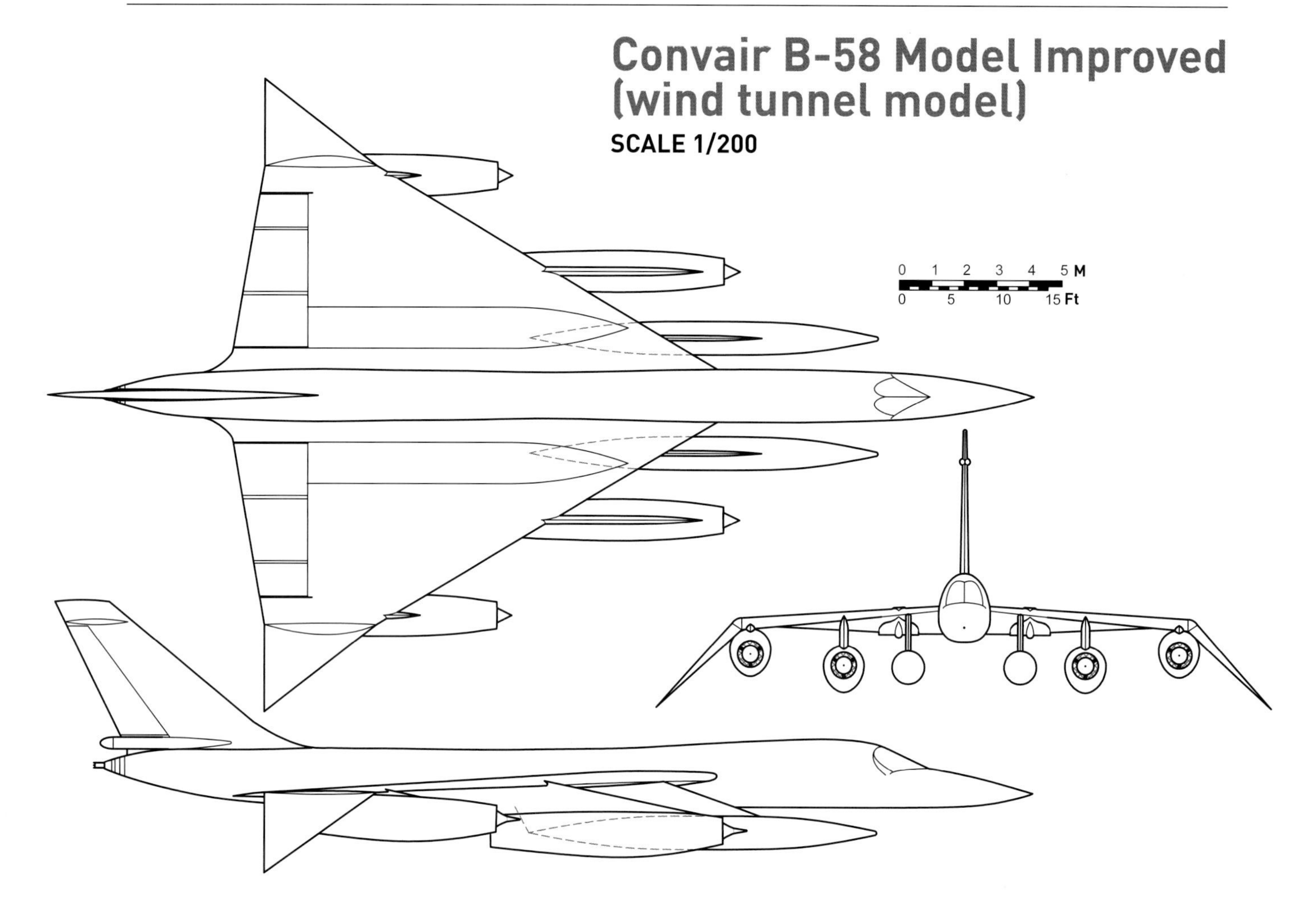

The most obvious difference between the two B-58MI configurations is the cockpit: one shows a more or less conventional cockpit for a B-58, while the other shows a cockpit featuring side-by-side seating. The former design had a somewhat stretched forward fuselage and, according to photos of a wind tunnel model, slightly different contours to the cockpit canopy. The aircraft used two slim external fuel tanks attached to forward-projecting pylons attached to the underside of the wings inboard of the inboard engines. It is unclear what the status of the tail armament would have been; the wind tunnel model modified the aft fuselage for attachment to the pylon, and the details of the tail gun, if any, are lost. Additionally, the model does not depict the canopy frame arrangement, so what is shown here is speculative. No weight or performance data is available.

The second B-58MI design had improved range and speed, with side-by-side seating for a crew of four each in conventional ejection seats rather than capsules. The canopy was entirely unlike that of the standard B-58; long narrow panes of transparencies were laid at very shallow angles to create a low-drag canopy with decent visibility for the crew. This is a somewhat unusual canopy arrangement, but the same basic layout appeared on several Convair supersonic bomber concepts around this time (see the Convair WS-125A nuclear powered supersonic bomber from 1956 in Volume 2). The forward fuselage was extended 8ft and was substantially wider than that of the standard B-58 in order to accommodate the side-by-side crew.

The J79-GE-5 engines would be replaced with the more powerful J79-9, capable of 18,600lb thrust. Gross weight for this version would have been 186,000lb with a maximum speed of at least Mach 2.2. Payload options were wide and included the use of both the centreline and inboard wing pylons. Under the centreline it could carry the BLU-2 two-component fuel/bomb pod with a Class C (using the nine megaton B-53) or a Class D (using the 1.5 megaton W-28) thermonuclear weapon, a single large Class A (25 megaton) or Class B (5 to 10 megatons) free fall bomb, a large air launched ballistic missile, a bomb bay pod, or recon equipment pod with high resolution radar, photo reconnaissance or 'ferret' reconnaissance equipment.

The wing pylons could each carry a free-fall bomb with a Class C or Class D warhead, a self-contained countermeasures package, an air launched ballistic missile (smaller than what could be carried under the centreline), a bomb bay pod for conventional or special munitions, or an expendable fuel tank with JP-4 or high energy fuel. Diagrams depict it carrying a two component pod similar to that carried by the

Convair B-58 Model 16 Tactical Bomber

SCALE 1/200

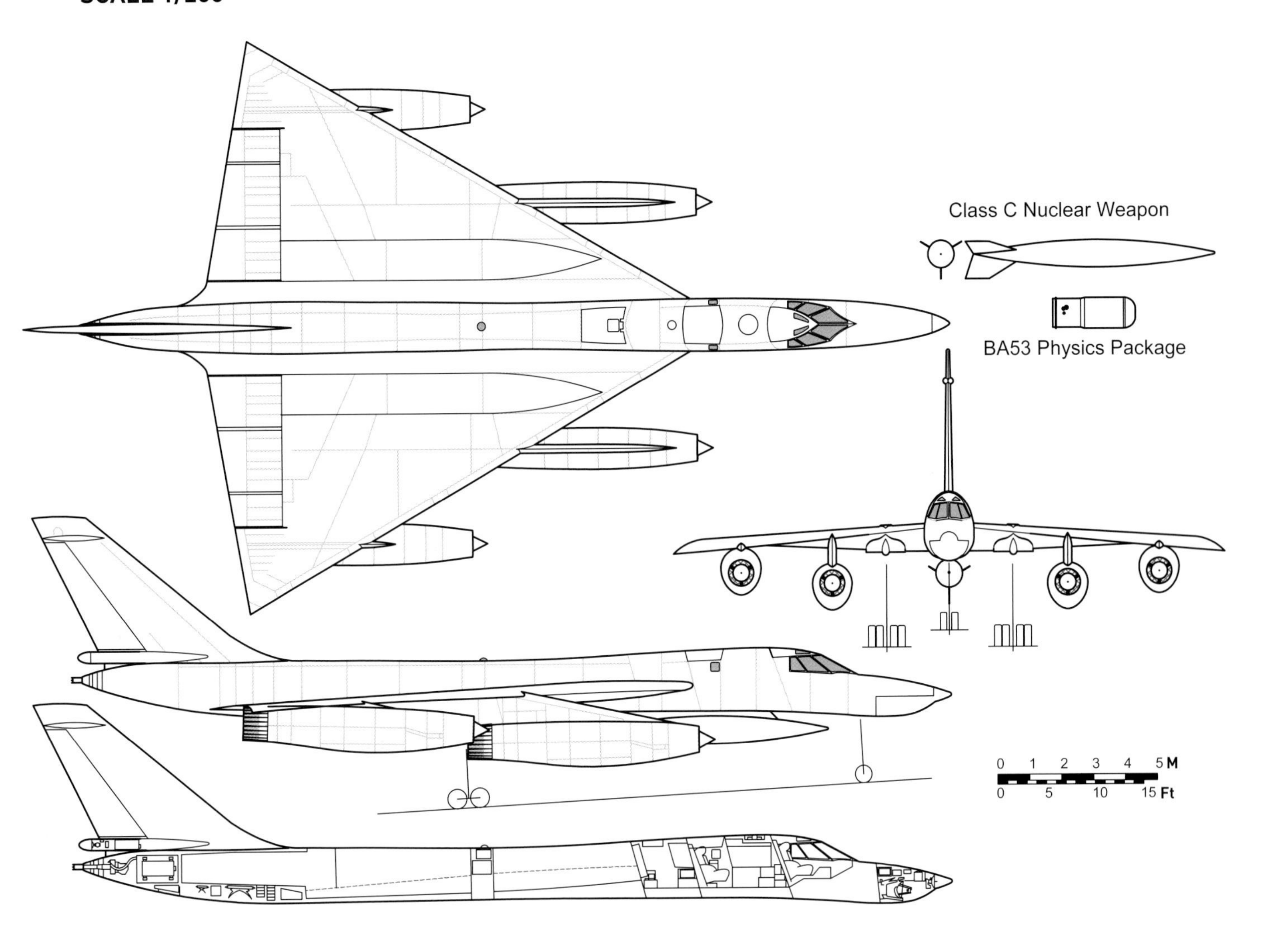

B-58A, but substantially stretched. A curious feature was that the outboard nacelles were to be jettisonable; available documentation does not say under what condition this would occur, but it would presumably be to reduce weight and drag post bomb release in order to extend range enough to make it to a safe base.

The tail armament seems to have been deleted; apparently the belief had swung back to 'it's too fast to intercept'. Rather than a tail gun, the B-58MI was to have been equipped with additional countermeasures, the details of which are currently lacking.

A single photo shows another display model depicted a B-58MI carrying a variant of the Super Hustler slung underneath. No further data is available on either the B-58MI carrier or the unusual Super Hustler variant.

Model 16 Tactical Bomber

In June of 1955 Convair reported on its Model 16 B-58 Tactical Bomber designed to System 302A requirements. This was largely the B-58A, but with a few notable changes allowing it to perform as a light tactical bomber in the 1962-63 timeframe. It was required to take off from widely dispersed bases and drop nuclear or conventional weapons from high altitude at supersonic speeds, or low altitude at high subsonic speeds.

Gone was the large pod; the requirements for long range and a large hydrogen bomb were dismissed. Added was a new ground-scanning radar under the nose, giving the aircraft the appearance of a cartoonish chin. With the deletion of the pod, a large mass of fuel was removed, dropping the gross takeoff weight of the aircraft greatly; this helped the aircraft to achieve a takeoff distance to a 50ft height of 2,860ft. Mission radius was 600 nautical miles. The maximum payload was 12,000lb with a design payload of two Class D nuclear weapons (using the 1.5 megaton W-28 warhead), each weighing 4,290lb. An alternate payload was a single Class C nuclear weapon using the nine megaton B-53 warhead.

B-58-C-1

SCALE 1/200

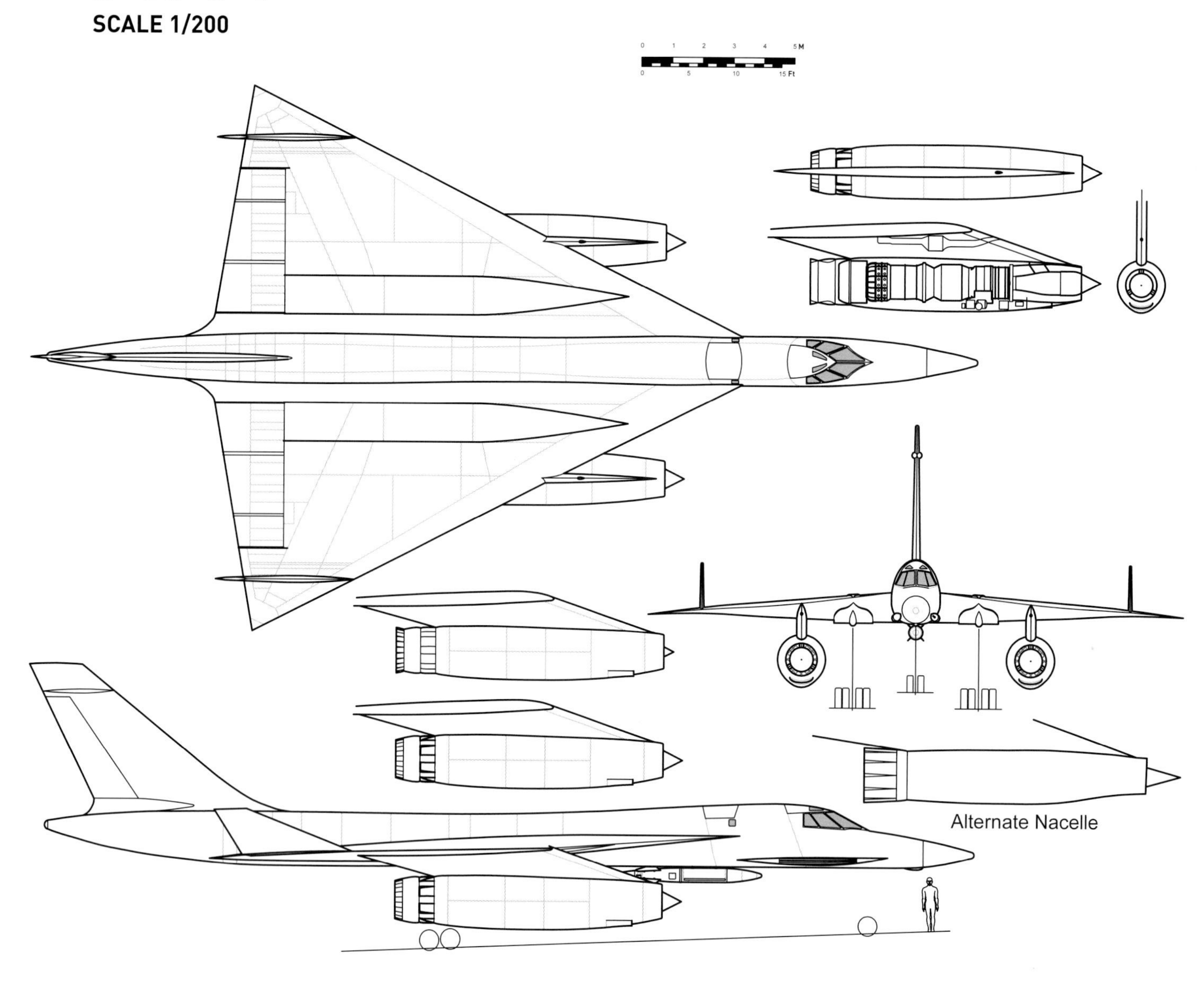

In a bomb bay pod – similar in concept to the B-58A pod, but without fuel – the Model 16 could carry a wide range of conventional weapons, such as 24 x 5in high-velocity aircraft rockets, 100 x 2in folding fin aircraft rockets, 3,000lb of high explosive bombs, 2,745lb of incendiary bombs, biological weapons, chemical weapons, napalm, even Lazy Dog bomblets (bullet-sized and bullet-shaped steel projectiles that simply fell from the sky at high speed, potentially doing great damage to soft targets). The crew was reduced to two, with the third cockpit compartment converted into an equipment bay. However, it retained the T-171 gatling gun in the tail with 1,100 rounds of ammunition.

Convair expected conversion to be straightforward and fast, with the first units to be available in the 1959-60 time period.

Convair B-58-C-1

In early 1960 Convair proposed to the USAF a tactical bomber variant of the B-58 equipped with two afterburning Pratt & Whitney J58 turbojets (the same engines used on the SR-71). This would permit a supersonic cruise at Mach 2.4 at 68,000ft, the maximum speed that materials then in use on the B-58 could withstand due to aerothermal heating. It would have a range of 5,200 nautical miles extendable to 7,500 nautical miles via inflight refuelling. The B-58-C-1, also known as the B/J-58, was equipped with two B43 thermonuclear weapons carried on the lower centreline. Each 2,100lb bomb had a yield of up to one megaton.

The M61 Vulcan gatling gun normally mounted in a tail 'stinger' on the B-58 was deleted from the B-58-C. The four engines and pylons on the conventional B-58

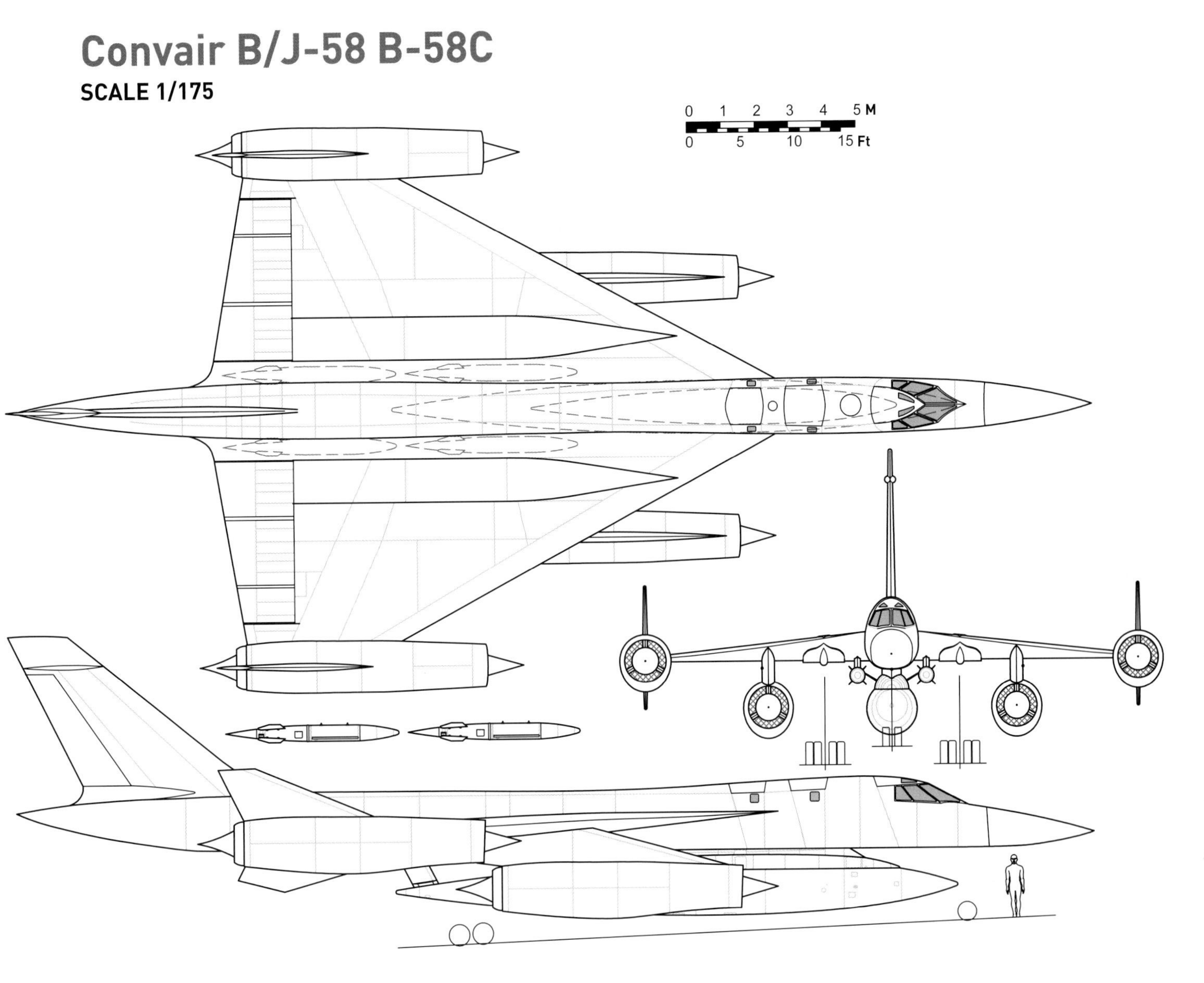

served as vertical stabilizers; to make up for the loss of two engines and two pylons, small vertical fins were added to the upper surface of the wings near the tips. AN/APQ-55 side looking radar antennae were added to the sides of the forward fuselage, while the copilot's position was deleted. The conical camber that characterized the wing of the B-58A was eliminated, producing a straight-camber wing.

Confusingly, this design was also designated the B-58D (the same configuration, but to be used as an interceptor) and the B-58E (seemingly exactly the same aircraft as the B-58-C-1, with the same role as bomber). The diagram here includes two different configurations for the J58 turbojet nacelles, as depicted on separate original diagrams. They differ primarily in the variable geometry exhaust nozzle. The J58 turbojet would have differed in an important way from the J58 used on the SR-71: it did not have the ducts used to divert air around the core, used to turn the engines into something of a ramjet at high speed. This was an innovation arrived at during the development of the Lockheed A-12, and likely was unknown to Convair's design teams.

Convair B/J-58

Also known as the B-58C, the minimally-documented B/J-58 from March of 1960 was for an improved all-supersonic version of the Convair B-58 bomber. The B-58 would normally cruise long distances at subsonic speeds, only dashing to Mach 2 over the target or to escape interception. But the B-58C would be re-engined to permit supercruising.

The B-58C was equipped with four non-afterburning J58 engines with conical plug nozzles. Without afterburners the maximum thrust and maximum attainable speed of the J58 engines was greatly reduced, but with much improved fuel consumption at supersonic speed. With some aerodynamic refinements – a stretched fuselage and the outboard engines mounted on the wingtips, with vertical wingtip stabilizers – the B-58C was able to supercruise at Mach 2 for the bulk of its journey. The wings were cropped, having slightly less span and area than the basic B-58A; this reduced the lifting area, but also reduced drag. The efficiency of the wing would be improved by the wingtip nacelles and fins, producing much the same aerodynamic benefits as given by modern wingtip fins. Being a supercruiser,

Convair B-58 Minuteman carriers

SCALE 1/144

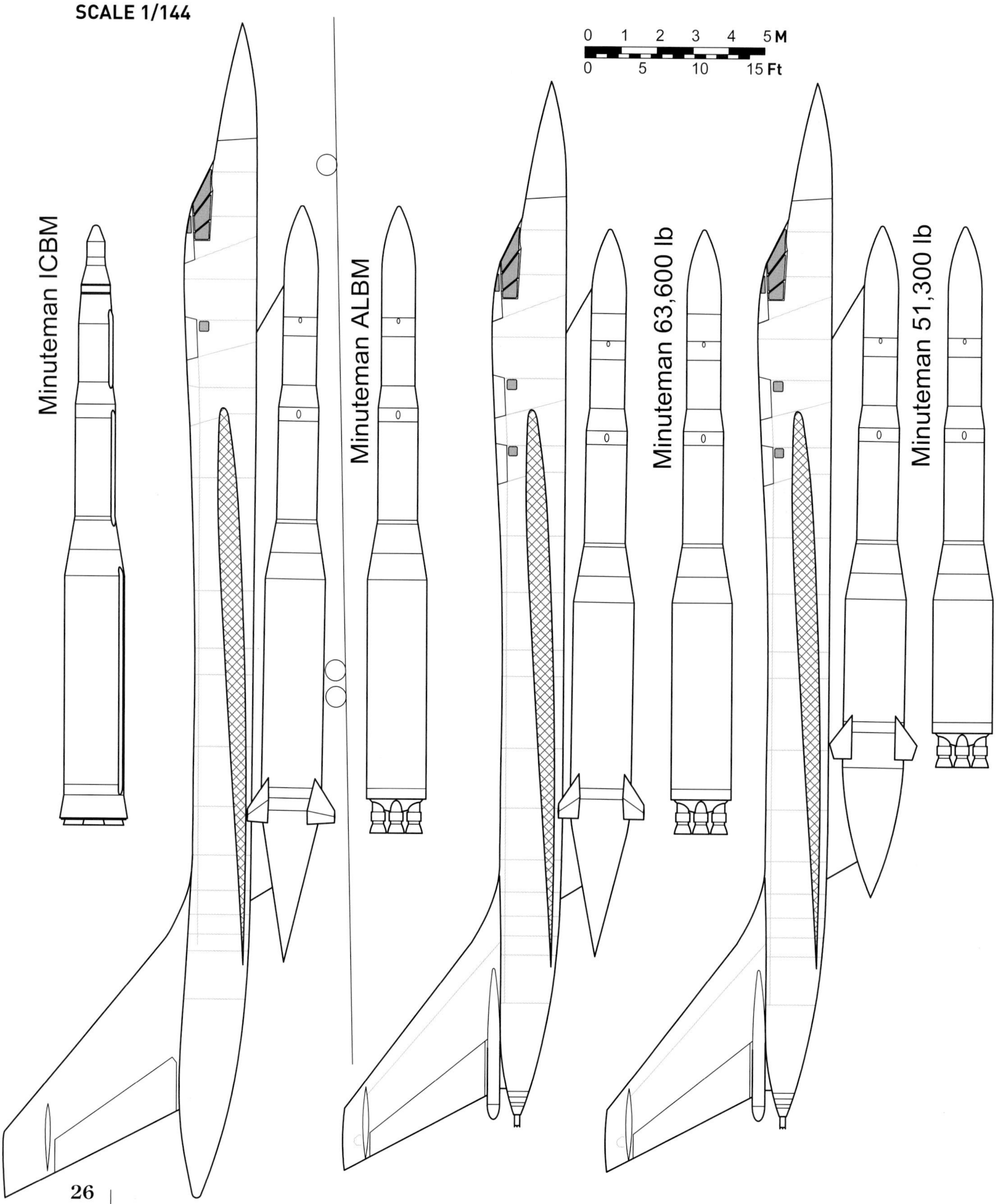

0 1 2 3 4 5 M
0 5 10 15 Ft

Minuteman ICBM

Minuteman ALBM

Minuteman 63,600 lb

Minuteman 51,300 lb

no defensive tail gun was fitted. For offense, it carried a BLU-2 two component pod, flanked by two TX-43 (later B43) bombs on either side.

Neither B-58C concept seemed to make it past April 1960.

B-58 ICBM launchers

The Air Launched Ballistic Missile programme and its relationship to the B-58 was described previously. But the ALBM was not the only ballistic missile concept to be considered for the B-58. The B-58 could carry a number of ALBMs... or it could carry one large missile, a true intercontinental ballistic missile. In 1962 Convair reported on the use of the B-58 to carry and launch a true ICBM, with multiple missile designs put forward. Unfortunately, the available documentation on this effort consists of briefing charts that focus on the practicalities of carrying and dropping variously-sized large rockets; the performance of the system is not given. Similar studies of the time included the use of large boosters carried by the B-58 for the purpose of launching satellites into orbit; it may be that that was a goal here as well, but mention is made of the range of the missiles carried by the B-58, indicating that a strike role was also envisioned.

It can be assumed that the rockets, derivatives of the Minuteman ICBM, would have ranges roughly equivalent to that of the Minuteman. With the added benefit not only of a high altitude launch likely at high subsonic speed, but also the ability to be carried thousands of miles from the original air base, the reach of such a system could well have been superior to a silo-launched conventional Minuteman. All of the missiles would be attached to pylons that would make use of the same attachments used by the MB1 and TCP payloads.

Along with a largely unmodified Minuteman, two sizes of smaller Minutemen were looked at. Both were based on the 68,000lb, 667in long solid-propellant Minuteman missile with an XM-35 first stage (nominally 292in long), XM-56 second stage (154in long) and XM-57 third stage (86in long) with a 135in payload nose cone. The smaller missile was 51,300lb and 577in long, achieved by removing a 90in long barrel section from the Minuteman first stage. This was the largest missile that could be carried that required no substantial modifications to the B-58A structure, though a few minor ones were needed such as modifications to the autopilot, an additional attachment point between the pylon and the aircraft structure, and additional controls added to the second crew station panels.

The larger missile weighed 63,600lb and was 645in long after removing a 22in segment from the first stage. This was the largest rocket that could be carried underneath the B-58A without major modifications. The aircraft would still require strengthened wing spars and a reinforced aft pylon attachment to the fuselage.

The stock B-58A would struggle to carry a full-size Minuteman, both in terms of the mass of the payload and its dimensions. Consequently, for a full Minuteman missile the B-58A would not do as the missile was simply too long. To position it under the B-58 so that it would not shove the aircraft's centre of gravity too far aft, the nosecone would interfere with the B-58's nose landing gear. Extending the fuselage by 22in would be adequate to solve the problem, but it was desired to use existing design knowledge from prior studies.

The Convair study team looked back to the B-58B and appropriated certain design aspects of that long-cancelled programme. The third crewman and all associated equipment would be deleted; behind the now emptied station a 5ft fuselage extension would be added and used as additional fuel volume. As with the B-58B, the vertical stabilizer would be modified for greater area to compensate for the longer nose. The tail cone would be modified in contour and the tail gun and associated equipment deleted, the tail now used as a fuel tank.

This full-size Minuteman was not considered attractive given the nature of the changes required to the B-58, in comparison to the relatively minor increase in length and capability of the missile over the 63,600lb missile. However, the added length would allow a missile perhaps 40in longer than the Minuteman to be carried.

All three Minuteman missiles required the addition of a drag-reducing tailcone to the missile as well as four small fins. These would provide stability after drop and before thrust vectoring of the four first stage nozzles took over roll, yaw and pitch control after ignition. The two lower fins, as the missile was mounted beneath the B-58, would need to fold upwards while on the ground to provide adequate clearance.

Super Hustler

The direct progenitors of the final B-58 design were meant to be carried aloft by larger, slower aircraft. But soon the B-58 itself ended up being proposed as a carrier for smaller, faster aircraft. As the design of the B-58 progressed and transitioned to manufacturing the prototypes, in 1955 engineers and designers at the Fort Worth, Texas, Convair facility were already looking at ways to greatly improve upon its performance by way of replacing the engines, stretching the fuselage, refining the aerodynamics and so on. Over the next few years numerous studies were made to increase speed to Mach 4; advanced fuels, turboramjets, auxiliary ramjets and rocket engines found their way into the designs, all to somewhat dubious value due to uncertainties regarding cost, performance and materials. Irritatingly, while it is known that such studies were performed, to date these reports and the associated diagrams have not been seen by this author.

In late 1957, not long after the B-58 began its test flight programme, Convair began studying another approach to expanding the performance envelope of the B-58: a small parasite aircraft.

The initial concept called for a single manned vehicle to be carried under the centreline of a stretched Hustler in the position normally occupied by the bomb/fuel pod. As initially conceived, the parasite would be ramjet powered and designed to cruise at Mach 5, but there was a problem: geometry. With any practical single vehicle, the B-58's main landing gear would be blocked by the parasite's wings. Soon a solution was found by splitting the parasite into two components. Echoing the early days of the GEBO, GEBO II and MX-1626, the parasite, dubbed the 'Super Hustler', had an expendable first stage equipped with two ramjet engines and a ramjet-powered cruise stage with a single pilot. Unlike the earlier 'podded' parasite aircraft, the powered expendable stage was not underneath the manned stage, but behind it as a 'pusher'. Both stages also had their own wings. This split the lifting surfaces fore and aft; positioned under the B-58 carrier aircraft, the gap between the fore and aft wings provided clearance for the B-58 landing gear to extend and retract.

The design specifics varied from iteration to iteration, including manned stages that were split into two separate slim fuselages, side-by-side. By early 1958 the initial concept had crystalized into a detailed concept with a crew of two. The booster had two side-by-side Marquardt ramjet engines in the rear of a stubby fuselage, each fed by a rhomboidal external-internal compression inlet on either side of the fuselage. Swept shoulder-mounted wings featured

Convair Super Hustler Configuration 121

SCALE 1/125

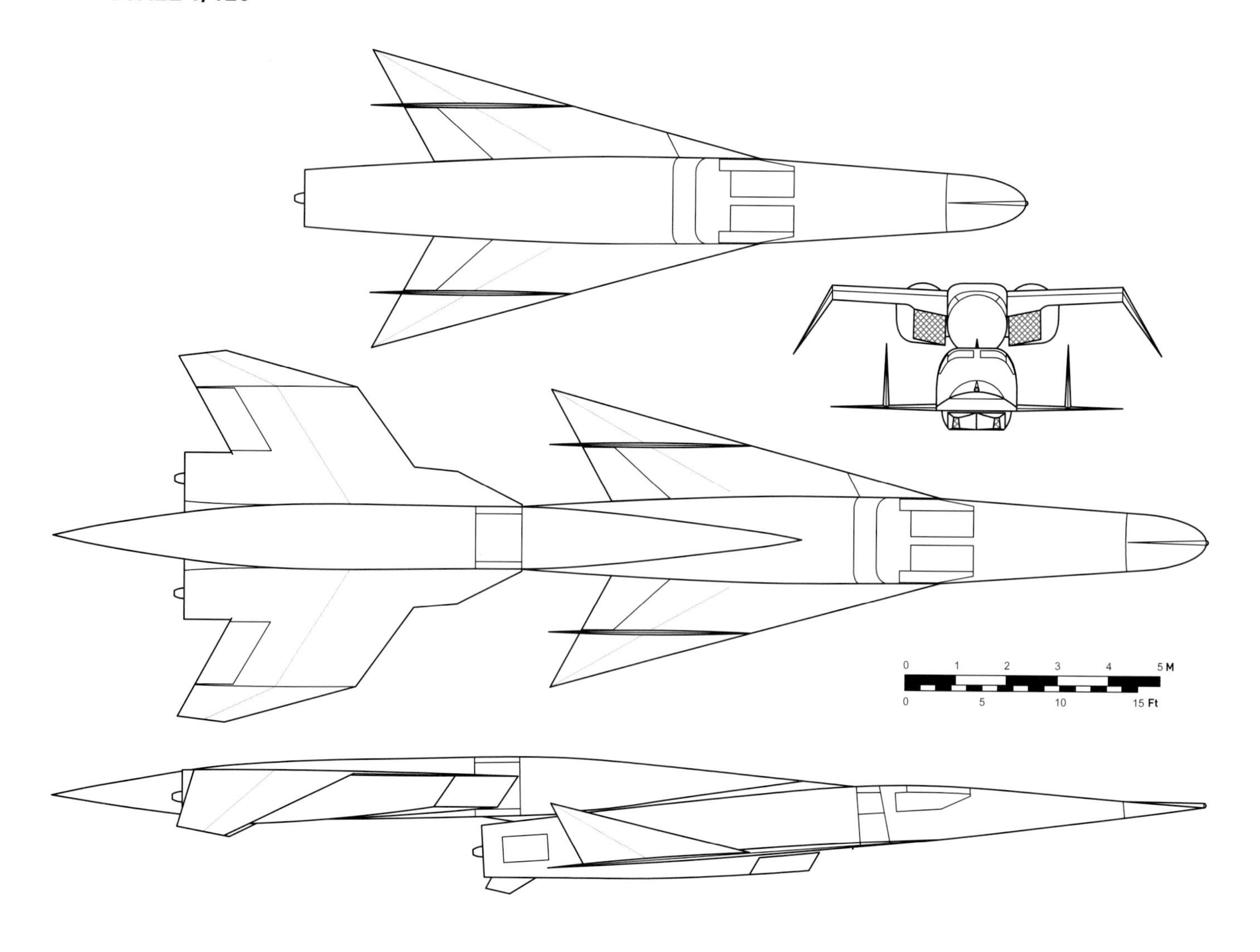

sizable downward-angled wingtip fins. The sharply pointed ogival nose of the booster fuselage contained a single 'Class C' (nine megaton B53) thermonuclear warhead, the underside of which mated to the upper rear fuselage of the manned cruise vehicle. The cruise vehicle had a flat underside, sharply swept arrow-shaped faceted wings and similarly shaped vertical fins at about mid-span. The baseline Super Hustler had a single ramjet engine in the cruise stage; an alternate design had two side-by-side ramjet engines. Both designs used an underslung inlet for the ramjets, with an auxiliary small J85 turbojet (tucked either under the single ramjet, or in the diverted between the ramjets for the two-engine version) used for landing.

The B-58 would carry the Super Hustler to a speed of Mach 2 and an altitude of somewhere under 40,000ft. The Super Hustler would be released and would fire up the ramjet engines in the booster, accelerating to a cruise speed of Mach 4 and an altitude of 73,000ft. Speed would stay at Mach 4, but altitude would gradually increase as fuel was burned off. A standard mission would see the booster separate from the cruise vehicle around 2,000 miles from B-58 launch at an altitude of 80,000ft. After separation, the warhead would separate from the booster stage and would plummet towards the target, with an expected circular error probability of 1,410ft. The warhead would deploy an aft skirt for stabilization. A skirtless lower-drag design would reduce CEP to 1,100ft. The manned stage would continue to cruise at Mach 4, climbing to a maximum of 91,000ft. The manned stage would land after travelling some 4,290 nautical miles from B-58 separation.

The Super Hustler manned stage was a small, compact vehicle, yet it could attain high speed, high altitude and substantial range. This was due to the fact that it was designed to stay at on-design conditions. A ramjet engine is generally considered to have poor fuel economy; this is due to the fact that ramjets do have poor fuel consumption when flown at anything other than their optimum design condition. Acceleration from low speed and climbing from low altitude will drain a ramjet's fuel tank in no time flat. But the Super Hustler manned stage had the advantage of being boosted to its design condition, and could thus operate at maximum efficiency. This would come in handy with a proposed alternate use of the Super Hustler: as a dedicated reconnaissance vehicle. With the bomb

Convair Super Hustler Configuration 124

SCALE 1/125

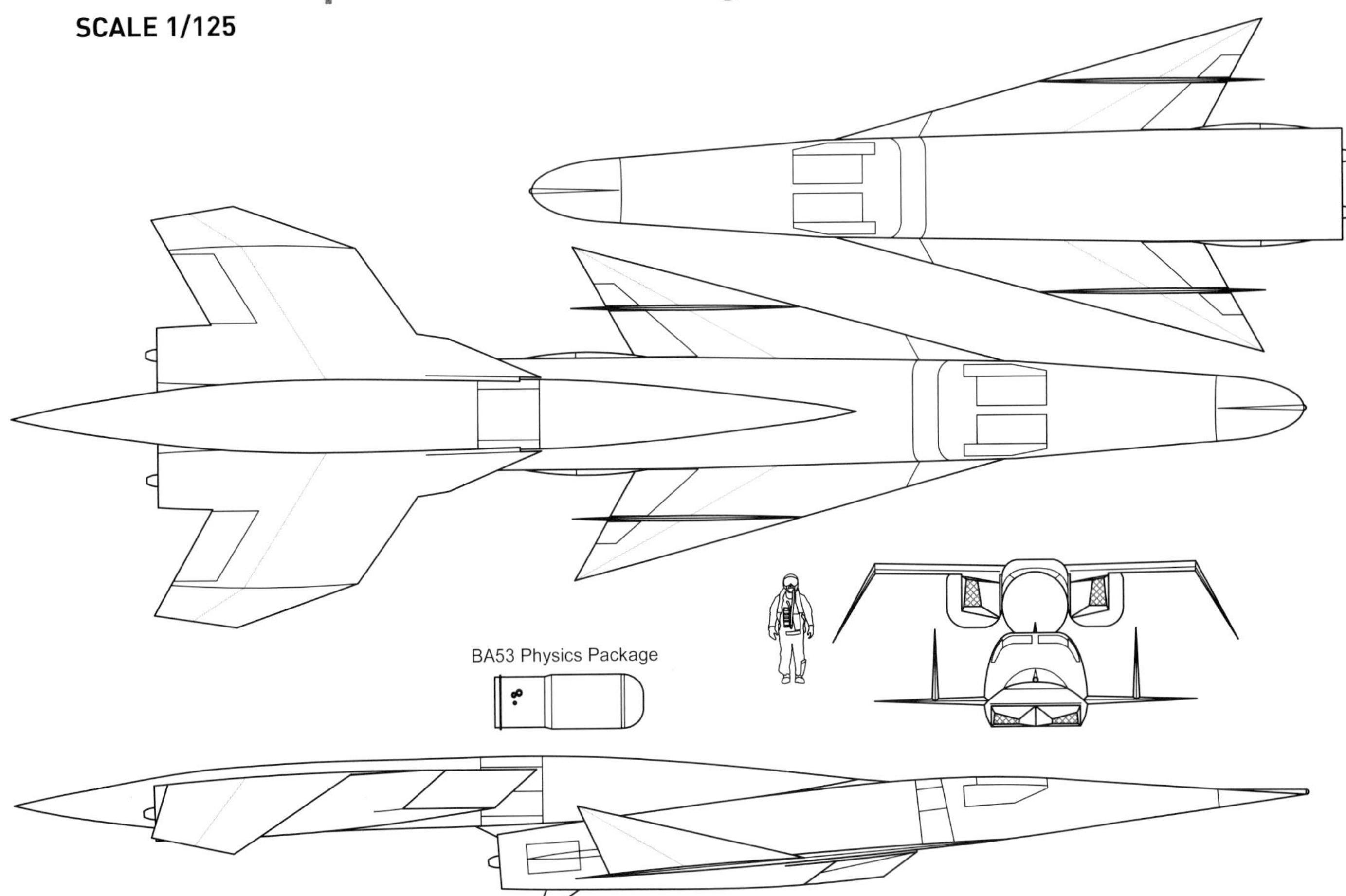

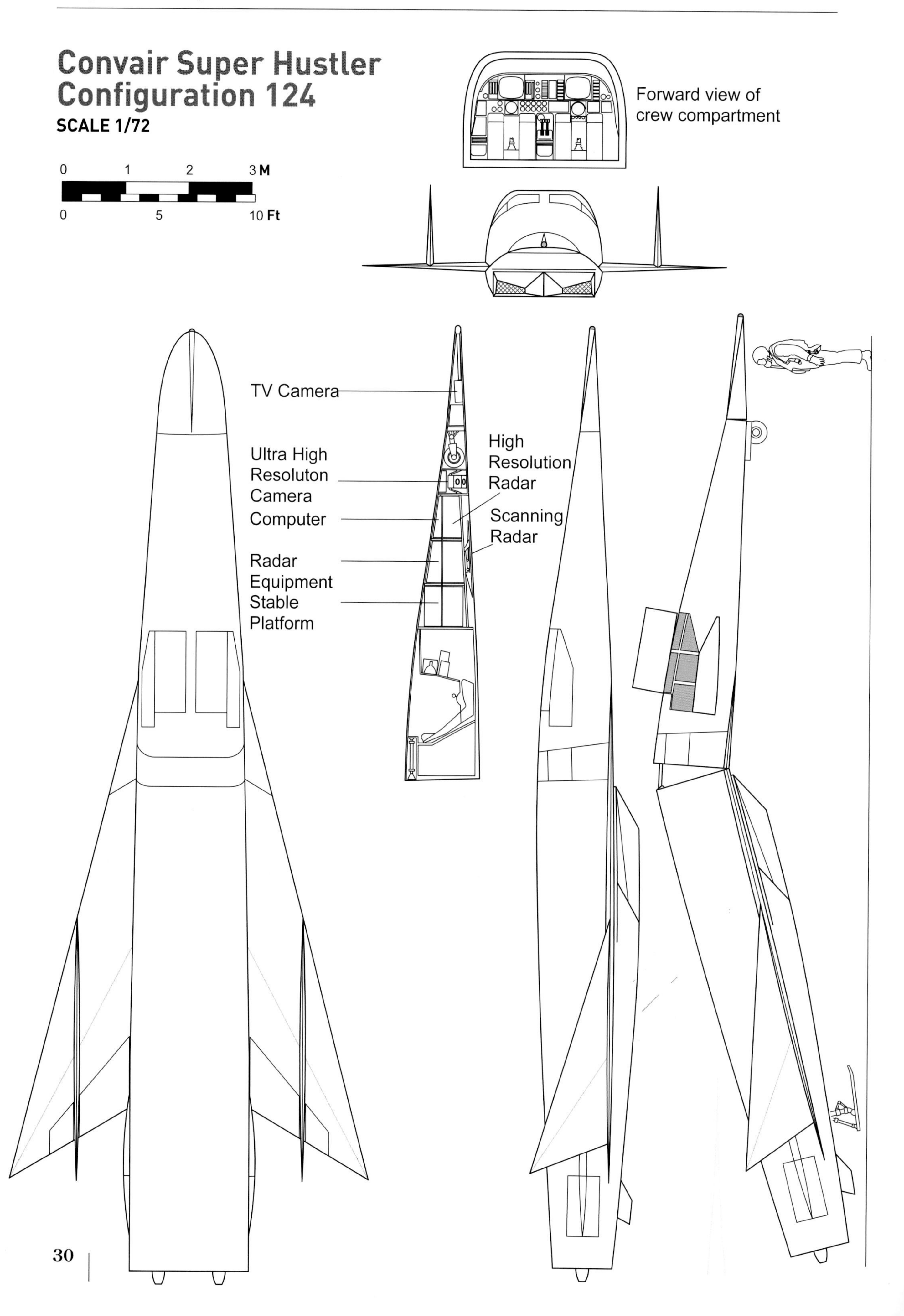
Convair Super Hustler
Configuration 124
SCALE 1/72
0 1 2 3 M
0 5 10 Ft
Forward view of
crew compartment
TV Camera
Ultra High
Resoluton
Camera
Computer
Radar
Equipment
Stable
Platform
High
Resolution
Radar
Scanning
Radar

replaced with fuel, the booster could attain greater range, and thus the vehicle as a whole could as well. With a high resolution camera system in the nose along with several radar systems (a 360° scanning radar with a range of 180 nautical miles and a high resolution X-band ground mapping radar with a resolution of 200ft at a distance of 20 nautical miles), the vehicle could reach somewhere around 6,600 nautical miles range after launch from the B-58.

The nose of the manned stage was required to fold down and back to provide clearance for the B-58s landing gear. This was hardly the only area of unusual variable geometry, however. The Super Hustler was low and flat and did not have a raised cockpit canopy; given the relatively low lift-to-drag of the vehicle, it would have needed to land at a high angle of attack. This would have precluded any realistic possibility of the pilot having anything remotely resembling decent forward vision during landing.

The aircraft was equipped with a television camera in the extreme nose, but for a safe landing at high speed something better than I Love Lucy tech-level TV would have been needed. So the entire nose from just aft of the cockpit could tip downwards twenty degrees, akin to the drooping nose of the Concorde but with the cockpit in, rather than behind, the nose. The end of the nose would also tip upwards to provide some clearance for the nose gear. A series of doors that covered transparencies over the cockpit would open up allowing the crew to actually see outside.

Alternative schemes were looked at including having the nose forward of the pilot roll 90°; the nose gear were be stored in and deploy 'sideways' from the underside of the forward fuselage. Other ideas had the cockpit tip upwards to give the pilot adequate forward visibility for landing, or tip out to the side; the nose ahead of the cockpit could drop like that of the Concorde, or panels could jettison from the underside, exposing windows that would provide the crew a downward and somewhat forward view.

Aerodynamically, the manned stage would have been an interesting mess as it came in for a landing on a nose wheel and two tail skids. This would seem to be an aspect of the design that would require a great deal of wind tunnel testing, and flight before it could be considered safely justified.

The fact that the forward fuselage could angle away from the fuselage created a useful opportunity. In the event that the aircraft was stricken, the entire forward fuselage would break away, accelerated forward by a solid rocket motor. It would deploy stabilizing flaps until it had slowed below Mach 1. At 30,000ft and Mach 0.9 it would release a drogue chute to slow it further; two 60ft diameter recovery chutes would deploy at 25,000ft and Mach 0.25 and lower it safely to the surface. This ejectable capsule was a feature that was fairly unique for its time... but it would become an operational feature of a vehicle that would ultimately descend from it.

The Super Hustler was to have been fuelled with conventional JP fuel, but considerable range advantage was envisioned with the use of high energy propellants (boron-based 'zip' fuels). Launching from Spokane, Washington, on the west coast and Loring Air Force Base, Maine, on the east coast, the B-58 carrier could fly the Super Hustler to a launch point 2,270 nautical miles out, heading towards the Soviet Union.

The JP-fuelled Super Hustler could access all of the USSR except the south-western portion before it would need to turn around and fly home; with high energy fuels, the Super Hustler could easily reach every point in the Soviet Union, drop the booster and the bomb, turn around, fly over the Soviet Union again and return home. Given access to bases beyond the Soviet Union such as in Pakistan, the JP version could reach all points in the USSR from two bases in the continental United States.

Range with a B-58 carrier aircraft was such that the entire Soviet Union would be accessible from virtually any direction. This would necessitate that the Soviets not only ring their entire vast country with surface-to-air systems, but systems that could counter a remarkably small vehicle travelling at Mach 4 or greater, 80,000 or more feet high. Some effort was devoted in the design process to reducing radar and infra-red signature; while by no means a stealth aircraft as it would be understood later, the Super Hustler would be difficult to detect at a great range and a nightmare to intercept.

The maximum temperature the aircraft structure would be exposed to due to aerothermal heating would be 950°F at the nose, 700°F along the flat underside. Boundary layer cooling was used on the nose to protect the structure; much of the rest of the vehicle, in particular the cockpit and equipment bays, used active refrigeration. The heat was pumped out of those sections and, via heat exchangers, into the fuel which was then fed into the engines. The cockpit was to be kept as a comfortable shirtsleeve environment, an interesting comparison with the Lockheed A-12/SR-71 in which the cockpits were virtual low pressure ovens, requiring special high temperature-capable 'space suits' for the crews.

Marquardt and Convair foresaw the possibility of raising the top speed to Mach 6 with advances in the ramjet. Mach 8 was seen as the theoretical limit with ramjets; while not discussed in available documentation, anything faster would most likely have required either rocket propulsion or scramjet engines.

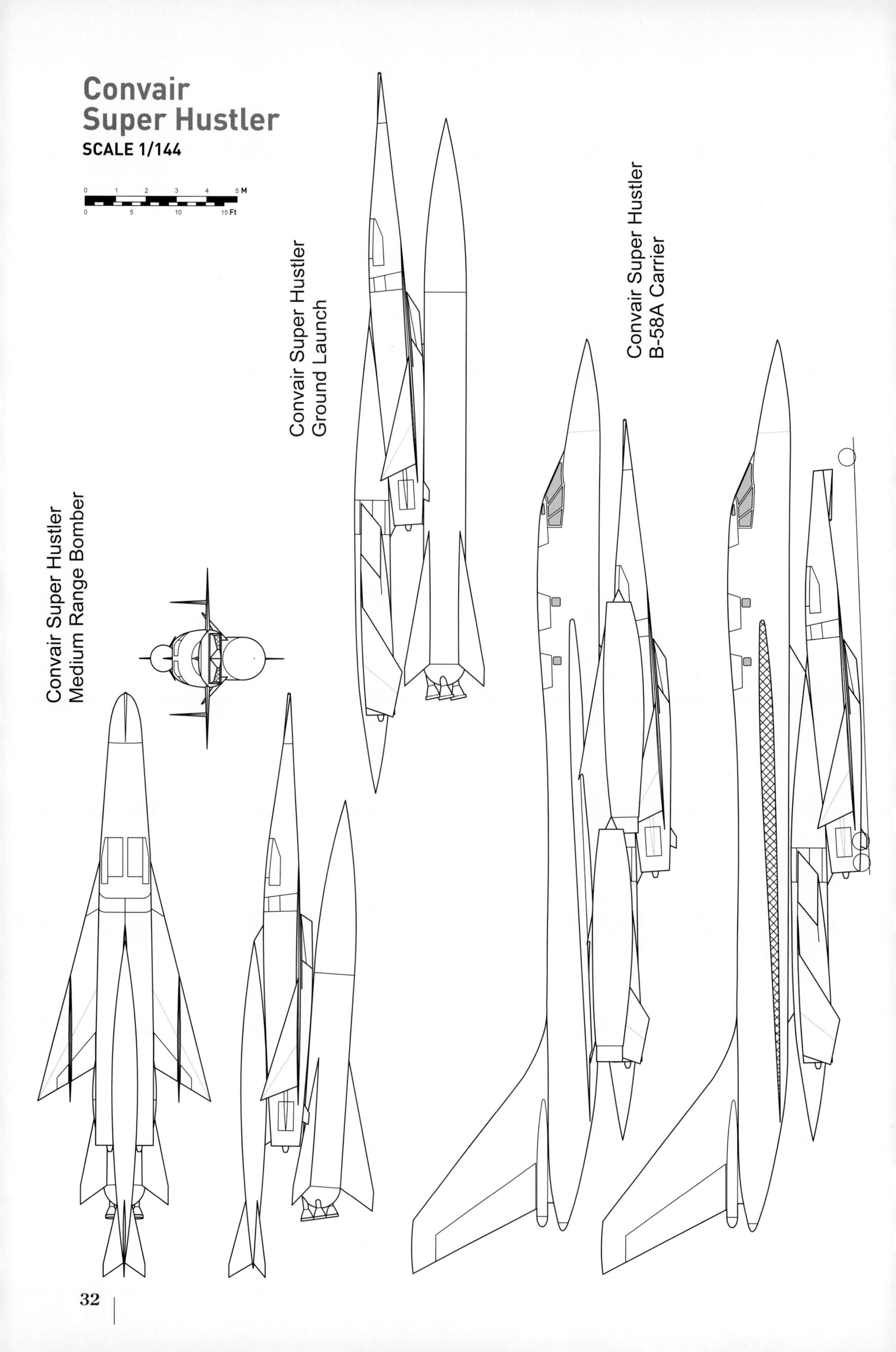
Convair
Super Hustler
SCALE 1/144
0 1 2 3 4 5 M
0 5 10 15 Ft
Convair Super Hustler
Ground Launch
Convair Super Hustler
B-58A Carrier
Convair Super Hustler
Medium Range Bomber

Navigation for the Super Hustler would have started with the B-58 carrier aircraft's astrotracker, providing high precision location and heading information up to separation. After that navigation would broadly be down to an inertial navigation system, with precise navigation and bomb aiming turned over to a down-looking radar sighting system in the nose. This would have looked through a radar-transparent flat panel.

Due to the small size of the aircraft, Convair estimated that first flight would occur three years after go-ahead, with production vehicles becoming available about four and a half years after go-ahead.

Convair proposed an alternate means of launching the Super Hustler: a large solid rocket motor could loft the composite aircraft to speed and altitude. This could not give it the initial range extension that the B-58 could, but it would allow the Super Hustler to be based in widely dispersed locations. The booster rocket envisioned was a solid propellant motor some 54in in diameter and 722in long (including the nose cone) weighing 61,600lb; the motor could produce an average thrust of 140,000lb for 90 seconds. It had four fins to provide stability during separation. It would loft the Super Hustler and its booster to an altitude of about 57,000ft and a speed of Mach 2.6, somewhere more than 30,000ft downrange. From here the ramjets in the booster would take over and the Super Hustler would fly an otherwise normal mission.

With high energy fuels, the mission radius would be 4,190 nautical miles. One hypothetical concept of deployment was in the region of Smoky Hill Air Force Base (now the Salina Municipal Airport) in central Kansas. Individual launch sites would be scattered around rural Kansas farmland in a radius of about 100 miles around the Air Force Base, requiring little more than road access for a series of trucks to transport the vehicles, launch equipment, fuel and personnel.

The Super Hustler could be launched from either prepared launch sites, or from road-mobile truck-based launchers. In the latter case, seven ground vehicles would be needed: a truck to carry the booster rocket and to serve as the launch platform; a truck to carry the manned stage; a truck to carry the ramjet booster stage; a crane truck; a fuel truck; an equipment truck; and a personnel truck. This would not be as seemingly simple and straightforward as the launch of a road-mobile solid propellant ICBM; some considerable effort would be required to assemble the vehicle onto the launch truck, and once assembled, the entire process would need to be reversed if they decided to move again. But once assembled, the vehicle could launch on short notice.

Essentially no liquid oxidizer was needed; unlike the contemporary Atlas ICBM, the system would not need to have vast dewars of cryogenic propellant on standby, only loaded onto the vehicle just before launch. The Super Hustler would rely on solid rocket propellant and JP-4 (or high energy fuel), all of which can be stored at normal conditions. Assuming the Super Hustler's fuel tanks didn't spring a leak, the vehicle could sit and wait for days to weeks. If it did spring a leak, and if it was filled with boron-based high energy fuel, the leak would have been immediately detectable due to the green flame as the fuel spontaneous combusts upon contact with air. The leak would have been in further evidence when, shortly afterwards, the entire vehicle would have exploded in a green-tinged fireball due to the small leak turning rapidly into a blowtorch which would have cut a progressively larger hole in the tank.

In the case of permanent launch facilities, the Super Hustler could be given hardened underground launch sites. Similar in concept to the early Atlas facilities that stored the ICBM unfuelled and horizontal in long reinforced concrete 'pits' with gigantic armoured doors overhead, the Super Hustlers would be stored horizontally in rectangular pits 85ft long by 25ft wide. Covers 91ft long by 31ft wide (and about 5ft thick based on diagrams) would protect the Super Hustler from weather and attack and would roll away when the time came. The Super Hustler and its booster rocket would be raised 65° upwards for launch.

A single Super Hustler base was assumed to have 45 Super Hustlers with 72 combat ready crews. The exact mix of fixed hardened launch sites and road mobile launchers is not available. The Super Hustler in this role would serve essentially as an alternative to the as yet unproven ICBM. Slower than an ICBM, more likely to be intercepted, the Super Hustler had the advantages of being recallable and, it was assumed, being more accurate.

An ICBM at the time was assumed to likely drop its warhead anywhere up to a mile or more from its target, but a manned bomber such as the Super Hustler could not only aim the bomb precisely via radar and optical fixes, it could also do on-the-fly bomb damage assessment. This would mean that sites that had not been adequately nuked could be nuked again; those that had been sufficiently converted into radioactive glass and clouds of angry vapour could be stricken from the 'nuke 'em again' lists.

A Medium Range Bomber variant was studied that also used a solid rocket booster for zero-length launch. In this case, the ramjet-equipped booster would be dispensed with; the twin-ramjet Super Hustler would carry a bomb pod – much like that of the B-58 – on its back, attached to the same latches that would have connected to the booster. The bomb pod, some 34ft 9in long and 32in in diameter, would contain a single nuclear warhead and additional fuel.

It would not have an additional propulsion system; it would drop unpowered.

One iteration of the booster rocket was 522in long, had four gimballed nozzles, a weight of 38,770lb and a thrust of 86,200lb for 90 seconds. Stability was provided by three fins at the rear of the booster.

Unfortunately, the available information on the Medium Range Bomber does not include range. However, given that the standard Super Hustler manned stage would fly approximately 4,290 nautical miles after releasing the booster and bomb, it's reasonable to assume that the Medium Range Bomber would have somewhat comparable range performance. This would preclude its launch from the continental Unite States to strike Soviet targets; but from European, Middle Eastern or east Asian bases, its range would doubtless be sufficient to serve a secondary strike role against Soviet targets. The Medium Range Bomber would doubtless have been launched from non-permanent launch facilities, like as not from the backs of large trucks.

As of January of 1959, the USAF saw the Convair Super Hustler as generally superior to the Lockheed Skunk Works-designed A-3 for the role of high-altitude, high-speed strategic reconnaissance. However, as Lockheed continued to work on their design, zeroing in on the eventual A-12 configuration, this evaluation would change. The logistical problems not only of a parasite aircraft, but a parasite that shed a large fraction of the carried aircraft, began to cast the Convair design into a bad light. As a nuclear bomber, shedding half an aircraft in the pursuit of a mission is cost effective... after all, the entire ICBM is expended in the goal of hurling thermonuclear warheads. But as a reconnaissance platform meant to fly with some regularity, during peacetime as well as wartime, throwing away entire aircraft with each mission seems a bit much.

So (as described in greater detail in *Lockheed SR-71 Blackbird: Origins and Evolution*) Convair greatly reworked the Super Hustler into the FISH: First Invisible Super Hustler. This was still a B-58-carried parasite aircraft, but one without an expendable booster stage. It also incorporated all the latest innovations in radar and infra-red signal reductions, producing a respectable stealth aircraft. But even so it remained a parasite. So the design was revised further into the single-stage Kingfish, which competed directly against the A-12... and lost.

While the Super Hustler, a parasite composite aircraft, was a throwback concept, it was sold as a step towards the future. The performance it would have provided would have been a considerable advance over what the B-58A could provide, flying around twice as fast more than 50% higher while carrying the same payload and presenting a smaller target. What's more, Convair saw it as a step between currently available and projected manned aircraft such as the B-58, B-52 and B-70 (known then as WS-110A) and what might have been the ultimate bomber concept of the late 1950s: RoBo, or Rocket Bomber. This predecessor concept to the X-20 Dyna Soar would have been, in Convair's view, a two man 'space bomber', a spaceplane launched into orbit while carrying a separate thermonuclear device to drop onto the enemy. Convair designed two slightly different RoBo vehicles, and while they had flowing curves and smoothly faired features in contrast to the Super Hustler's sharp edges and sharp corners, the fuselages and overall designs are suspiciously familiar.

The rocket-launched Super Hustler would, it was expected, provide a great deal of useful experience for developing and operating the RoBo vehicles. The ground and flight crews would already be aware of the procedures for launching large rocket vehicles; the flight crews would already have experienced the launch accelerations and vibration/noise environments. For all intents and purpose, the Super Hustler would be a space launch training programme. But it was not to be.

2 CHAPTER Boeing XB-59

Running parallel to Convair's development of the B-58 was Boeing's effort to design what would eventually be designated the B-59. Where Convair began the B-58 with supersonic designs from the outset, Boeing went through a convoluted path that included distinctly subsonic designs.

Boeing began work on the XB-55 in 1947; it was to be an all-turboprop subsonic strategic bomber similar in general configuration to the later B-52. However, in 1948 it was decided that the all-jet B-52 would out perform the XB-55, which was midway in size between the B-47 and B-52. Perhaps more importantly, the XB-55 would compete against the B-52, potentially damaging the possibility of the B-52 entering service. This was a problem because the B-52 was a favorite of SAC General Curtis LeMay, as it was the ultimate expression of a 'big stick'. Thus the XB-55 was cancelled.

The Boeing MX-1022 grew out of the XB-55 work – a study comparing smaller all-jet high-speed bombers with the XB-55. Instead of the full defensive armament that the XB-55 was to carry, the MX-1022 designs were intended to rely upon speed for defence. The MX-1022 study was continued after cancellation of the XB-55. The initial relatively conventional XB-55-like designs turned into delta winged vehicles and eventually began to gel into swept-wing designs.

In February 1951, Boeing began a Phase I contract with the USAF to develop a medium range strategic bomber capable of supersonic dash. This became Project MX-1712 and built upon aerodynamic research carried out under the earlier MX-1022 project. Boeing Model 484 was originally something of a catch-all designation for a wide variety of jet propelled bomber concepts (including flying wings of several types), but it had been assigned under MX-1022 so although the MX-1712 studies started with the Model 484 designs, these had to be redesignated Model 701.

Initial requirements for MX-1712 included a basic mission radius (with a 200 nautical mile supersonic dash) of 1,737 nautical miles, with a gross takeoff weight of 200,000lb. Cruise speed was to be 530 knots with a basic mission dash speed of 860 knots and a maximum speed of 1,150 knots. The engines were to be Wright J67-W1 turbojets with afterburning and the payload was assumed to be a single 10,000lb nuclear bomb.

Strategic Bombardment General Operating Requirements SAB-51 from December of 1951 and Strategic Reconnaissance General Operating Requirements SAR-51 from February 1952 began to lay out the requirements for what would become the XB-59. Boeing programme MX-1965 was an outgrowth of MX-1712. MX-1965 was seen by the USAF as a conservative backup to the more aggressive Convair MX-1964. It does not seem that there was ever any great enthusiasm in the Air Force for MX-1965, but there was concern that the more experimental MX-1964 might fail utterly, and the MX-1965 provided a fallback.

Project MX-1965 was an effort to develop a bomber capable of a subsonic unrefuelled mission radius of no less than 2,300 nautical miles, or 4,000 nautical miles with inflight refuelling. Supersonic dash – but not cruise – was a requirement of the design. The Wright J67s were replaced with a new General Electric engine, the J73-X-24A, which was predicted to have improved specific fuel consumption. The warhead was reduced in size and combined with a jettisonable fuel tank. The bomb/tank combination was to weigh in at 7,700lb, a substantial reduction from the MX-1712 baseline. Other advanced technologies were to be utilized... a high velocity 30mm cannon in the tail for defence, new aluminium and titanium structural alloys, inflight refuelling and new electronics and avionics.

With the great success being demonstrated by Convair, the MX-1965 programme was cancelled in 1953. The ultimate design, Boeing Model 701-299-1, dating from August 1953, was what has become known as the XB-59. But even though the MX-1712/1965 programmes were relatively short lived, a wide variety of designs were put forward.

Boeing Model 484-2-2 (twin engine pods)

Three early (March 1951) designs for MX-1022 were each labeled Model 484-2-2. They shared largely identical wings and fuselages, but differed in engine layout. In each case the fuselage was a straight-walled tube – easier to make than Convair's complex curvature, but aerodynamically unambitious with no concession to area ruling. The nose of the fuselage was a sharp straight-walled cone that quickly flared out to the full fuselage diameter.

Boeing Model 484-2-2
Dual-engine nacelles
SCALE 1/175

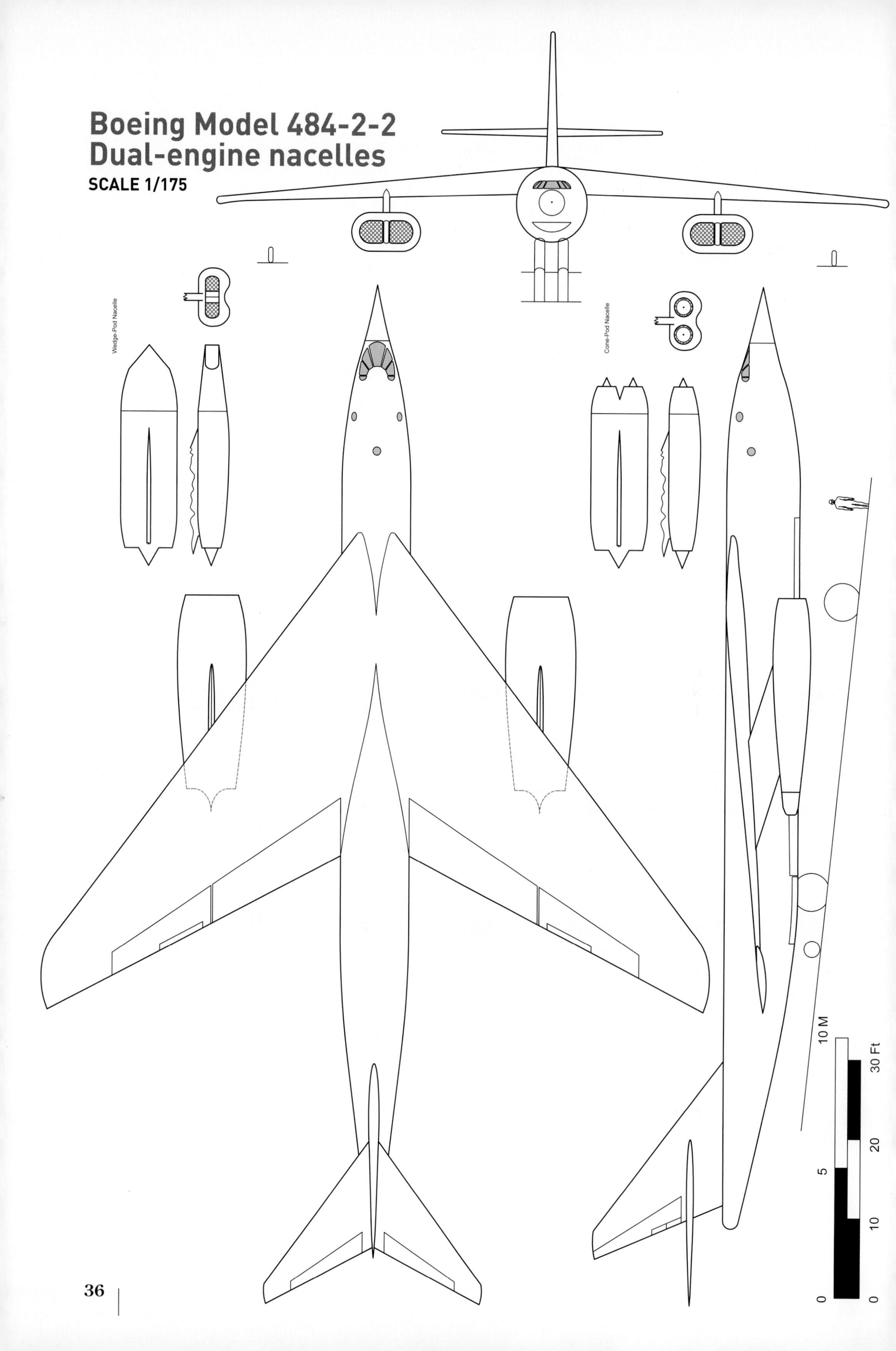

The crew were all in a single pressurized compartment at the front of the aircraft, equipped with flush canopies. The pilot would seem to have had a decent view of the world, but the ECM officer behind him had only two small side windows while the bombardier at the rear of the compartment had only a single small window in the top of the craft. The cockpit is wide enough that it seems likely that the crew could get up and likely change positions in flight.

The wings and tail were aggressively swept but not very innovative in configuration. The basic impression of the design is rather generic.

The Model 484-2-2 had a single bomb bay in the fuselage and a remote control turret in the tail with a pair of .50 calibre machine guns (it was expected that a superior weapon system would replace the two .50s). By removing a single fuel tank, the bomb bay could be extended aft, creating space enough to carry a single large standoff missile. The bomb bay could also be filled with photographic equipment for recon missions.

The first of the Model 484-2-2 designs used four jet engines in two underwing pods. Where the final Convair B-58 had four engines in individual pods, the Boeing design used pods similar to the Siamese nacelles designed for the Convair MX-1964. Several variants of the pod design were put forward and wind tunnel tested. These nacelles had long inlets optimized for supersonic flight with several concepts studied including conical spike inlets, 2D ramp inlets and simple flat inlets.

While the Model 484 design was essentially competing against the Convair design effort, the performance expected was nothing like what the B-58 would produce. The Model 484 designs would cruise subsonically and have a dash speed of only Mach 1.3. The conservative design ethic produced a design that was clearly inferior to the B-58 in terms of performance.

Boeing Model 484-2-2 (wing root engines)

The second of the Model 484-2-2 designs used four jet engines in wing-root nacelles. This reduced drag compared to the externally podded configuration at the expense of putting the engines in a less accessible position, making maintenance more difficult. Additionally, this necessitated long internal inlet ducts, reducing engine performance slightly. The trailing edge location of the engines also greatly reduced the size of the wing flaps. Other than these changes, though, the configuration was much like that of the podded-engine version, including internal arrangement.

This variant of Model 484-2-2 was, when MX-1022 gave way to MX-1712, redesignated Model 701. Some minor design changes were incorporated; the most visible was a change to the wingtips. Model 484-2-2 used small outrigger landing gear that folded up into thickened wingtips; Model 701 used spindle-shaped nacelles to store the outriggers. This design feature would reappear on future Model 701 designs.

A third Model 484-2-2 was drawn up. It had engines on pylons under the wing, similar to the first design, but only a single engine per pylon. Another engine was added to each side of the rear fuselage, the inlets just under the trailing edges of the wing roots. Otherwise, this design was basically that of the first design.

Boeing Model 484-415

One unconventional side road taken in the development of the XB-59 was Model 484-415. The diagram seems to be dated from June 1950, but is likely from a year later. If so, that might indicate that this aircraft was designed in response to the April 1951 US Navy requirement for a Seaplane Striking Force, which gave rise to the Martin P6M SeaMaster.

Model 484-415 was much like Model 484-2-2 but had one major difference: it was a flying boat. Numerous modifications were required to make this work:

1) The fuselage was deepened.
2) The landing gear was deleted and replaced with a hydroski.
3) Floats were added to the wingtips.
4) The engine inlets were moved to the leading edge of the wings to distance them from water spray.

Other details of the design are unavailable. The diagram shown on p39 compares it to the Martin P6M, showing that it is roughly the same scale and configuration. Since the P6M was not a supersonic aircraft, it seems that the Boeing Model 484-415 would have struggled with supersonic flight; the basic Model 484 was only barely supersonic, and the modifications to turn it into a seaplane would have added considerable weight and drag.

Boeing Model 701-238

Model 701-238 from January 1952 was an early design in the trend away from the fuselage used in the earlier Model 484-series. Thinner and sleeker, these designs relegated the bomb load to an external missile or pod rather than a conventional internal bomb bay. While this would have increased drag until weapon release, it would have lowered structural weight and post-release drag. Additionally, by using an external weapon pod the same benefits that were expected for the B-58 (using the pod for fuel tankage, for instance) were expected here.

Model 701-238 also included deployable canards behind the cockpit. Data is lacking, but the intent was likely for stability at low speed... takeoff, landing and possibly low altitude manoeuvring.

Boeing Model 484-2-2 Wing-root engines

SCALE 1/175

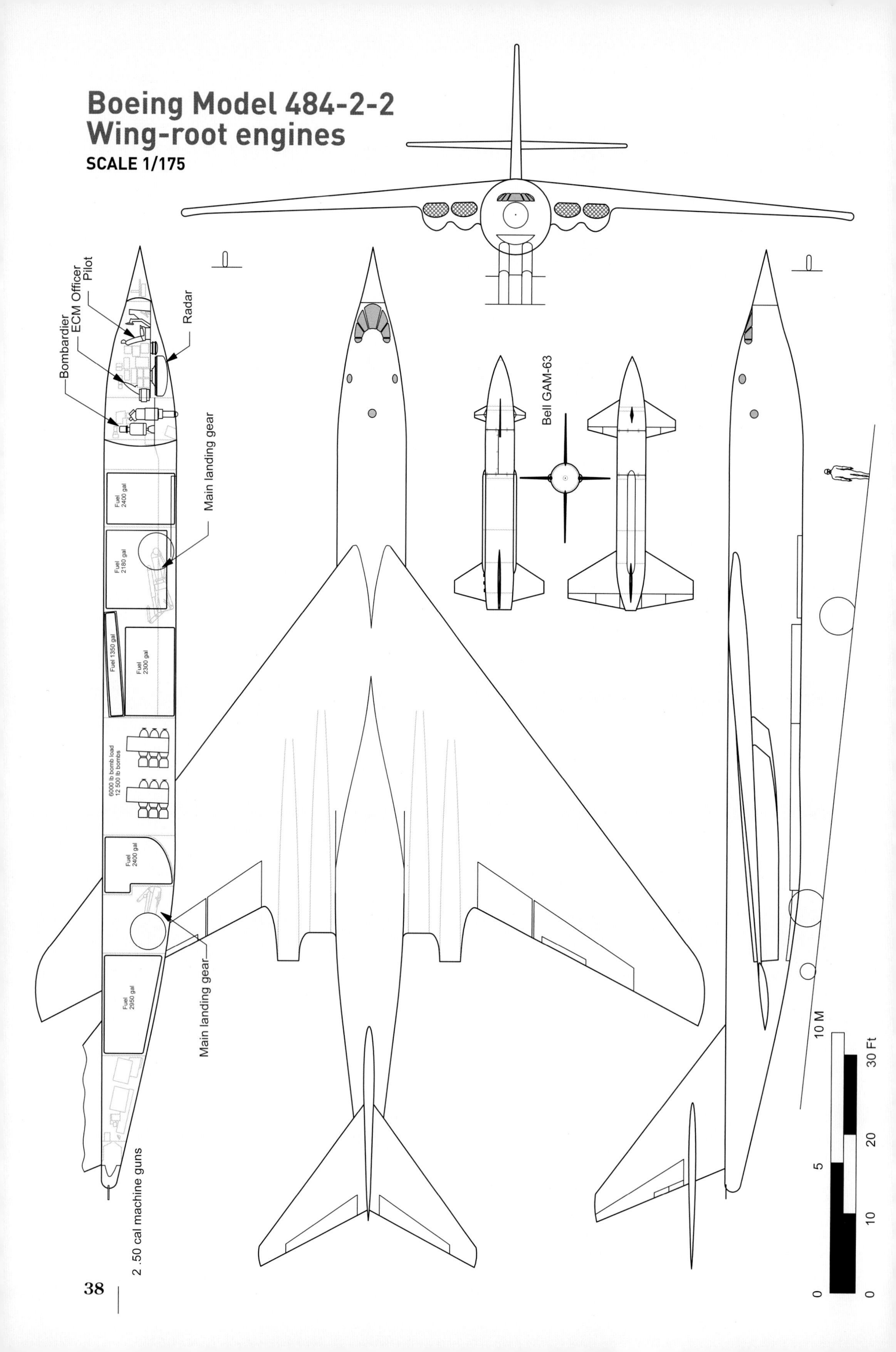

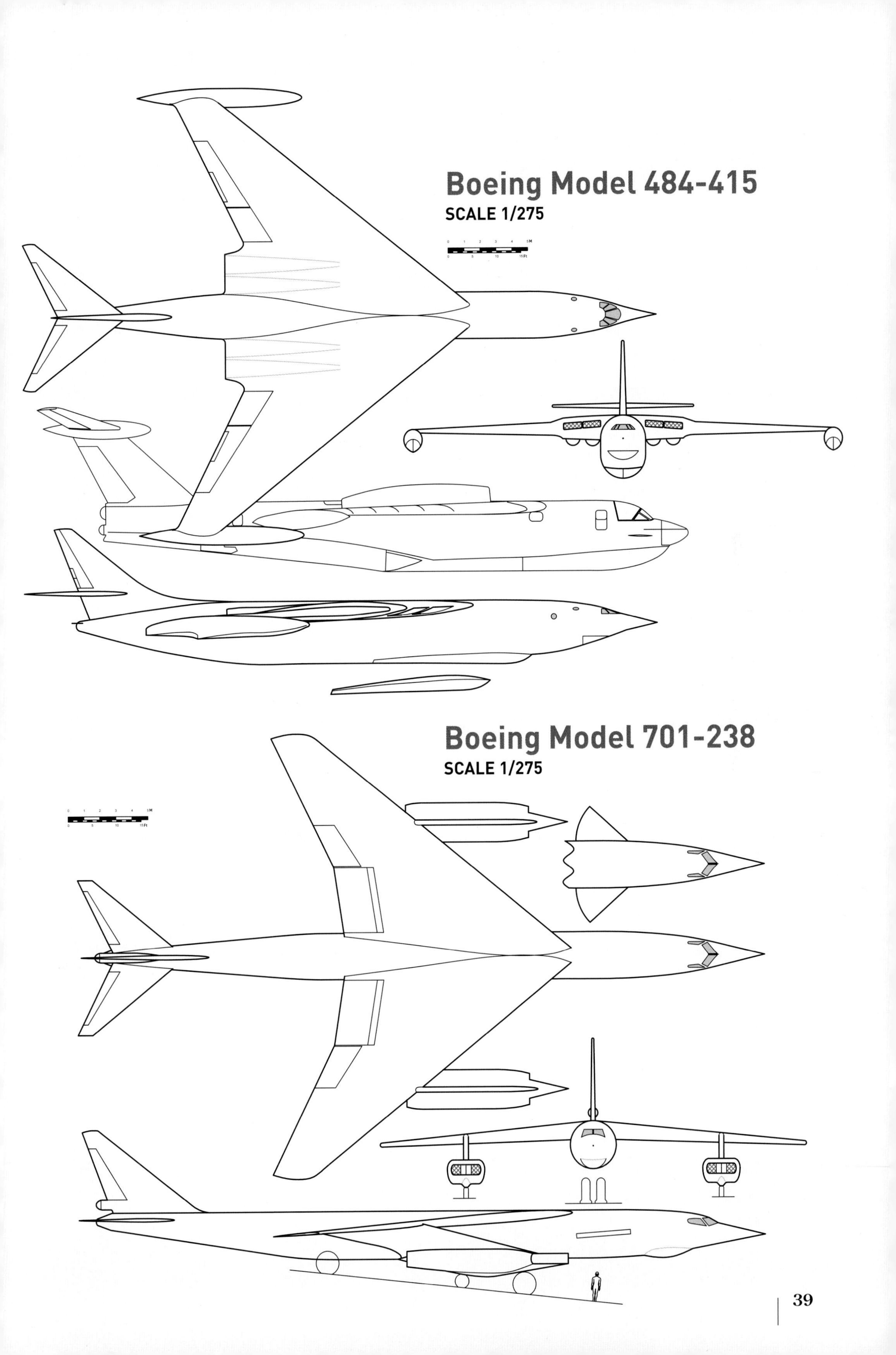
Boeing Model 484-415
SCALE 1/275
Boeing Model 701-238
SCALE 1/275

Model 701-240 was similar in configuration, but with a rounded nose and without the long inlet wedges. Model 701-242 split the four engines into individual nacelles.

Boeing Model 701-299-1

Model 701-299-1 followed a long series of prior designs... not only at least 298 prior Model 701 concepts, but a great many Model 484s too. The ultimate XB-59 design was an elegant configuration, if somewhat technically underwhelming compared to the futuristic Convair B-58. This was something of a reversal from the state of affairs with the conservative Convair XB-46 and the futuristic Boeing B-47 from only a handful of years earlier.

The XB-59 was a conventional configuration, a long, relatively slim fuselage with shoulder mounted modestly swept wings with distinct anhedral. The tail unit contained a rearward looking radar in a bullet-like fairing where the horizontal stabilizer intersected the vertical stabilizer. The radar was used to control the single 30mm cannon located in a flexible turret in the tail of the fuselage.

Model 701-299-1 was intended to be a missile carrier as well as a bomber. For the missile role, Boeing designed a stubby-winged turbojet-powered vehicle. The range on the missile was only 50 miles. For the standard bomber role, Boeing designed a large bomb casing that would be carried within the bomb bay... but which would also serve as a fuel tank, holding 1,000 gallons of fuel.

The XB-59 used the bicycle landing gear that Boeing had grown enamored with starting with the B-47; small outrigger stabilizing wheels would drop down from wingtip pods. The four engines, General Electric J73-X24 turbojets derived from earlier J47 engines, were embedded within the wing roots much like the engines of the British de Havilland Comet jetliner. This is aerodynamically clean, but makes maintenance more difficult.

A recon version of the XB-59 could be created by installing equipment in the bomb bay. Night photography would by made possible by carrying a number of illumination bombs that would light up a sizable region.

The Boeing MX-1965 design was put up against the Convair MX-1964 design at the Wright Air Development Center in 1952, and did not do well. It was too conservative, and was judged unlikely to meet its performance requirements. At the same time, the Convair MX-1964 was given high ratings, and went on to become the B-58.

It is interesting to speculate what might have happened had the XB-59 triumphed over the B-58. For that to have happened the Convair design would almost certainly have had to show some fatal flaw, allowing Boeing's more conservative design to win. That conservatism might have allowed the B-59 to have a longer, more successful career than that of the B-58.

The B-58, advanced as it was, was forever plagued with maintenance and cost problems. Worse, the introduction of Soviet high-altitude capable surface-to-air missiles meant that the B-58, designed to fly high and fast, needed to fly low and subsonically to avoid being shot down, negating the whole point of the aircraft. But the B-59, designed for subsonic cruise with only relatively brief supersonic dash – and relatively slow supersonic dash at that – might have been able to do better in that environment. Given the longevity of the B-52, it is conceivable that the somewhat pedestrian B-59 may well have served for many decades.

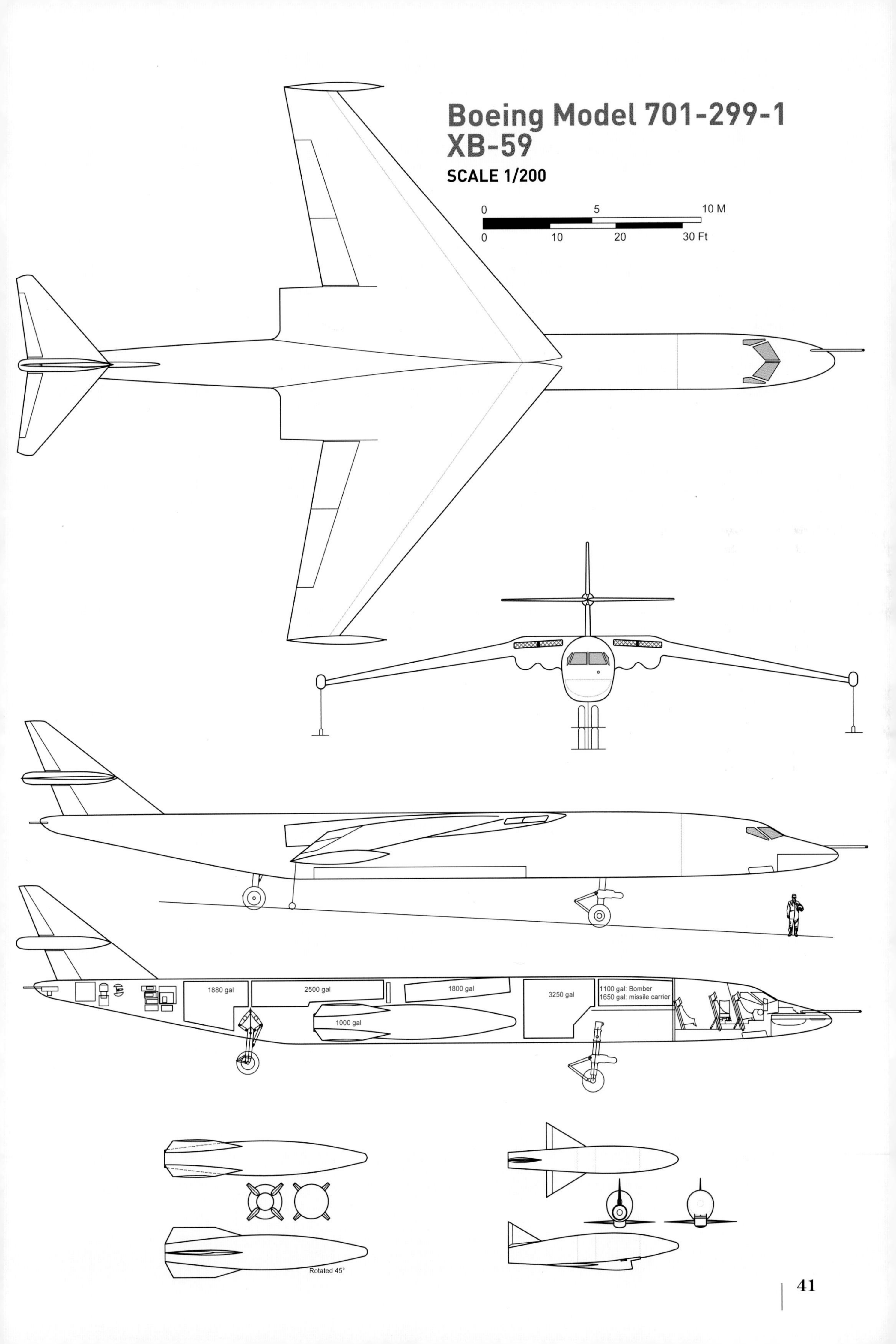

Boeing Model 701-299-1
XB-59
SCALE 1/200
0
5
10 M
0
10
20
30 Ft
1880 gal
2500 gal
1800 gal
3250 gal
1100 gal: Bomber
1650 gal: missile carrier
1000 gal
Rotated 45°

Chapter 3 Martin XB-68

The USAF's Weapon System 302A of July 1954 called for a supersonic tactical bomber that would fill the Martin B-57/Douglas B-66 role but faster. Its standard payload would be a 4,000lb bomb (later revised down to 3,500lb) but with the ability to deliver an 8,300lb bomb (revised up to 8,500lb) to a reduced range if necessary.

Companies including Douglas, Boeing and North American tendered designs and the contest, such as it was, took place from 1954 to 1956. While data is a bit lean there is at least enough available to describe these submissions.

Douglas Model 1364

The Douglas entrant of 1956 was similar in layout to the Lockheed F-104 Starfighter. Its long, slim fuselage had stubby shoulder-mounted trapezoidal wings a bit aft of the midpoint; the tail was equipped with aft-swept horizontal stabilizers and a vertical fin that looked slightly odd for the design. A single turbojet was suspended directly underneath the midpoint of each wing.

Curiously, Douglas did not opt for bicycle landing gear, even though the nacelles provided obvious and convenient locating points for outrigger stabilizer gear. Instead it had tricycle gear, with a dual-wheel nose bogey and two four-wheel bogeys for the mains. The four wheels were all side-by side, resulting in a fairly wide stance. The tandem cockpit gave the pilot sizable windows to look through, but the navigator seems to have only had small rectangular side windows.

The rear fuselage aft of the wing was lifted upwards slightly, presumably to provide ground clearance for rotation at liftoff. No particular effort seems to have

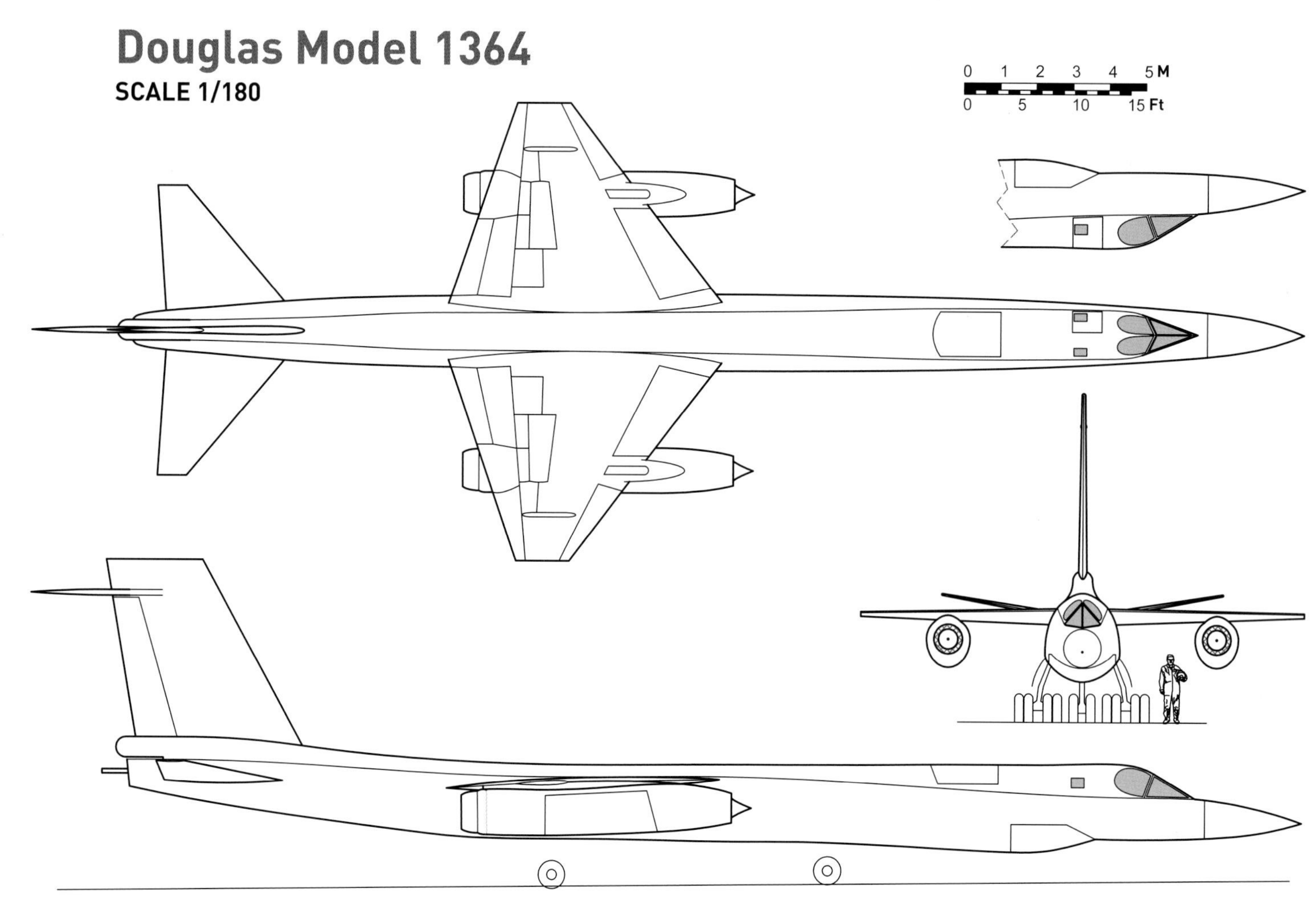

been devoted to area ruling the aircraft. A bulging 'chin' radome aft of the cockpit covered the ground-mapping radar.

Boeing Model 721

It would have made sense for Boeing to submit something like its B-59 for the WS-302A role, but the actual submission, Model 721 from 1955, was quite different. While the Model 484 and 701 concepts seemed to have resisted application of the area rule concept, Model 721 embraced it. The result bore a vague resemblance to the Republic F-105, but with its two engines bolted to the sides of the rear fuselage. From the side the fuselage seemed fairly deep and straight, but seen from above it displayed a considerable fluidity of lines in order to conform to the area rule principle.

The crew of two were seated under fighter-style tandem canopies, which look disproportionately small due to the relatively large size of the Model 721 fuselage. Landing gear was of the bicycle variety, with outrigger stabilizer gear folding up into narrow forward-protruding nacelles near the wingtips. The bomb bay was central and a tail turret, seemingly much like that of the Convair B-58, provided defence.

North American WS-302A submission

Unfortunately, North American's submission is known so fragmentarily that not even an actual designation is currently available. It is known largely from scraps... some notes with the basic data and some display models. It is from those model photos that the three-view presented here was created.

The North American WS-302A submission from circa 1954 was very much in the mould of the slightly later A3J-1 – a fighter-like plane with twin turbojets at the aft of a long fuselage, with two side-mounted ramp inlets, minimally swept shoulder wings, large swept horizontal stabilizers and twin tails. A casual glance could easily mistake the WS-302A for the earliest Vigilante configuration, as built as a mockup; undoubtedly work on the WS-302A informed the early A3J-1 design. Unlike the Vigilante however, the WS-302A had a conventional, if apparently small, bomb bay located in the centre section of the fuselage.

There are a few odd features to the layout. The inlets are at the front of fairings that continue straight aft to tail cones, with no deviation or broken lines; but the engines themselves are not within these fairings. They are moved inboard, mounted nearly touching, side-by-side. Thus there are two tail cones outboard

Boeing Model 721

SCALE 1/180

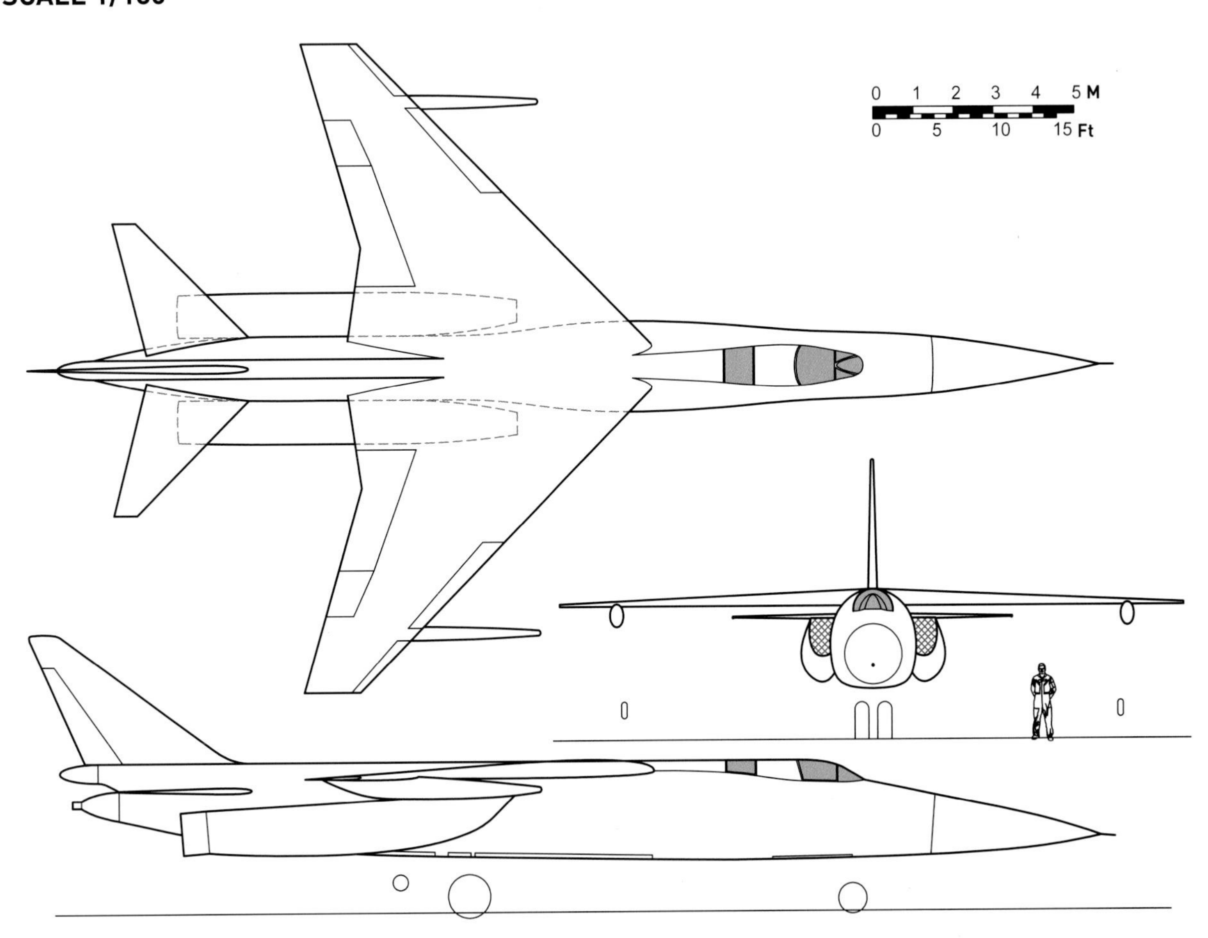

of the engines; the port cone ends in a T171 gatling gun turret; the starboard cone has the gun aiming radar. The fuselage was in the end very wide but quite thin; it doubtless would have provided a large proportion of the total lift generated by the aircraft.

Martin Model 281-5

Slightly preceding official WS-302A work was the Martin Model 281-5 from December 1952. One of a string of designs for subsonic and supersonic bombers, Model 281-5 was specifically designed for high speed at high altitude.

The Martin Model 281-5 was designed for maximum aerodynamic performance. The cockpit was fully faired into the nose; the wings and tail surfaces were all well swept deltas. The engines were in long nacelles, two side-by-side under each wing about two thirds of the way out along the span, the nacelles attached directly to the undersides of the wings.

The fuselage was long and slim, a rounded triangle in cross-section. Like the Boeing B-47, it had bicycle main gear with stabilizer gear deploying from the middle of the nacelles. It had a sizable downwards-looking search radar on the underside of the fuselage just aft of the cockpit; when not in use the underside of the fuselage was kept flush, but when needed the radar would rotate 180° around the roll axis, projecting from the fuselage and protected by a teardrop-shaped radar transparent fairing.

Armament is shown as consisting of a Mk 8 atomic weapon, which looks rather small sitting in the aircraft's bomb bay. The Mk 8 was an early ground-penetrating weapon, around 3,300lb with a 30 kiloton gun-type fission warhead. The wide lower fuselage would seem to suggest an ability to carry two.

With all that, it was only nominally supersonic, capable of 719 knots at sea level, or about Mach 1.08. It seemed to be optimized for that; at cruise altitude it would reach 517 knots (Mach 0.78). Presumably there was a high altitude dash at a substantially higher Mach number.

Model 281-5 was one of at least 11 Model 281 variants. Among the others were subsonic types with swept rather than delta wings, with the engines below and behind the wing roots rather than in nacelles further out along the span. No further data currently available.

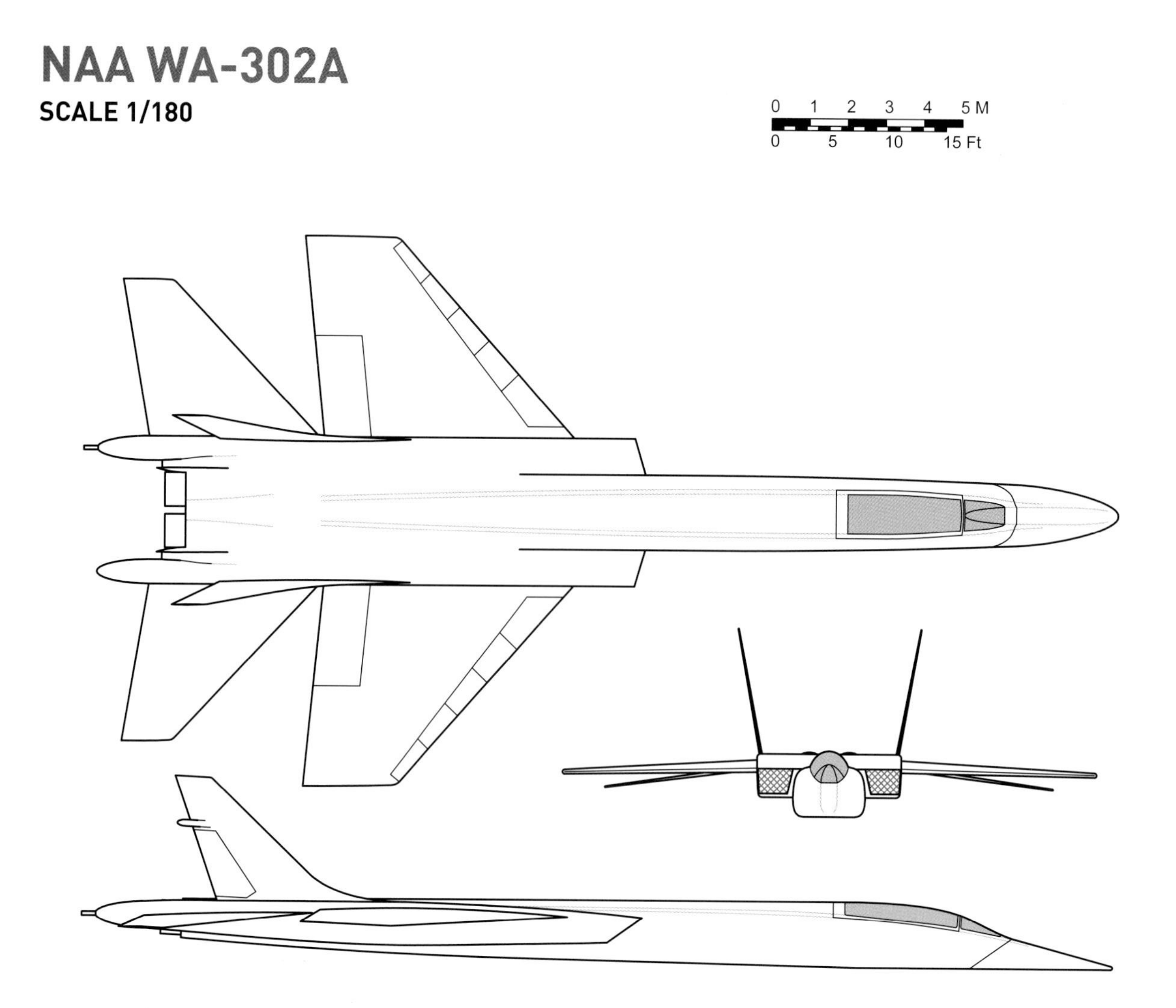

Martin Model 281-5

SCALE 1/180

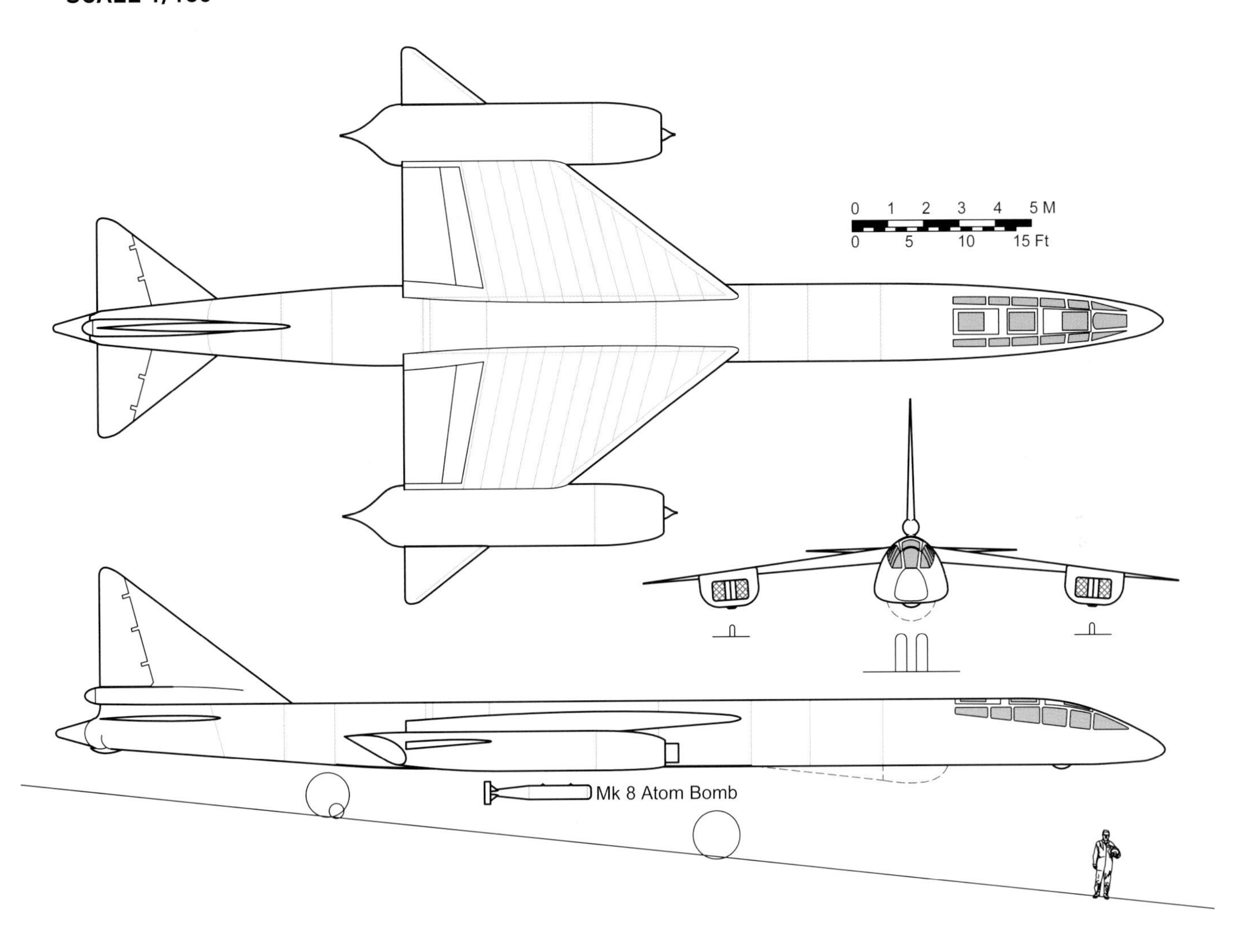

Martin Model 316

The first Martin submission to WS-302A came along in early 1955. Model 316 bore little obvious relationship to Model 281-5; it did, however, somewhat resemble the subsonic members of the Model 281 family in that it had swept wings with substantial anhedral and engines (two this time, with afterburners) attached to the rear fuselage, behind and below the wings. The cockpit was not as smoothly faired into the fuselage; a more conventional stepped canopy following aft of the nose cone. It had two crew – the navigator sitting behind the pilot under his own canopy, with reasonably sized windows to permit an exterior view. At the rear of the fuselage was a radar unit and a gun turret much like that on the Convair B-58. Above the tail gun was a tall vertical fin topped by an all-moving horizontal stabilizer.

Model 316 was to be capable of Mach 2 at altitude and range would be extended via in-flight refuelling using a probe-and-drogue system. The probe would deploy from the starboard forward fuselage, parallel to the pilot.

The landing gear was of bicycle arrangement, with two nose wheels up front and four main wheels further aft. Outrigger gear would deploy from pods at the wingtips.

Martin XB-68

Model 316 continued to evolve, by October reaching the ultimate XB-68 configuration. While clearly similar to the original Model 316, there were numerous important changes, the most obvious being the replacement of the swept wings with short, stubby and almost unswept wings. To allow for a Mach 2.4 dash speed, the minimally swept wings were very thin (3.5% thickness) with a razor-like leading edge – the same solution chosen for the Lockheed F-104 Starfighter. In a dive the aircraft was expected to be capable of Mach 2.5 and the top speed was such that aerothermal heating was an important concern.

Martin Model 316

SCALE 1/175

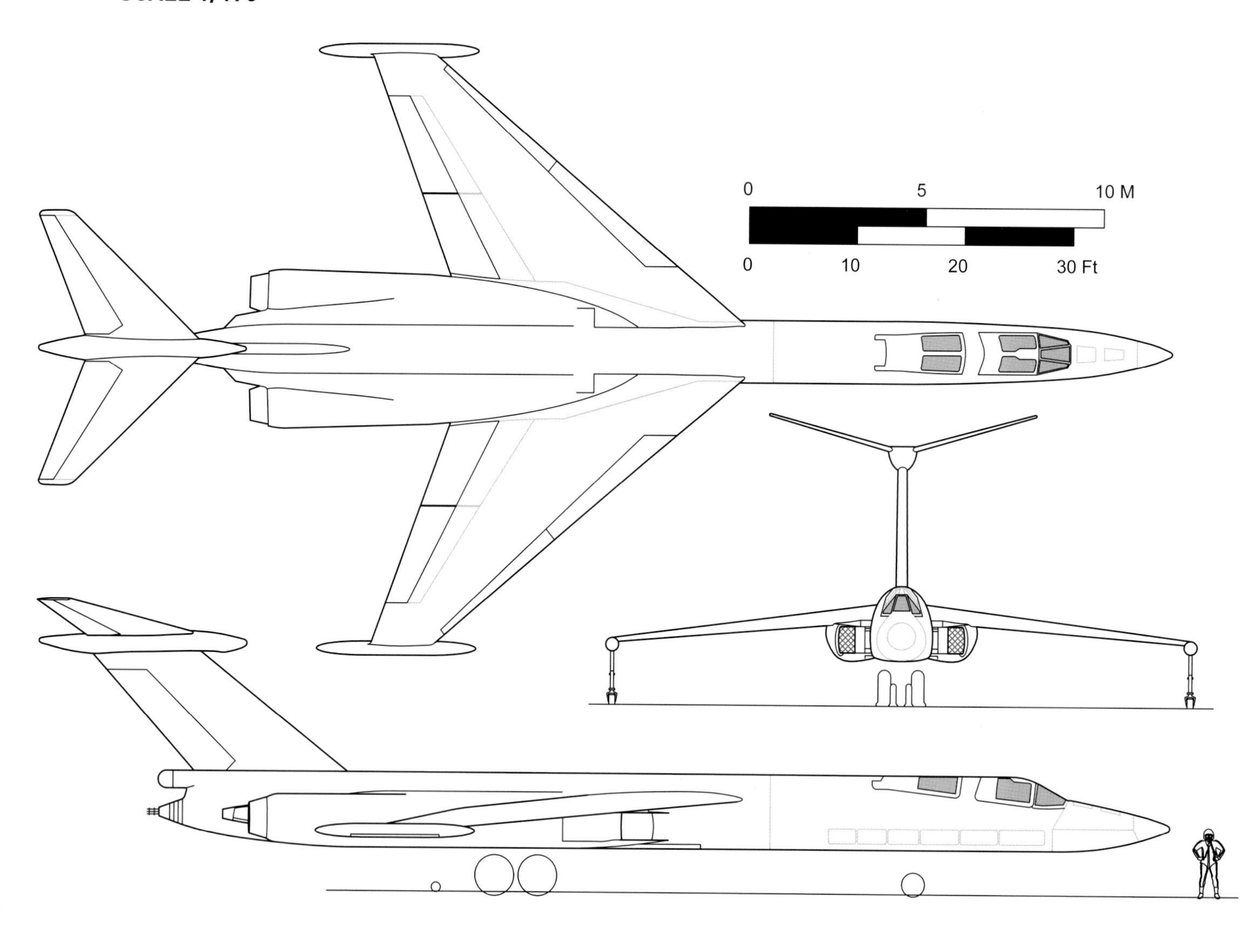

Honeycomb skins similar to those on the B-58 would be used; but unlike the B-58, the primary structural material would be steel rather than aluminium in order to withstand the heat. In places, titanium would be used; as with other American aircraft of the day – built and projected – the use of titanium was strictly limited due to the difficulty in obtaining the material. To keep the crew from cooking in the 350°F heat expected to be generated, an evaporative cooling system was planned for the cockpit.

The bulk of a B-68 mission would be carried out at high subsonic speeds and low altitudes in order to avoid detection by enemy radar, with a pop-up to high altitude and an acceleration to Mach 2.4 for penetration of enemy airspace.

The engine fairings were the other most obvious change. The afterburner exhausts were, as with the Model 316, quite near the fuselage tail; but the inlets now projected well ahead of the wing leading edge. These were to be variable geometry ramp inlets, akin to those later used on the Grumman F-14 and the McDonnell Douglas F-15.

Navigation relied on an inertial system, with radar fixing for assistance. The nose of the craft would include a terrain avoidance radar for low altitude operations, with the radar fixing antennae mounted just behind the nose. As with the Model 316, the tail also included a radar unit, used to aim the T-171E-2 gatling gun for defence.

Martin seems to have won the contract to build the XB-68 by mid-October 1956, but WS-302A was then cancelled in January 1957, a victim of budget cuts, priority changes and difficulties in developing the navigation system. By that time wind tunnel testing had been carried out and a full-scale mockup, clad in sheet metal, had been built. It does not appear that detailed and complete engineering had yet been carried out, though prototypes had been ordered. After

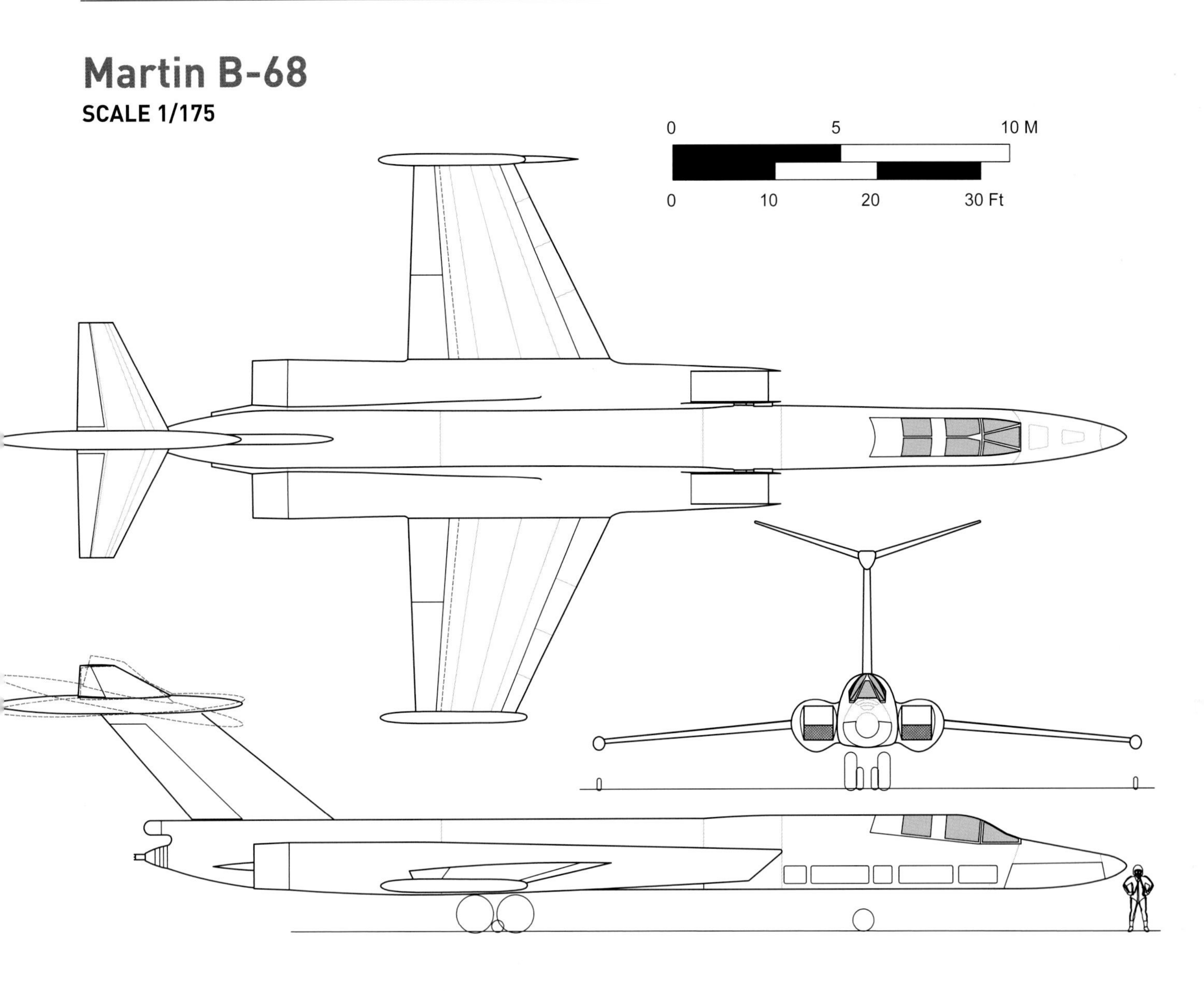

cancellation, the 'B-68' designation was transferred for a time to the Titan ICBM programme; the SM-68 designation was changed to HGM-25A in 1962.

NASA B-68 wind tunnel models

Cancellation of the B-68 was not the end of all work on the design. Several years later, in early 1960, NASA was still reporting on the results of wind tunnel model testing of configurations based on the B-68. The models tested depict it modified in various ways... the nose comes to a distinct point, the forward fuselage is stretched, the wings are reshaped slightly, the inlets are substantially different. The major changes revolve around the rear fuselage and the tail surfaces.

Two very different configurations were tested. NASA-Langley wind tunnel engineers fashioned a model of a modified B-68 with either a T-tail or a low tail. The T-tail was different from the original B-68 tail – longer, slightly more swept, with substantial ventral fins (either two fins or one longer central fin) and a smaller horizontal stabilizer than the B-68 original. The other modification stretched the engine nacelles further aft; the vertical stabilizer was much smaller, and the horizontal stabilizer was split into two fins, one on either side of the fuselage, attached to the extended nacelles.

It's unclear whether the models were based on Martin design work or were in-house NASA concepts. It may be that the tests used the B-68 configuration because the model and associated existing test data happened to be available, no longer required, and could be modified without irritating a customer. Or it could be that these tests were late-stage Martin B-68 design work, or perhaps even a post-B-68 Martin effort to wring some last bit of hope from the work that had been done. The available report does not describe the aircraft itself except to say that it is meant to cruise subsonically but then perform a supersonic dash at speeds approaching Mach 3. The T-tail configuration was found to be somewhat less stable at high angles of attack.

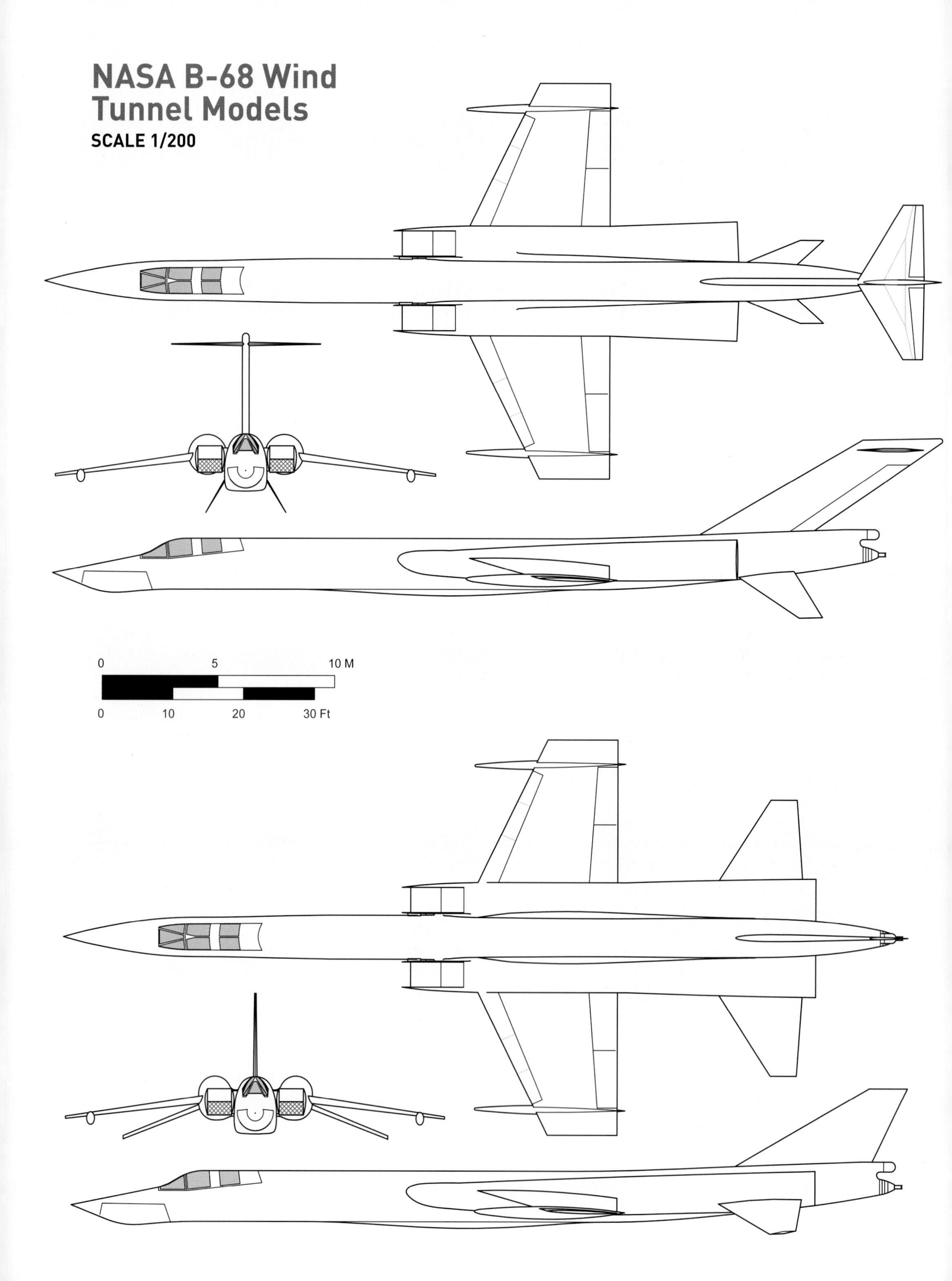
NASA B-68 Wind
Tunnel Models
SCALE 1/200
0
5
10 M
0
10
20
30 Ft

4 CHAPTER North American A3J-1

While it was not given a 'B' designation (due to the Navy eliminating the 'B' designation in 1946 in favour of 'A' for Attack), the North American A3J-1 Vigilante – later redesignated the A-5 – was very much a bomber. Unfortunately, though, very little is publicly known about the A3J-1/A-5 design evolution, and even less about proposed derivatives.

The Vigilante began life in late 1953 with the advent of the NAGPAW (North American General Purpose Attack Weapon) programme. This was originally a single-seat swept wing carrier-based subsonic aircraft using a novel way to deploy a single nuclear weapon. Instead of carrying the bomb externally, or within a fuselage bomb bay that would open doors on the underside and drop the bomb, NAGPAW called for a linear 'tube' within the body of the aircraft, running to the tail.

The bomb would be stored within that tube, situated at the aircraft's centre of gravity, with one or more cylindrical fuel tanks behind it. These tanks would be drained first and would be empty when the time came to release the bomb. At that time, the bomb would be projected aft through an opening in the tail, taking the empty fuel tanks with it. This method of bomb release was intended to solve a problem that had been discovered with high-speed bomb delivery – with a conventional bomb bay, sometimes the bomb did not so much drop from the bay as bang around inside it, buffeted by unfortunate and unwanted air flows. With a linear bomb bay, the separation of the bomb from the aircraft in a predictable fashion was virtually assured.

The NAGPAW aircraft was intended as a low-altitude bomber, 'tossing' the bomb and escaping at high subsonic speeds. North American suggested that prior to bomb release, speed for the penetration and pull-up manoeuvre could be improved with the use of a rocket engine attached to the rear-most fuel tank. For that purpose, one of the tanks would be full of hydrogen peroxide; jet fuel would be taken from the aircraft tanks to burn with the hydrogen peroxide in the rocket, substantially increasing the total thrust of the aircraft.

As well as having an unusual bomb stored within an unusual bomb bay, it was planned for the NAGPAW to deploy the bomb while undergoing an unusual manoeuvre. Typical bomb runs have the plane fly more or less straight and level over the target, dropping the bomb so that it starts off with the same airspeed as the bomber, and follow a modified ballistic drop to the target, sometimes several miles from the drop point. But as the NAGPAW would come in at low altitude, time from release to impact would be only a few seconds; as the jet was subsonic, it would be unlikely to escape the blast. So in this case the intent was to 'lob' the bomb.

Just short of the target the plane would pull up into a vertical climb; the bomb would be ejected from the bay when the plane reached ~10,000ft altitude, and would continue to coast upwards for another 5,000ft or so before coming back down. Immediately after release, the pilot would roll into a power dive to get away as quickly as possible. The bomb would drop vertically down onto the target, taking about a minute to do so, giving the plane and its pilot time enough to get to a safe distance before detonation.

The NAGPAW was submitted to the Navy in January 1954 as an unsolicited proposal. The Navy liked the concept, but wanted Mach 2 and high altitude performance rather than low altitude subsonic, as well as insisting on a second crewman to assist with navigation and targeting. North American went back to the drawing board and returned with a design dubbed 'Vigilante' in April of 1955. In July North American received a contract for NAGPAW II design studies, wind tunnel testing and mockup construction. Subsequently a contract with the Navy for two YA3J-1s was signed in September.

Currently, the configuration of the subsonic NAGPAW is known only from patent sketches and basic dimension and weight data; the path to the Mach 2 Vigilante through the almost wholly unknown NAGPAW II is quite unclear. However, photos of a full scale mockup and a diagram of an early wind tunnel model exist which show the Vigilante design at a few points prior to finalization.

The mockup is quite similar to the A3J-1 Vigilante as it would come to be. It is also similar to, though definitely distinct from, the North American submission to the WS-302A competition (see Chapter 3). It has two vertical stabilizers like the WS-302A, whereas the wind tunnel model has a single, taller vertical stabilizer.

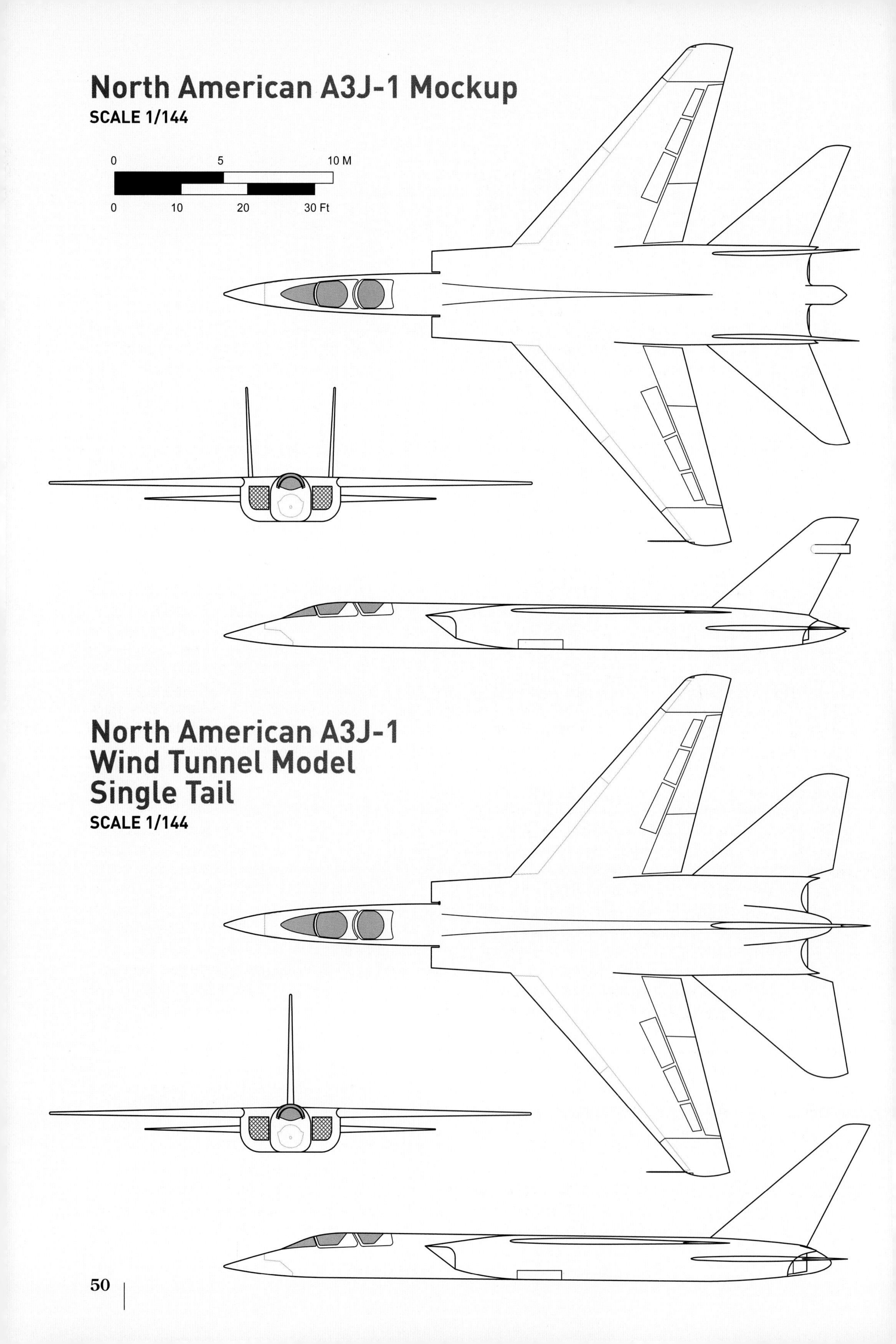
North American A3J-1 Mockup
SCALE 1/144
0
5
10 M
0
10
20
30 Ft
North American A3J-1
Wind Tunnel Model
Single Tail
SCALE 1/144

Doubtless the point of the two stabilizers in this instance was to reduce overall height in order to fit within aircraft carrier hangar decks, but a single larger foldable fin likely proved lighter and had lower drag. These early designs shared otherwise largely identical configurations, including sizable shoulder mounted swept wings, large horizontal stabilizers and tandem crew positions located well forward. The bombardier/navigator was given a sizable transparent canopy, while on the final Vigilante the canopy was largely solid metal with only two small rectangular windows. Both featured the same sort of ramp inlets as the Vigilante, but with unusual curved cutouts on the outboard sides of the inlet. Both featured the central tubular bomb bay flanked by afterburning turbojets, though the details of the tailcones were different.

North American A3J-1 in brief

The A3J-1 was largely built from conventional materials… steel and aluminium for the fuselage (with some titanium in high temperature areas of the engine bays) and aluminum-lithium for the wings and all-moving horizontal and vertical stabilizers. The vertical stabilizer could fold at about the half-span position for storage in aircraft carrier hangar decks. Similarly, the wingtips could fold upwards to reduce the aircraft's footprint on deck. The A3J-1 had full leading and trailing edge flaps for increased lift at low speed and a complex set of spoilers and deflectors for lateral control, while differential deflection of the horizontal stabilizers provided lateral trim.

This arrangement was sleek and low drag but by the early Sixties its limits were clear – the ability to carry just one bomb internally restricted the aircraft's usefulness.

The first prototype YA3J-1 – internal North American designation NA-233 – rolled out on May 16, 1958 from the company's Columbus, Ohio, facility. A slim and elegant-looking design, it was optimized for high speed at high altitude… quite different from its low-and-slow NAGPAW progenitor. Several months of flight test instrumentation installation, systems checkouts and ground run and taxi tests followed, with the first flight finally occurring on August 31. A second prototype soon followed with a first flight in November and a further nine early A3J-1s were delivered through 1959.

Service acceptance tests began in February of 1960 and concluded at the end of December 1962. These included carrier suitability tests aboard a variety of vessels as well as a weapon loading and bombing evaluation at Kirtland Air Force Base in New Mexico. The bomb originally planned for the A3J-1 was a Mk-43 device, capable of yields ranging from as low as 70 kilotons to as high as one megaton. The device was nestled within a cylindrical sabot, which held the small diameter bomb securely within the larger diameter bomb tube and connected the bomb to the first of two cylindrical fuel cans. At the rear of the assembly were four deployable fins to make the complete structure aerodynamically stable after release. The Mk-43 qualification for the A3J-1 internal bomb tube was cancelled in October of 1962, and subsequently the Mk-27 and Mk-28 were cleared for internal carriage. Additionally, the Mk-28, Mk-43 and Mk-57 were cleared to be carried externally.

The Vigilante utilized advanced electronics for the time, including a digital computer, a multi-mode Ku-band monopulse radar useful for terrain avoidance, an inertial auto-navigator that used radar for position updates, a television system, a heads-up display and an advanced integrated autopilot. For control, the A3J-1 was the first production aircraft with a fly-by-wire flight control system that replaced mechanical cables between the pilot and the control surfaces with electronics and wires. High pressure air was bled from the turbojet engine compressors to the trailing edge flaps to maximize lift at low speed.

North American built an improved version of the Vigilante by adding a hump to the back, noticeably changing the profile of the aircraft but adding a great deal more fuel volume. An additional hardpoint was added under each wing. This revised version was designated A3J-2 and first flew on June 30, 1962.

The A3J-1 was redesignated A-5 in September 1962 due to the Tri-Service aircraft designation system which unified the nomenclature systems of the US Air Force, US Navy (and US Marine Corps) and US Army. The A3J-2 and A3J-3 became the A-5B and A-5C respectively (more specifically, the A3J-3P became the RA-5C).

As the A-5 was entering service, the US Navy was undergoing a policy shift away from nuclear bomb-dropping aircraft and towards submarine-launched ballistic missiles. Impressive as it was, the A-5 was quickly becoming obsolete (at least as far as new policy and doctrine had it), as well as demonstrating reliability and maintainability issues. So procurement of A-5 bombers was ended in 1963… but production of the RA-5C fast reconnaissance version would continue for seven more years. The RA-5C dispensed with the nuclear bomb and filled the bomb bay with fuel tank cans and additional electronics; the hump from the A3J-2 was employed and a 'canoe' fairing on the underside held the recon equipment.

The RA-5C continued to be capable of performing bombardment missions, though the linear bomb bay was no longer where the armament was to be carried. Instead, the underside of the wing was scored for several hardpoints from which pylons could be attached; these could carry additional drop tanks, conventional ordnance and nuclear weapons such as the Mk-28 and Mk-43 bombs. The RA-5C never actually carried out

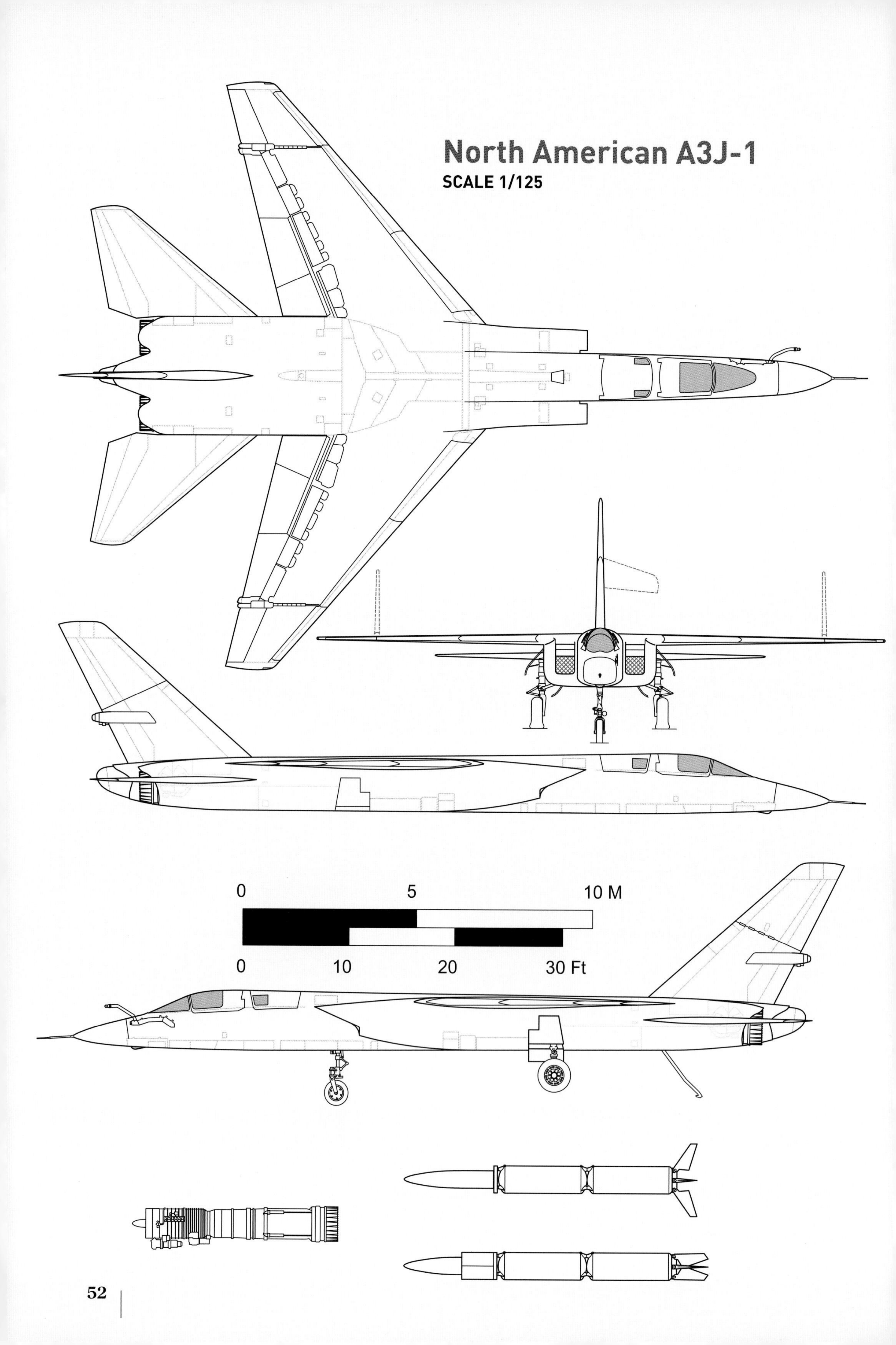
North American A3J-1
SCALE 1/125
0
5
10 M
0
10
20
30 Ft

the strike role in service however, instead providing admirable reconnaissance intelligence. The RA-5C soldiered on, performing largely reconnaissance roles, until the final Vigilante was retired in 1979.

Only a few derivative projects are known, and then only fragmentarily.

Retaliator

While the Vigilante was designed for the Navy, it only made sense for North American to try to sell it to the Air Force as well. It seems that several Vigilante-based proposals to the Air Force were made using the name 'Retaliator', including a 1959-vintage effort to create an interceptor. This would be armed with missiles carried externally and the linear bomb bay converted into propellant tanks for a Rocketdyne XLR46-NA-2 rocket engine to be used to boost speed and altitude. An earlier (circa 1957) 'Retaliator' was a bomber based on the A3J-1 vehicle, with not a whole lot to visually distinguish it from the naval version. Little is known about this other than the existence of various display models, which sadly conflict on some of the details.

The Retaliator was to be around 2,000lb heavier than the A3J-1. The biggest changes seem to be that the linear bomb bay was capped with a permanent tail cone, suggesting that the bomb bay was converted into a fuel tank and that all ordnance was to be carried externally (presumably on underwing pylons). The Retaliator arrived hot on the heels of the cancellation of the Martin XB-68; it is probable that the North American team proposed the Retaliator in an unsolicited bid in order to persuade the Air Force that it could still have the B-68 medium bomber role filled, but at lower cost, by adopting a modified version of the A3J-1.

Variable geometry studies

Through at least 1959 to 1965, NASA tested several variants of the A3J-1 configuration modified with variable geometry wings. As these are known solely from NASA wind tunnel test reports, details on just

North American Retaliator

SCALE 1/150

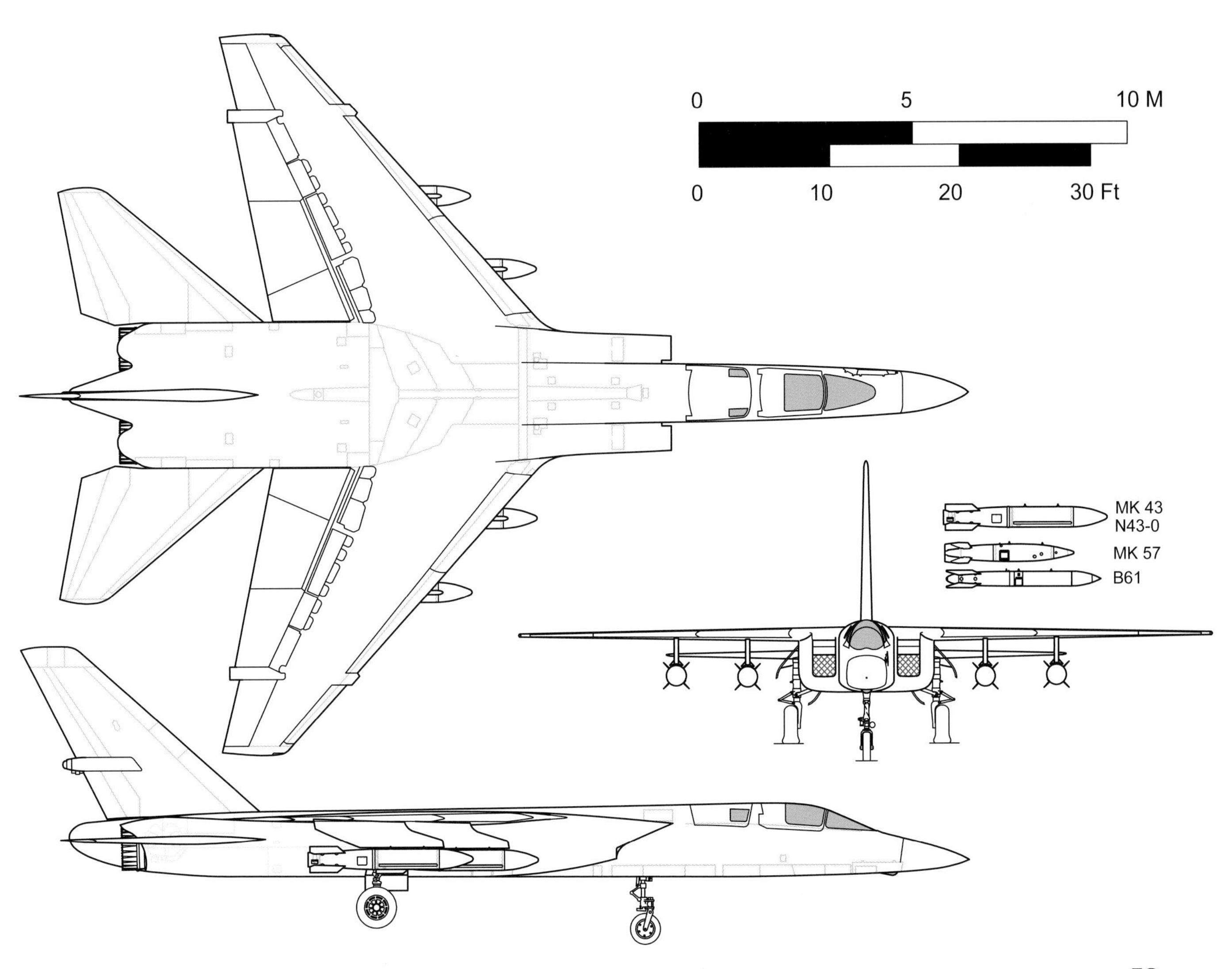

what the end goal was is unclear at best. These may have been tests done at the behest of North American, interested in expanding the marketability of the Vigilante; alternatively, these may have been purely theoretical studies, using the existing wind tunnel dataset of the Vigilante configuration as a baseline. In any event, the timing was not entirely accidental.

The late 1950s through the 1960s was the heyday of the variable sweep wing; it promised a combination of good low speed takeoff and landing characteristics, good subsonic cruise and loiter performance and low drag at supersonic speed. A number of aircraft emerged into operational service from this technological fad... the US fielded the F-111, the F-14 and the B-1; the Europeans the Panavia Tornado, the Soviets the MiG-23 and -27, Su-17, -20 and -22, Su-24, Tu-22M and the Tu-160, most starting life during the 1960s. Since then the excitement of variable geometry wings has faded; the Tu-160 entered service in 1981, the last variable geometry aircraft to do so. And while there have been subsequent proposals for VG aircraft, none have come close to production. The complexity and weight, coupled with advancements in aerodynamics, structures and computerized control systems have made variable geometry far less appealing.

But in its day, variable geometry was all the rage. So NASA tested a number of A3J-1/A-5 forms using several different sets of variable geometry wings. A very basic system of designations was applied to the various configurations; if there were any other designations, NASA or North American, they are currently lost.

Configuration 1 was wind tunnel tested at up to Mach 1.97. It featured the A3J-1 fuselage and tail mated to variable geometry wings with the pivot points located well outboard of the wing roots. This resulted in large fixed wing 'gloves' and smaller movable wing panels. The wings were swept aft to 75°. Canards were used in some tests, both with and without the horizontal tails. The use of canards led to reduced static margin as the wings swept aft. This would have likely required computerized controls; standard practice today, rather more challenging in the early 1960s.

Configuration 2 moved the pivot points inboard within the fuselage. This maximized the size of the wing that could actually sweep back and forth and resulted in a small wing 'glove'. This also meant that a large portion of the wings would retract into the interior of the fuselage, requiring a fair amount of space that could not be otherwise used for fuel or engines. It had, however, the advantage of putting the pivot within the thick fuselage, rather than the thin wing glove, meaning the pivot could be stronger to withstand the forces that will be applied to it from many directions.

The main disadvantage was that the aerodynamic centre of the aircraft would shift fore and aft a considerable distance as the wing moved, requiring that the wing either translate fore and aft to compensate (a heavy, complex and space-consuming system) or use large control surface deflections, resulting in considerable drag. The maximum sweep of the wings was 70.5°.

Configuration 3 was Configuration 1 modified to allow the wings to sweep even further aft: to 113°. This folded them back onto the fuselage, and resulted in an almost wingless configuration; lift would be generated by the fuselage and the stub wings formed by the wing roots. This configuration was considered most appropriate for a high-speed, low altitude attack aircraft. Clearly no ordnance could be hung under the wings, at least if the plane was going to fully sweep its wings; missile and bombs would have to be carried internally or hung from body-attached pylons.

The design was changed again to produce 'Configuration III', (no explanation was given for the change from Arabic to Roman numerals, nor for the re-use of 'Configuration Three') a double-inboard-pivot configuration. It had a large sweepable wing with an inboard pivot like Configuration 2, but was able to sweep the small wing glove as well. The advantage of this was that there would be no discontinuities in the wing leading edge as the wing swept fore and aft. This configuration, while more complex than the single pivot designs, demonstrated increased stability. It reduced the unfortunate contribution the glove makes to pitch-up with the wings at full spread. The wing glove retracting into the fuselage as the main wing extended would of course be more complex and require yet more internal volume... but it seemed to negate much of the aerodynamic centre shifting problems of Configuration 2. This design was tested at up to Mach 2.2. Maximum wing sweep was 71.5°.

Configuration IV was much like Configuration III, but with the wing and pivot point translated somewhat further aft.

Several years later, another variation was evaluated and reported on. A model with a 'free floating apex' was studied in hopes of reducing some of the problems with the double-pivot configuration. Rather than being retracted into the fuselage, the free-floating apex allowed the glove to pitch nose-down like an all-moving horizontal stabilizer. Thus the lift and drag of the glove could be adjusted for any flight regime; it could be positioned to have a zero angle of attack with respect to the airstream, eliminating lift generation altogether. By being free-floating, the glove would automatically adjust itself to the conditions at hand.

The NASA studies showed definite potential for variable sweep wings, but these were never applied to the actual Vigilante. They would, however, prove useful for the imminent TFX studies.

North American A3J-1 Variable Geometry Configurations

SCALE 1/180

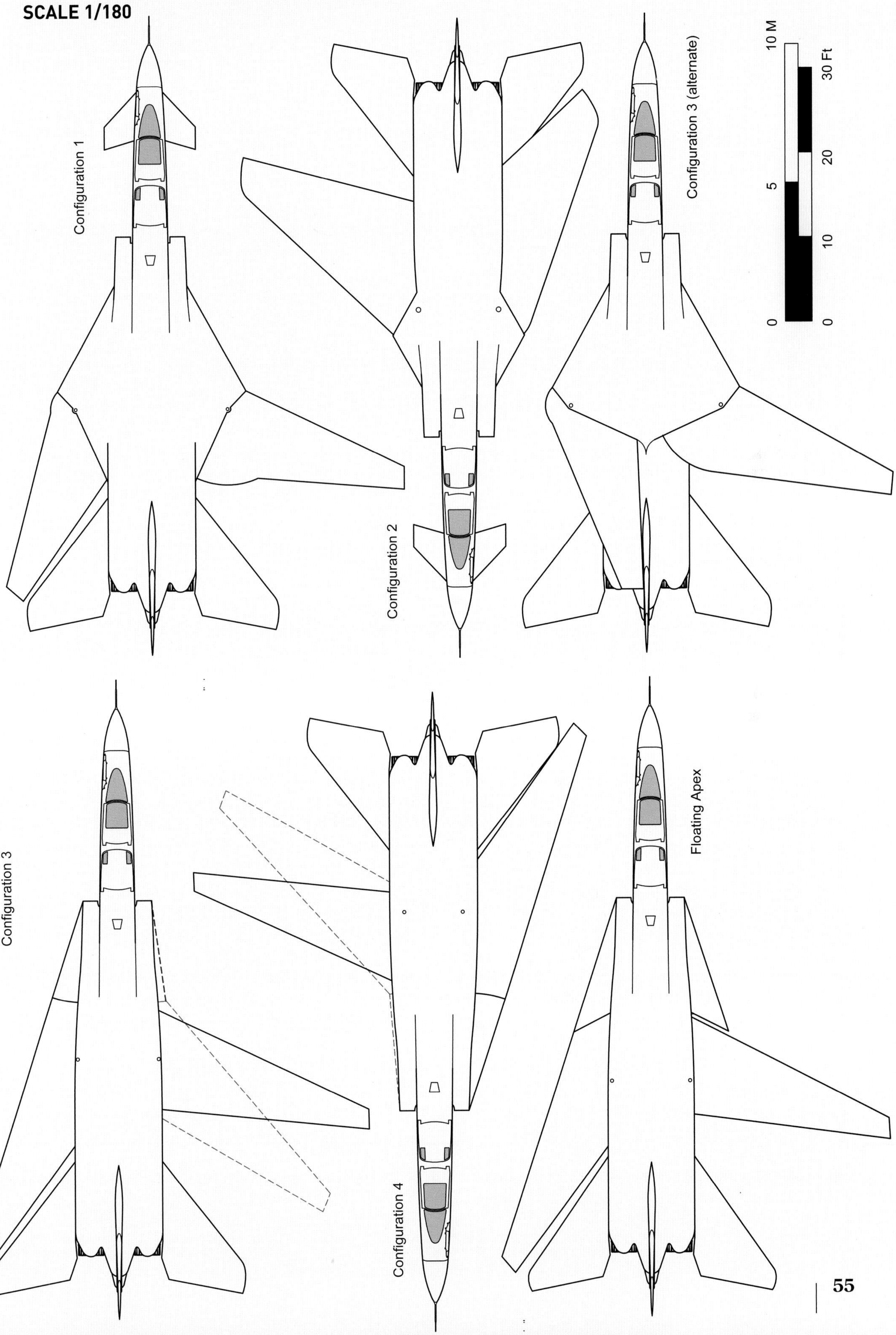

Configuration 1

Configuration 2

Configuration 3 (alternate)

10 M
5
0
30 Ft
20
10
0

Configuration 3

Configuration 4

Floating Apex

5 CHAPTER North American XB-70

Almost unquestionably, the North American Aviation XB-70 is the ultimate example of the supersonic bomber. It was big, fast, pretty, and very, very expensive. As it happened, one of these factors turned out to be much more important than all the others put together.

The year before the B-52 entered service in 1955, the USAF issued General Operation Requirement Number 38. GOR 38 called for the next generation of bomber, the plane to replace the not-yet-operational B-52. It was vague but looked towards the future, with both conventional turbojets and nuclear power as propulsion options.

At the time, nuclear powered *everything* was seen as not only likely but probable; nuclear powered cities and ships were already a reality (the USS *Nautilus* having entered service in 1954). The Army looked forward to nuclear powered tanks; the Ford Motor Company would soon begin to publicize their notion of a nuclear powered family automobile. Aircraft powered by nuclear reactors seemed entirely feasible, if perhaps technically risky.

Whatever the GOR 38 bomber would be, General LeMay wanted it to enter service in 1963. This was an important date because the earliest B-52s would start to retire by then and it was planned that the last B-52s would be built that year. And clearly, the B-52 would be horribly obsolete just a few years after that.

In late 1954 the Air Force decided to officially embark on a nuclear powered bomber programme under Weapon System 125A (which will be described in greater detail in Volume 2). This was still vague about exactly what kind of aircraft was to be built; supersonic cruise would be great, but supersonic dash with subsonic cruise would also work. It all would depend on what technologies could be ready in time.

And while there were those in the Air Force who seemed confident that nuclear powered bombers could be made operational by the mid-1960s, others were skeptical. A fallback option was put in place in the form of Weapon System 110A which called for a conventional chemically-propelled bomber.

While less impressive than a nuclear powered bomber of near unlimited range, the WS-110A at least promised an aircraft that would actually exist. To meet the operational deadline of 1963, the mockup would need to be inspected by October 1957, the first flight by September 1960, and the first operational aircraft would enter the Strategic Air Command inventory by November 1962.

The call went out to the American aviation industry in April 1955 to design a bomber that could carry free-fall bombs and missiles to targets deep within the Soviet Union. The bomber would need to launch within 30 minutes, cruise at a minimum of Mach 0.9, and possess a dash speed as fast as possible for at least 1,000 nautical miles, with 2,000 nautical miles preferred. The minimum unrefuelled radius was to be 4,000 nautical miles (5,500 nautical miles being desired) and the combat ceiling would be 60,000ft… 70,000ft or greater if possible.

Boeing 702 MX-2145

For project MX-2145, Boeing studied a wide variety of high altitude heavy bomber concepts, mixing subsonic B-52-like aircraft with supersonic designs, turbojets with turboprops, chemical fuel with nuclear propulsion. Reported on in January of 1954, before the WS-110A programme began, these designs were apparently quite preliminary parametric studies to get a sense of what could and should be possible. Payloads ranged from 10,000lb to 20,000lb to 40,000lb, with the bomb bay set as the same size as that of the B-52 due to a lack of specific detail on possible payloads.

Radius of action was set at a minimum of 3,000 nautical miles, 5,000 nautical miles maximum (a maximum that would certainly have been exceeded had the nuclear propulsion systems come to pass). Both inflight refuelled and unrefuelled were to be considered. All designs were meant to be manned, with a crew of six. A first flight of 1959 was projected.

One of the designs – not given a designation in the fragmentary report on hand, but apparently a Model 702 – set the stage for the Mach 3 studies to come. A remarkably long and slim fuselage of 'Coke bottle' shape for area ruling was fitted with a large swept wing and a conventional swept tail. Much of the wing served as fuel tankage; any volume in the fuselage that was not devoted to the bombs, the landing gear or the cockpit was similarly stuffed with fuel. However, the landing gear, which appears on the relatively simple diagram to be similar to the quadrupedal gear of the B-52, took up a surprising amount of space in the fuselage.

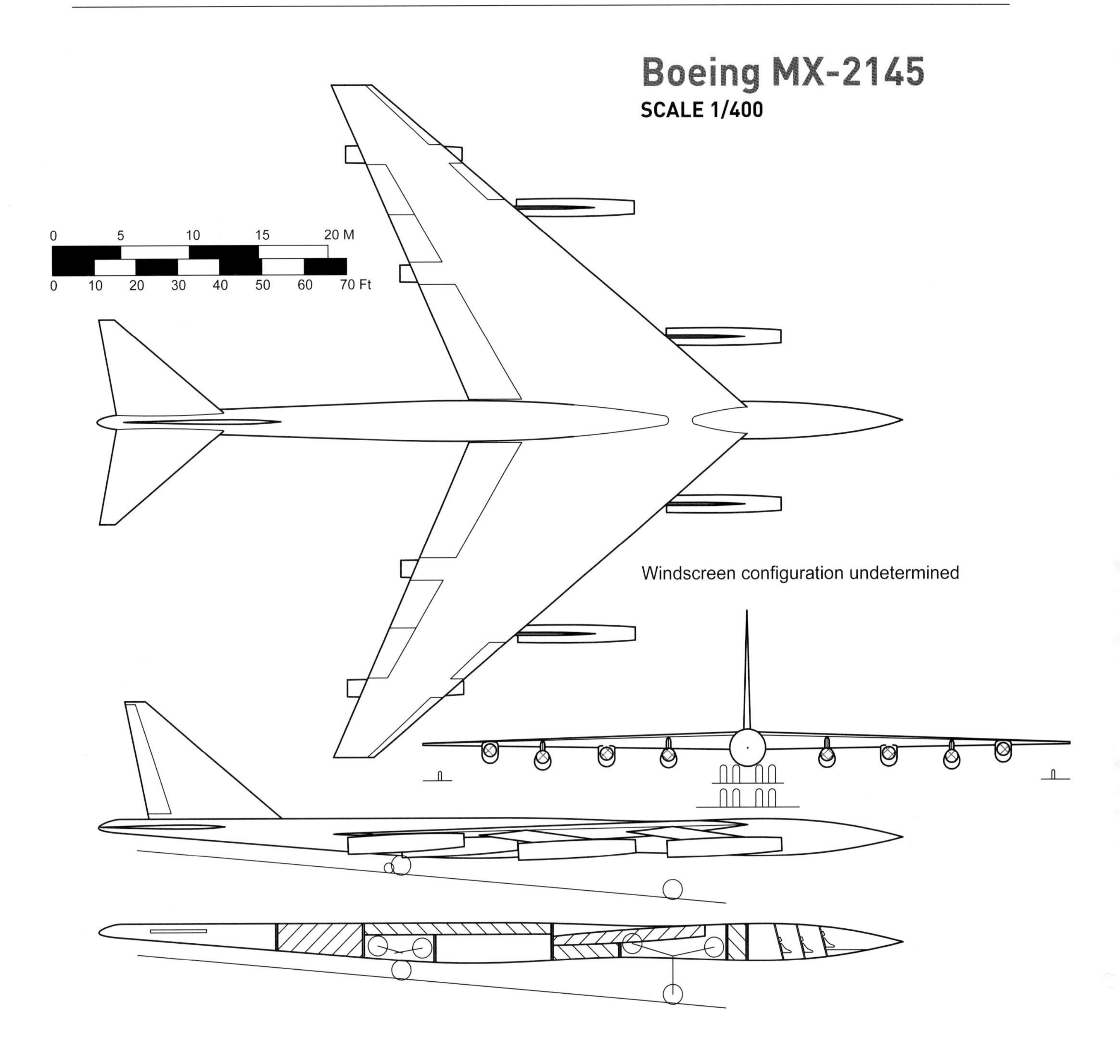

Each wing had four turbojets underneath it, all in separate nacelles… two attached directly to the underside of the wing with their nozzles just aft of the trailing edge, two projecting forward beneath pylons, the nozzles just below the leading edge. The design was modified into smaller versions with six and four engines, and 4,500sq ft and 3,000sq ft of wing area respectively. Apparently the eight-engined aircraft could theoretically fulfill its mission, at the cost of a 600,000lb gross weight.

Boeing 713

Initiated in June of 1954 and reported on in August, the Model 713-1-101 was a further advancement on the MX-2145 studies. Again both nuclear and chemical systems were considered; in this case, both propulsion systems were considered for this same aircraft. Shown here is the fully chemically fuelled version. The nuclear propelled version (Model 713-2-102; chemical designs received a -1, nuclear designs a -2) was largely identical in configuration except for the inclusion of notably larger nacelles. The reactor in that concept would have been installed into the fuel tank just behind the bomb bay. The crew cabin would also have to have been massively shielded.

The chemical version was a fairly conventional supersonic design, vaguely like a stretched Convair B-58. The wings were swept, not truly delta; relatively small horizontal stabilizers were fitted to the tail of the fuselage.

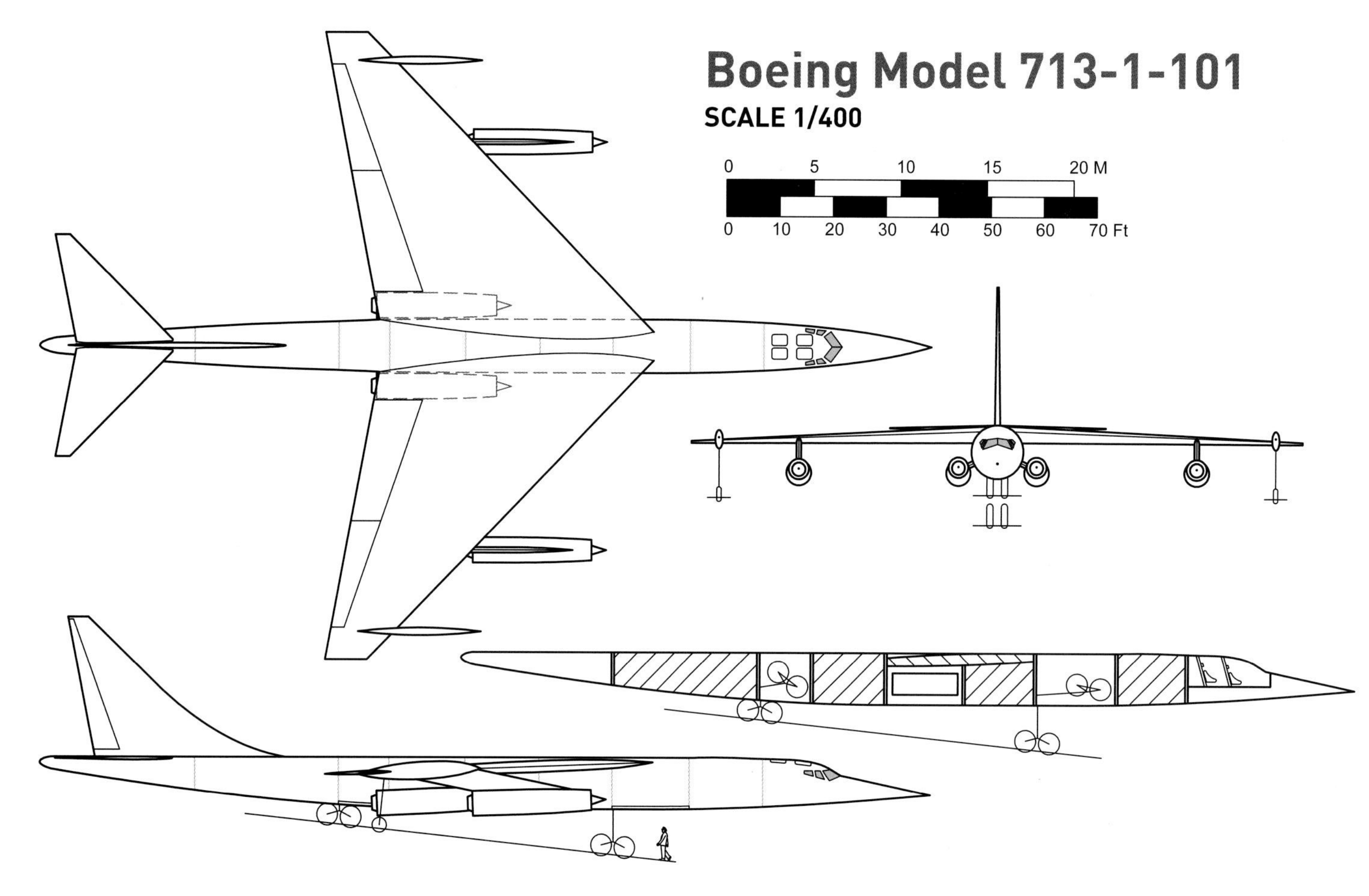

One engine nacelle (with an afterburning General Electric X-84 turbofan, an unbuilt engine that was also proposed for the Lockheed A-12 along with other advanced aircraft concepts of the time) was suspended via a pylon a little outboard of mid-span on each wing, projecting well forward; another nacelle was attached to the side of the fuselage, just under the wing root. Landing gear was of bicycle variety, with outrigger stabilizer gear stored in slim nacelles projecting well forward from near the wingtips.

Several hundred designs followed on after the -1-101, many only slight variations but some wildly divergent, including what appear to be giant mutant versions of the B-52 with up to 16 engines (see: *Boeing B-47 Stratojet and B-52 Stratofortress: Origins and Evolution*). Most were equipped with nuclear propulsion, but none seem to have exceeded Model 713-1-101 in terms of speed.

Those intended for supersonic flight topped out at a maximum airspeed of 1,150 knots, a chosen standard for Model 713. The final known Model 713 design, Model 713-299, was vaguely similar to the 713-1-101 in general layout, and flew a similar sort of mission. But all of the non-nuclear designs had the same problem: lack of range. So Model 713-299 was modified to increase fuel load. This was done by adding giant fuel tanks to floating wingtip extensions. This study, from December of 1955, set the stage for the official Boeing study for WS-110A.

Three ship formations

Turbojets from the mid-1950s were vastly more capable than those of only a few years prior; very large aircraft could now be designed that could be relied upon to reach Mach 3 or greater. But what they couldn't do was fly long range at high speed. Those turbojets drank fuel at an astonishing rate, limiting range even with the use of inflight refuelling.

Aircraft designers knew that there were several ways to increase range, including improved engine performance, improved aerodynamics, improved structural materials and design and simply adding more fuel. Inflight refuelling was a successful way to add fuel to an aircraft, but it was logistically limited… the Soviets, for example, were unlikely to allow American tanker aircraft to overfly their territory. And Soviet territory was vast, meaning that American bomber aircraft would have to have substantial unrefuelled range to have a hope of penetrating deep into the USSR, never mind making it to a base at the end of the mission.

Improvements in engines, aerodynamics and structures tended to be slow and incremental, with little hope of major changes on a prescribed schedule. And there is only so much space in an aircraft in which to cram more fuel. External tanks can be added of course, but those add drag and mass. And an aircraft only has so much wing area and can only lift so much weight.

There was, however, a way to bypass what was otherwise a hard limit. If the added fuel tanks came with more wing area, the aircraft could in principle lift off with a greatly increased gross weight. Boeing had previously studied the idea of extended wings with large external fuel tanks in 1950, applying the concept to both the B-47 and B-52 configurations. Boeing's Model 450-36-10, for example, was effectively a four-engined B-47 with substantial wingtip extensions, known as 'floating wingtips'. The extensions were attached to the wings with hinges allowing them to 'flap'. Model 464-79-0 was the same concept applied to the XB-52 configuration. Both designs used the wingtip extensions not only to increase wing area but also as attachments for new large external fuel tanks (both designs are covered in *Boeing B-47 Stratojet and B-52 Stratofortress: Origins and Evolution*).

These aircraft benefitted not only from a substantial increase in wing area but also an increase in aspect ratio. As demonstrated by sailplanes, long, thin wings more efficiently generate lift than short stubby ones, so the extended wings would noticeably improve the range performance of the aircraft. It is not clear whether these wingtips, and the fuel tanks integrated into them, were intended to be jettisoned after the tanks were emptied.

Boeing was neither alone in studying the floating wingtip concept nor the originator of it. Engineer Richard Vogt had studied it in Germany during the Second World War; after being brought to the US as part of Project Paperclip, he worked with Wright Field to further develop the concept, flying a C-47 with a single Q-14 Culver Cadet that could – and did – dock to a wingtip. This demonstrated the aerodynamic benefits, as well as the difficulties, of docking two aircraft in flight wingtip to wingtip.

Further efforts continued into the 1950s with a Boeing ETB-29A modified to dock one Republic EF-84D to each wingtip. This also demonstrated aerodynamic benefits... until the composite aircraft crashed after one of the EF-84D's flipped up and over, crashing into the wing of the bomber, taking all three aircraft down. The concept continued on to Project Tom Tom, where one Republic RF-84F was docked to each wingtip of a Convair B-36. The intent was to provide the B-36 with escort fighters for the long trip into Soviet territory, but even though the concept proved at least technically feasible it was not developed to operational status.

Despite the failure of these efforts to provide an operational composite aircraft, the aerodynamic benefits were well known to Air Force personnel and planners. The Air Research and Development Command supported the idea of floating wingtip extensions with additional fuel tanks as a way to allow large aircraft to cruise subsonically for great distance... and by dropping the extensions and the tanks to reduce weight and drag and optimize aerodynamics for a high-Mach dash. Consequently, the contractors vying for the WS-110A contract prioritized that unconventional arrangement.

Boeing Model 713-299 Modification

The earliest known of the floating wingtip designs is the previously mentioned Model 713-299 modified with extended wings. With the addition of two extensions each of 1,795sq ft and carrying 82,740 gallons of fuel, the aircraft had a gross weight in excess of 624,000lb... massive, but only slightly greater than that of the eight-engined MX-2145 of about two years prior. The extensions increased the basic airplane span of 118ft 4in to 241ft 0in.

This began to show one of the rather dire aspects of the concept: in order to keep the wingtip fuel tanks from dragging along the ground, each was fitted with its own takeoff gear (which would drop after takeoff). The distance between the tank takeoff gear was 168ft 6in, meaning that not only could the complete aircraft not land again – every takeoff would expend the wingtips and the tanks – but the aircraft could only take off from runways wide enough to take it... probably 200ft or so wide. Very few air bases would ever be able to handle such a monumental requirement for concrete and real estate.

North American NA-239

North American Aviation also produced design studies on wingtip extensions, though information on these is limited. NA-239 was a twin-tailed, rear-winged design with a sizable canard and four engines laid in a horizontal row at the rear of the fuselage fed by two ramp inlets on either side of the fuselage. The wings used the inlets as the wing roots and were swept, stubby trapezoids. The canards were mounted at the extreme nose, blocking much of the forward and downwards view from the nearly flush cockpit.

All of the NA-239 designs featured the extended wingtip/fuel tank concept, but as the design evolved between March 1955 and June 1956 its wingtips and tanks grew. This was because the NA-239 was initially intended to use high-energy boron-based pentaborane 'zip' fuel. The boron would have, in theory, greatly improved engine performance, requiring substantially less fuel to perform the same mission... but in practical fact the problems of boron, from toxicity to the combustion products being glasslike sludge that would tend to plate out onto the engines, meant that zip fuel never met its promise.

The loss of zip fuel meant that the NA-239's wingtips and fuel tanks grew considerably in size as the aircraft had to use more conventional hydrocarbon fuel. But given the B-70's serious troubles with leaky fuel tanks, that was a fair and sane trade to make.

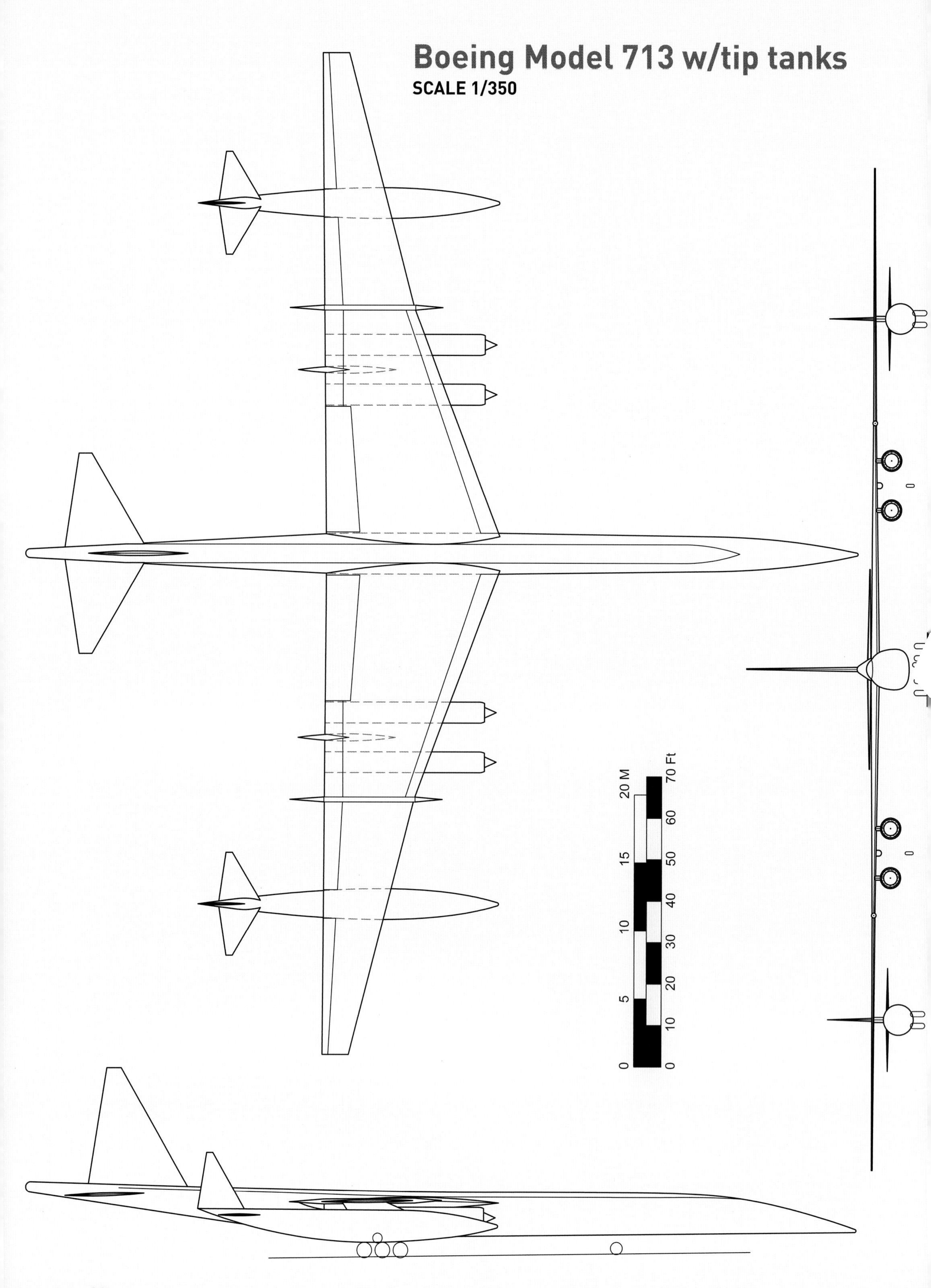
Boeing Model 713 w/tip tanks
SCALE 1/350
0 5 10 15 20 M
0 10 20 30 40 50 60 70 Ft

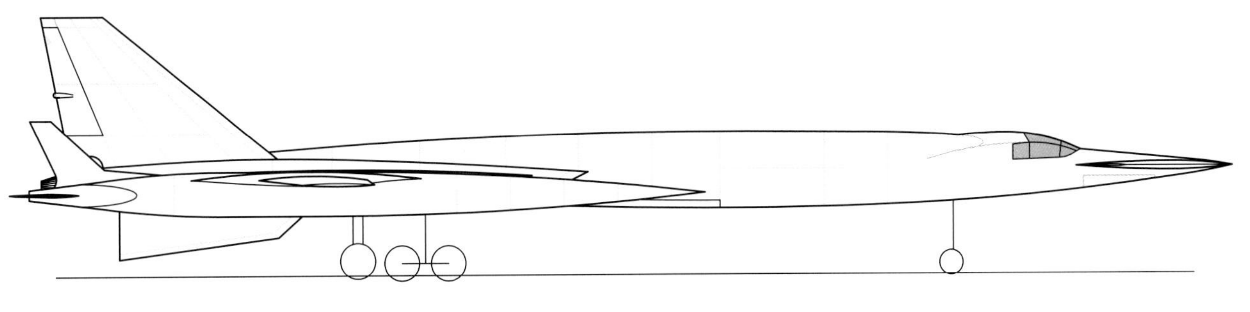

North American WS-110A

SCALE 1/300

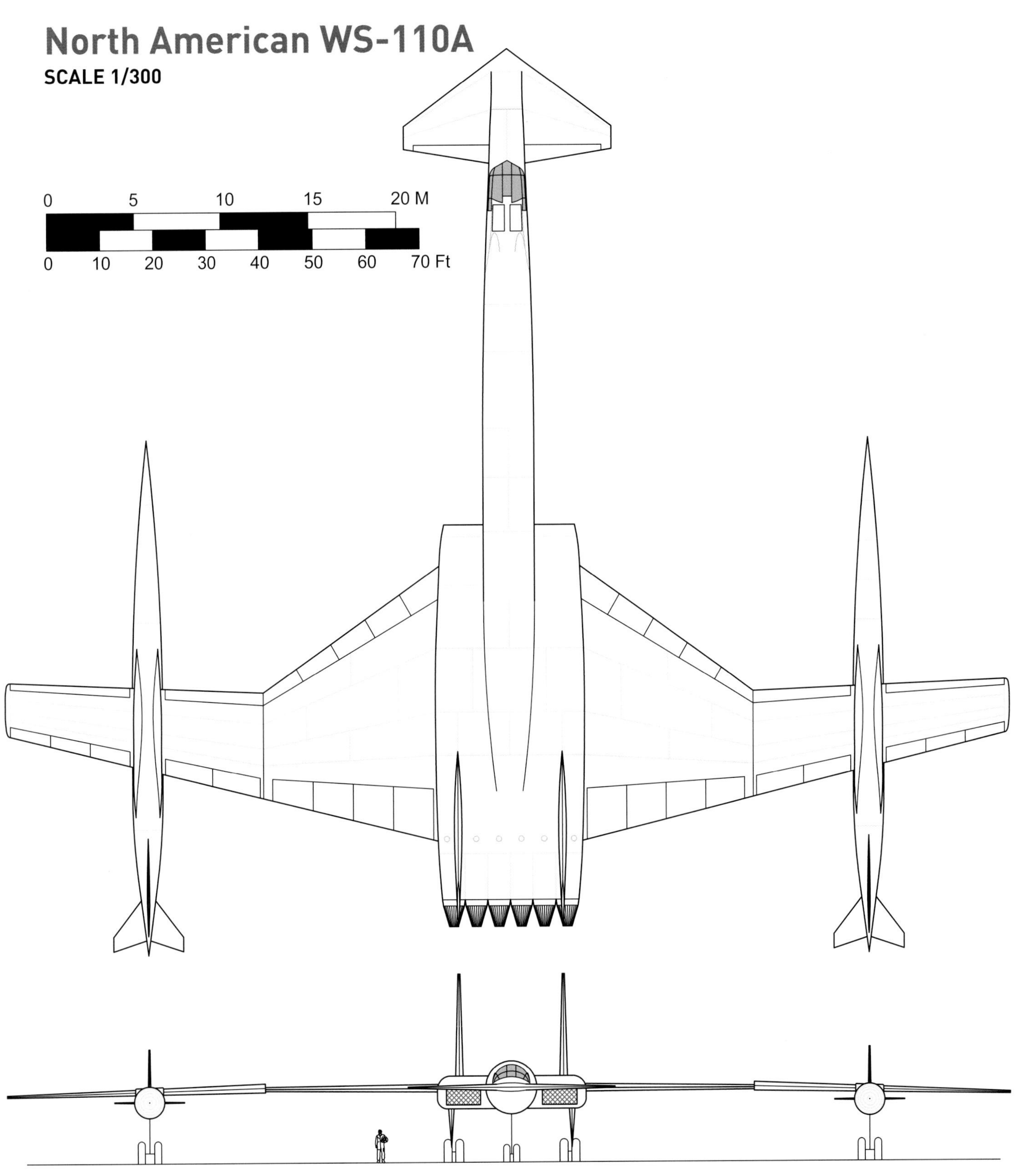

Relatively little information is available on the final North American Aviation WS-110A submission. The configuration remained more or less the same as it had begun with, though the canard had shrunk somewhat and was less sharply swept. The cockpit was raised, rather than flush, though the view forward and down for landing would have still been virtually nonexistent.

The use of JP-4 fuel meant that the aircraft required large wingtip panels, large external fuel tanks and six, rather than the initial four, General Electric X279A turbojet engines.

It had a relatively small bomb bay, not quite 20ft long, which could carry a relatively small 10,000lb bomb load. It could also carry external stores; a supersonic airbreathing missile similar to the AGM-28 Hound Dog was planned. Photos of display models show this missile being carried under the port wing. The same location (under both port and starboard wings) could also be fitted with 1,500 gallon drop tanks; two smaller jet-engine equipped standoff missiles, type unknown, could be carried under the fuselage.

Boeing Model 724-13

Boeing embarked on a new series of bomber designs to meeting the WS-110A specification in December 1955. As these were designed from the outset to incorporate floating wingtips they were granted a new model number to distinguish them from Model 713: 724. The first, Model 724-1, was similar in configuration to the modified 713-299, the only major difference being an increase in sweep of both the wing and the extensions.

The configuration had changed substantially by Model 724-13 from March 1956. The wing was now relatively small, trapezoidal and located well aft; the horizontal stabilizers were turned into canards mounted aft of the cockpit. The wingtip extensions were longer and slimmer; swept, with a fair aspect ratio for good aerodynamic efficiency.

Model 724-13 retained four engines; one under each wingtip, the others mounted alongside the rear fuselage well below the trailing edge of the shoulder-mounted wing. The pilot and co-pilot sat side by side and an aerodynamic fairing would angle up to shield the forward windscreens during high speed flight and lower to permit forward vision during cruise and takeoff and landing.

The bombardier/navigator sat directly behind the co-pilot on the starboard side of the fuselage; the 'battle director operator' sat directly behind the navigator. The crew were able to get up and move about with a retractable bunkbed positioned directly behind the pilot. Model 724-13 retained the single relatively small bomb bay designed for a single 10,000lb weapon.

Boeing Model 724-15

Model 724-15 of April 1956 was Boeing's official submission for WS-110A. It was a large supersonic bomber with four General Electric X-278A engines and highly swept rather short-span wings. There were also two long-span wing extensions, each with its own large fuel tank. The wings themselves were full of fuel too; the result was that for takeoff and long range subsonic cruise the aircraft had a whole lot of additional fuel (22,400 gallons of fuel per wingtip) and a whole lot of additional wing area (tripling that of the basic aircraft).

The jettisonable wingtips – similar in concept to those used on Model 464-79-0 and large structures in their own right – had their own model number, 724-1003. The canards of the Model 724-13 reverted to conventional horizontal tails.

Model 724-15 had the same sort of variable geometry windscreen fairing as Model 724-13 though the nose as a whole was fixed, unlike the drooping noses of most supersonic transports. The aerial refuelling receptacle was on the upper surface of the starboard side of the nose ahead of the fairing.

The baseline payload was a single undefined 10,000lb 'special' weapon – a large hydrogen bomb. Other weapons loads were considered, including a single 25,000lb hydrogen bomb. Diagrams present several configurations of bombs ranging from 1,750lb up to 25,000lb; they are unusual configurations, shown without much detail. It may be that these are simply the envelopes that such bombs were expected to fit within and do not depict actual configurations; however, the text seems to indicate that these shapes were developed after wind tunnel testing, indicating that these finless bodies of rotation were actual proposed bomb configurations. Also shown in the diagram here is a B41 bomb, the sort of weapon that would have been available for this aircraft.

During a standard mission, the Model 724-15 would cruise at 460 knots for 1,960 nautical miles, at an altitude of 32,100-36,100ft. It would then jettison the wingtips and begin to climb and dash supersonically, cruising at 1,725 knots while ascending to 63,100ft. After dropping its 10,000lb weapon it would turn around, fly another 1,070 miles at 1,725 knots while ascending to 67,600ft. Then it would drop to 37,800ft and 518 knots and cruise the rest of the way home subsonically. The crew were positioned much as they were in Model 724-13, each in a standard ejector seat.

Model 724-15 was presented to the Source Selection Board Evaluation Team on July 24-26, 1956. Boeing planned for a mockup inspection in November 1957 and a first flight in March 1960. As with the North American submission, the Boeing design was rejected outright. General Curtis LeMay famously derided the designs as more like three-ship formations than proper

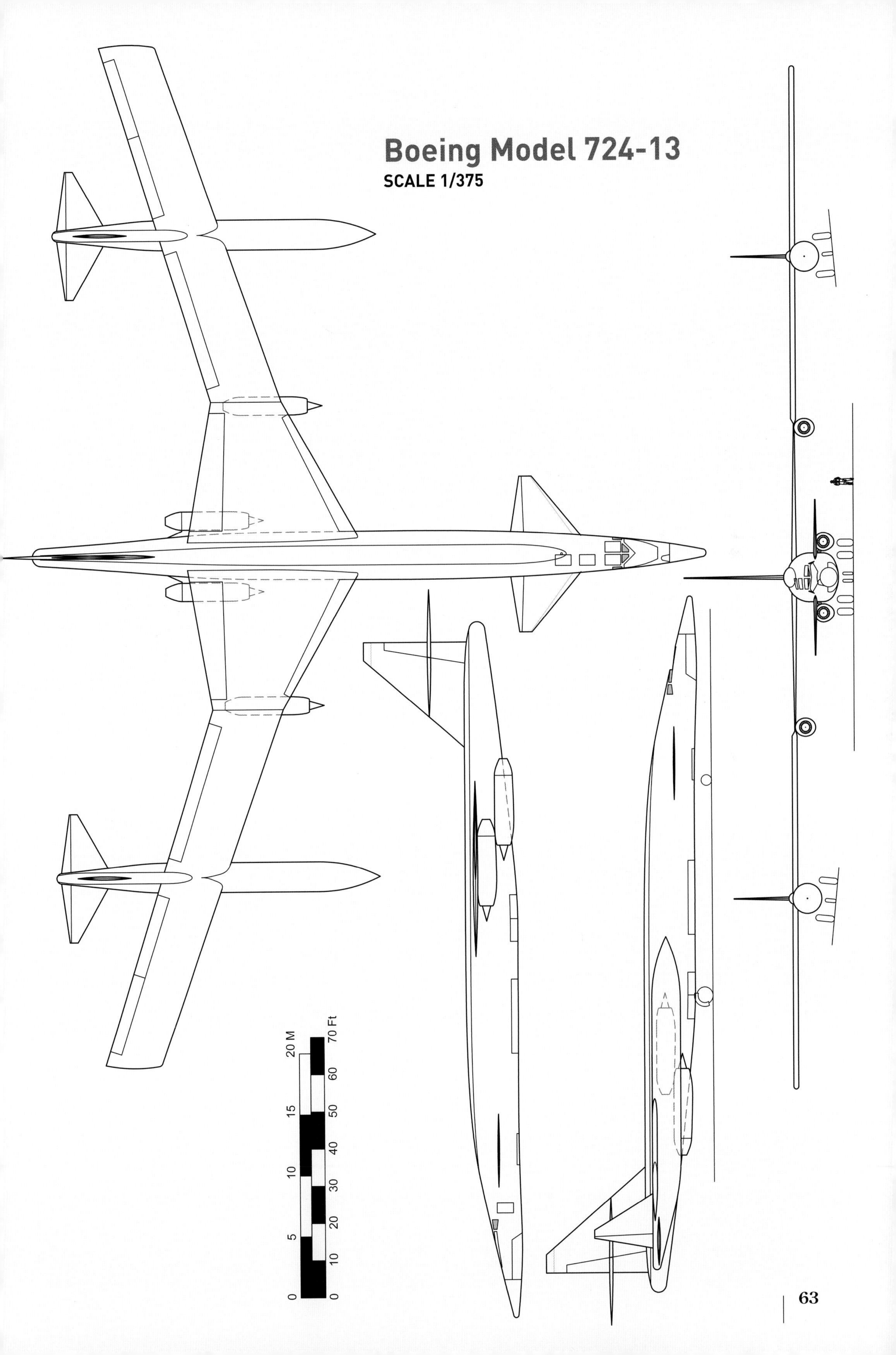
Boeing Model 724-13
SCALE 1/375

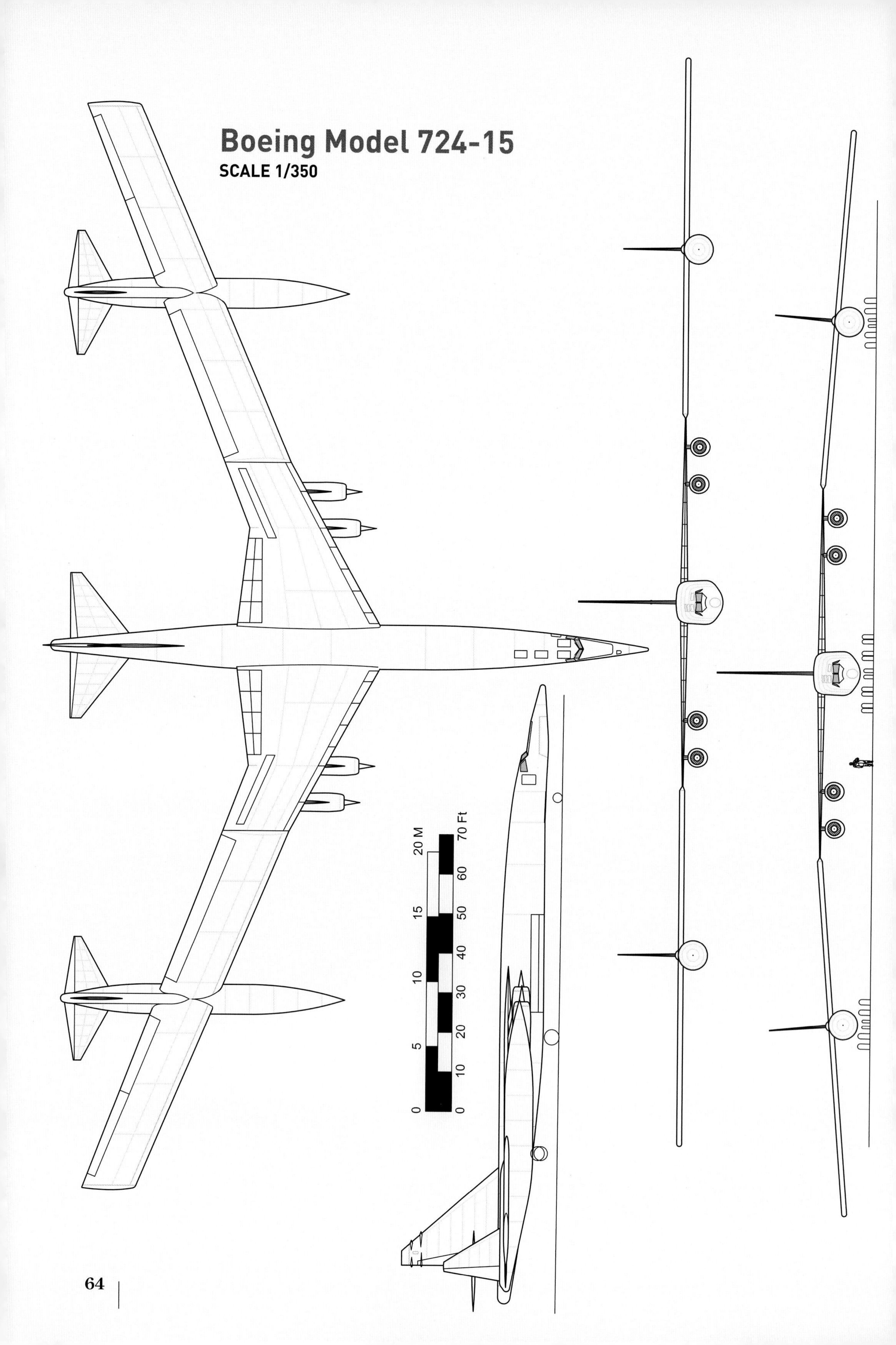
Boeing Model 724-15
SCALE 1/350
0
5
10
15
20 M
0
10
20
30
40
50
60
70 Ft

aircraft. As a result, both North American and Boeing went back to the drawing board.

Boeing Model 724-16

Proposed alongside Model 724-15 was Model 724-16. This was much the same configuration as 724-15, but scaled up for a 25,000lb bomb load. It included larger and more powerful General Electric X279A engines but the most obvious design change was to the nose. Instead of the simple variable geometry windscreen fairing, the entire nose would 'droop' at low speed much like that of Concorde. When raised for high speed flight, the forward fuselage would be fully faired in with no drag inducing discontinuities... and no forward vision.

The aerial refuelling receptacle was on the upper surface of the starboard side of the droopable nose. The pilot and co-pilot would have had flush-mounted windows to their sides, but these would have been of no assistance during inflight refuelling. The nose would have had to droop downwards to permit the bomber crew to see forward and upwards during rendezvous with the tanker.

The crew were repositioned compared to Model 724-15. The pilot and co-pilot still sat side by side, but so did the navigator/bombardier and the defence system operator. Each had a B-58-style ejector capsule... and the two back seaters were facing backwards. This doubtless would have made ejection interesting, since the trajectories of the front ejector capsules intersected with those of the rear ejection capsules. Even though 724-16 was a larger aircraft than 724-15, it does not appear that there was room for the crew to move about; no bunk, retractable or otherwise, is shown in the available diagrams.

Convair Water-Based 110A

In most histories of the B-70, Boeing and North American are the only corporations to receive much mention. The reason is clear: only those two companies left much readily accessible information on their designs for WS-110A, and only they seem to have officially submitted designs to the Air Force. However, they were not alone in studying the possibilities of WS-110A: Convair studied it too and came up with rather different designs.

Two Convair WS-110A concepts are known, reported in December of 1956. Both, perhaps unexpectedly, proceed from flying boats rather than landplanes. This is not to say that Convair only looked at flying boats, just that the sole known source of information on Convair WS-110A studies deals exclusively with water-based strategic aircraft.

In the available report, the proposed WS-110A configurations are described as being based on what was believed to be the land-based 110A configurations. Given that this report was dated some six months after the USAF Source Selection Board had already told Boeing and North American to go back to the drawing board after they turned in their 'three-ship formation' designs, it seems probable that Convair was not heavily invested in WS-110A. This study seems to have been a way to use an ongoing Air Force programme to feed into a long-existing Convair desire for seaplane bombers.

One of the concepts is a tug-tow design... a supersonic dash aircraft towed into and through the air by a much larger subsonic tow plane. The other is in line with the early Boeing and North American designs, featuring gigantic expendable fuel tanks attached to wingtip extensions.

Convair proposed that the USAF institute an intercontinental seaplane bomber force composed of a mix of nuclear and chemical propelled seaplane bombers. The so-called Advanced Base Force would position a 28-wing force of medium bombers at six theatre forward bases and four supporting rear area bases. These could be positioned far closer to Soviet territory than landplane bases in the continental United States, allowing shorter-range aircraft to strike just as deeply into the Soviet Union.

Another obvious advantage is that no amount of bombing could destroy the surface of the sea, where a single good bomb run can tear up a runway. The bombers would normally be based in ice-free secure waters in and around the United States, but would move to advance bases at times of crisis. They would be serviced by special logistic seaplanes or modified submarines, using hidden caches of submerged jet fuel. The bombers suggested were heavily modified Convair B-58s, turned into seaplanes.

In addition to the medium bomber seaplane B-58s, truly intercontinental range high-altitude heavy bombers based on the WS-110A requirements were produced. The first design considered was a floating wingtip design similar to what Boeing and North American had proposed. This aircraft was a supersonic flying boat somewhat like the Martin P6M SeaMaster in configuration. A long, slim, wasp-waisted flying boat hull was given relatively short and stubby shoulder-mounted swept wings with a conventional swept T-tail at the rear for stability and control. Two turbojets were located in a long nacelle mounted above each wing, presumably well above water spray height.

In order to achieve the sort of range required, the bomber was fitted with wing extensions and fuel tanks, as Boeing and North American had already tried. But due to the need to take off from water surfaces, the fuel tanks were also flying boat hulls; the wings were not single oblique panels, but were swept aft on either side of the fuel tank hull forming symmetrical wings.

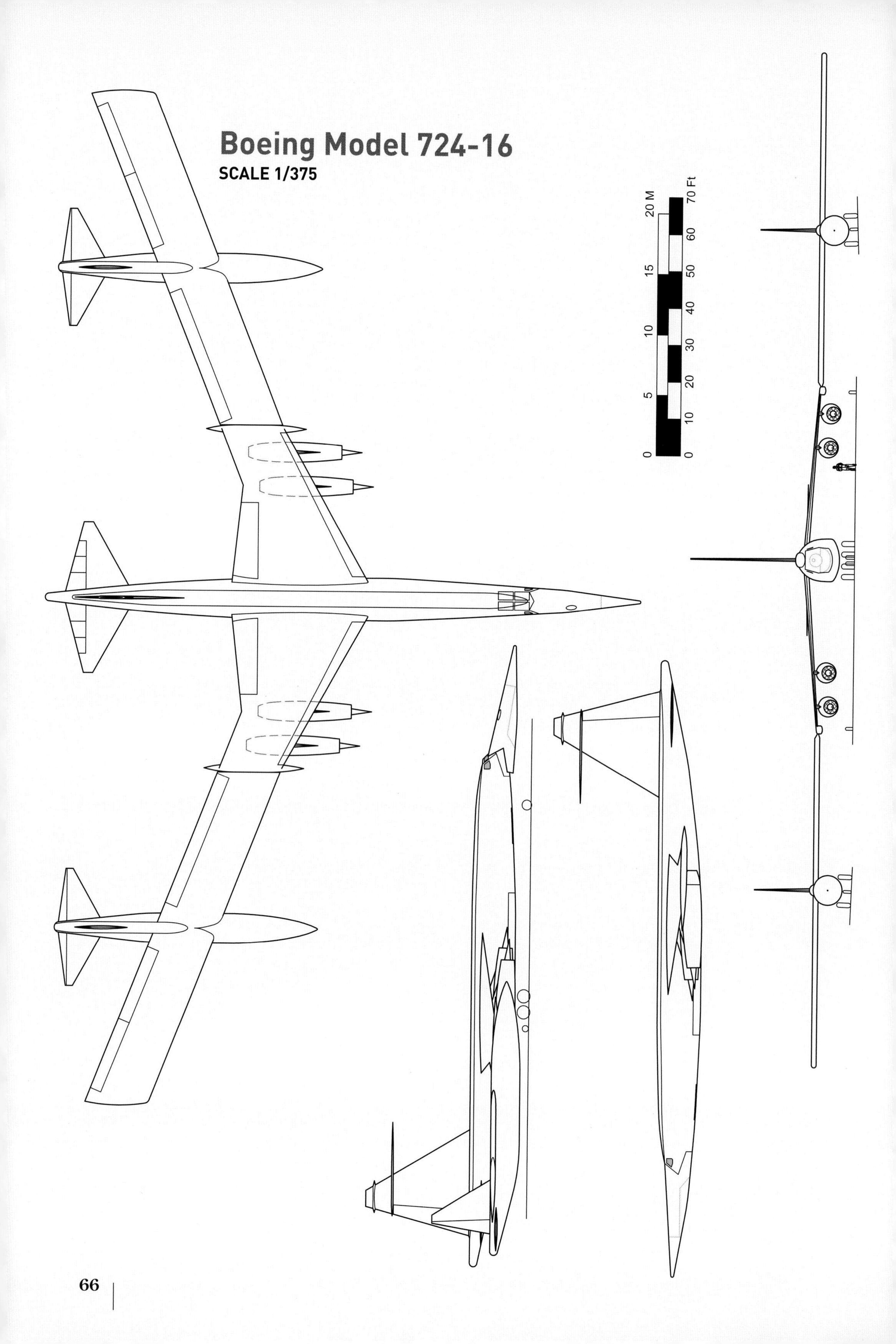
Boeing Model 724-16
SCALE 1/375
0 5 10 15 20 M
0 10 20 30 40 50 60 70 Ft

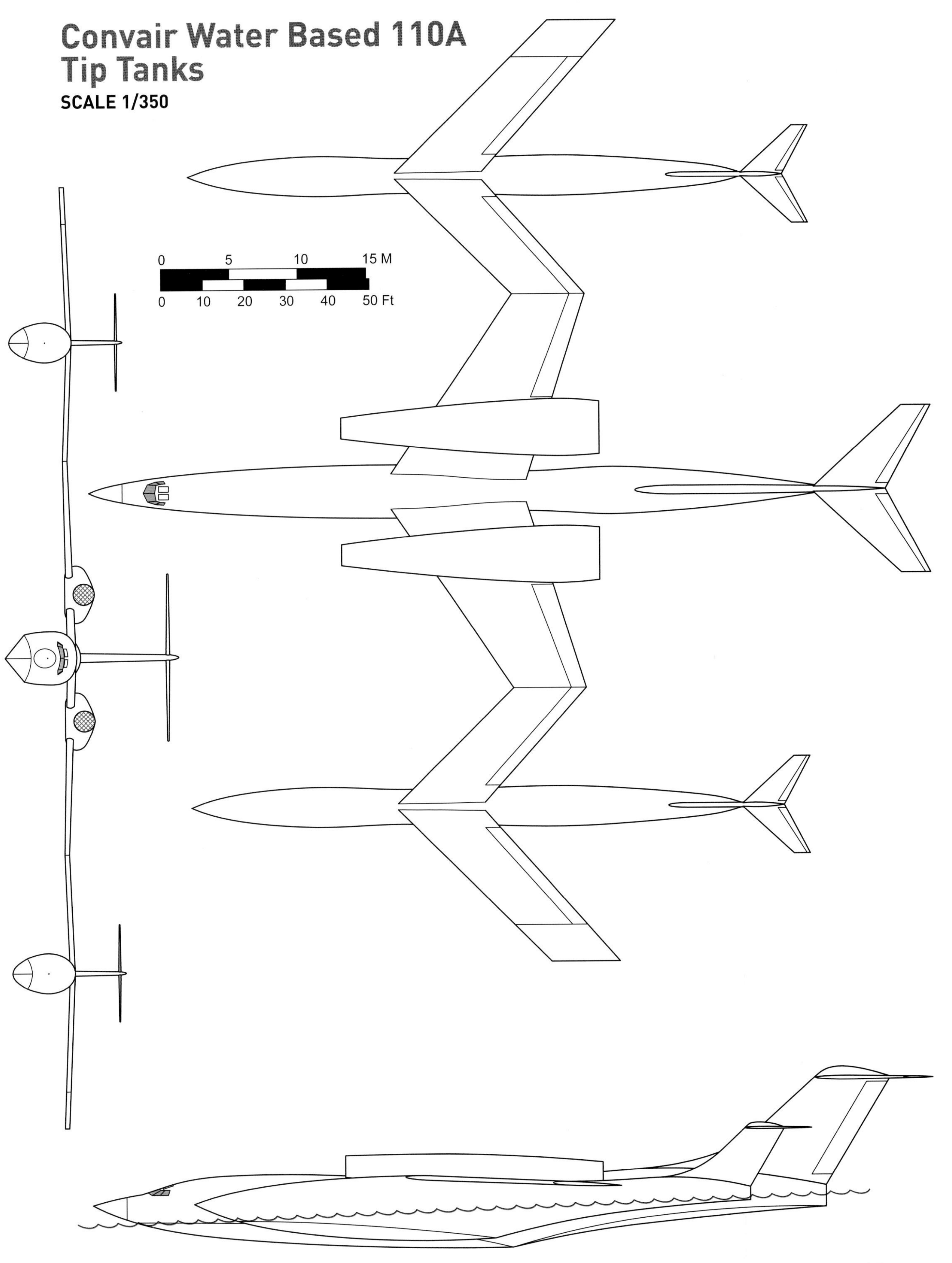
Convair Water Based 110A
Tip Tanks
SCALE 1/350
0
5
10
15 M
0
10
20
30
40
50 Ft

Convair Water Based 110A Tug-Tow
SCALE 1/750

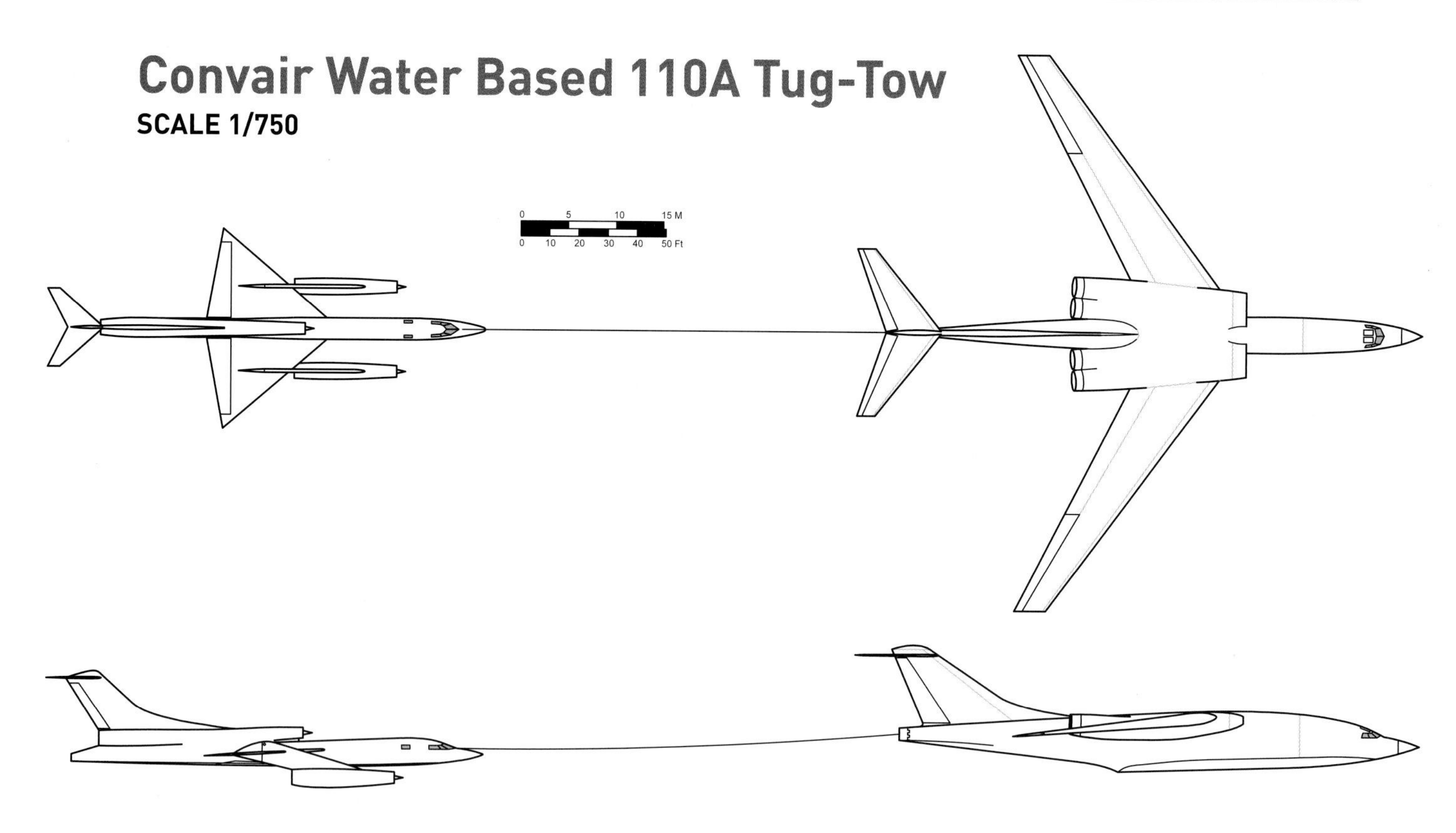

Convair Water Based 110A Tug-Tow
SCALE 1/350

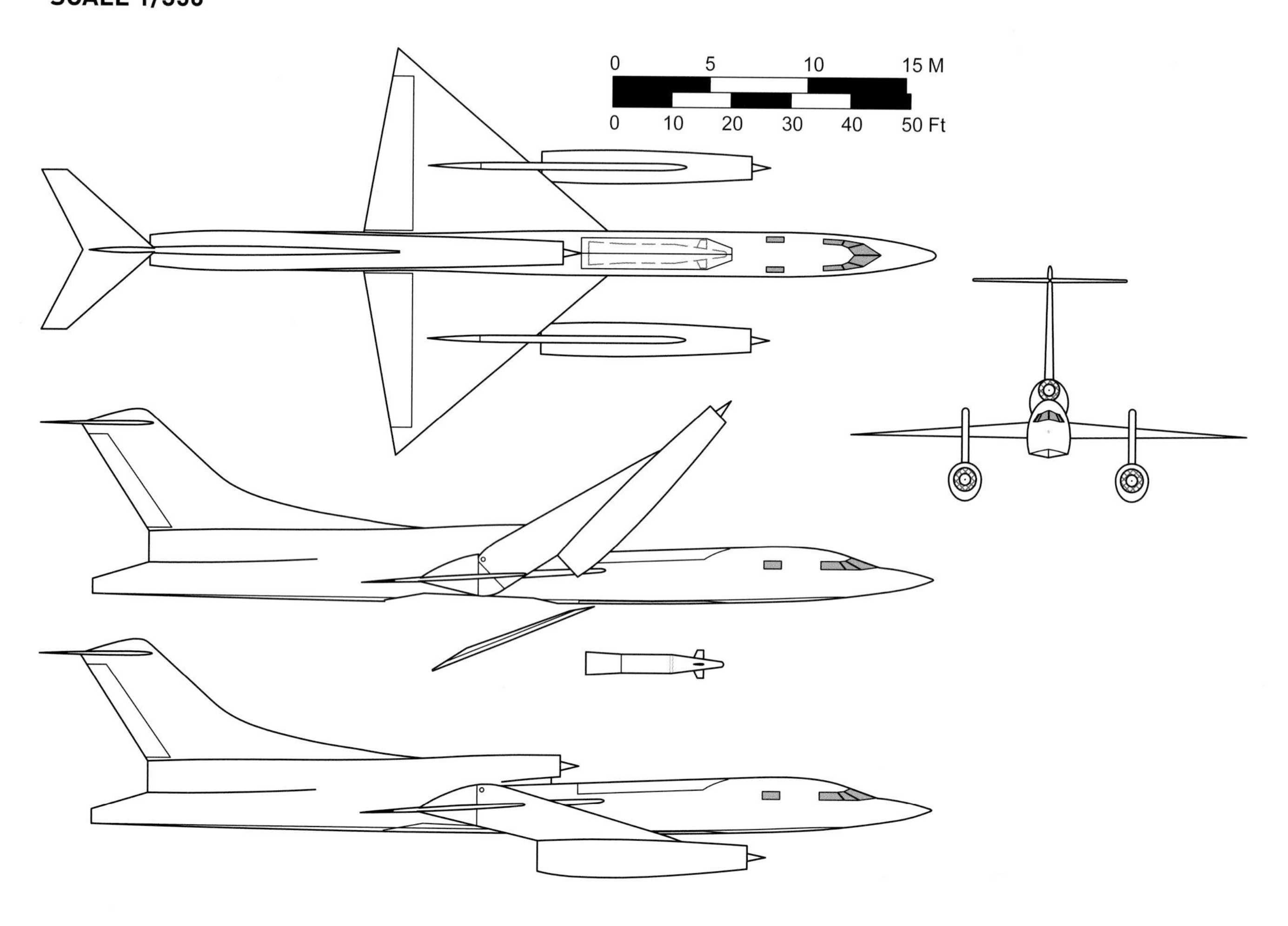

The outboard wing, however, was fitted with its own wingtip extension; at tank jettison, the outboard tip extension was jettisoned. This meant that the port and starboard wings of the fuel tank would create equal lift, theoretically providing the tank with a smooth, non-rolling jettison. At the rear of the tank was a full T-tail.

The result was a complex configuration that the Convair designers quickly realized would be a nightmare to launch from any water surface that was not glassy smooth. The fuel tanks would bounce on their own waves at times and frequencies unlikely to line up healthily with those banging into the main aircraft or the other tank. Coupled with the added complexity of multiple jettisonings, the designers realized that the floating wingtip flying boat was a loser of a design. So they went back to the drawing board.

The first alternative was a piggyback concept… a large subsonic aircraft carrying a Mach 3 dash component on its back. This would have been hydrodynamically much more straightforward than the floating wingtip concept but it was quickly realized that for a dash component weighing 160,000lb, the carrier aircraft would have to weigh well over one million pounds. The piggyback concept seems to have been abandoned before drawings could be made.

So another concept was floated: a tug-tow arrangement. A large subsonic flying boat would tow a much smaller Mach 3 dash flying boat. This was found to be much more practical than the preceding concepts. The tug aircraft was a large conventional design with four Pratt & Whitney JT-9A turbojets in shoulder wing-root installations. The tug had large high aspect ratio (8.56) wings swept 35° at the quarter-chord line, making it an efficient flyer; when not used as a tug, it could serve as a logistics carrier or as an independent subsonic bomber.

The tail of the tow plane contained a reel installation which could retract the cable into the aircraft after separation. The tow cable would connect to a retractable hook on the dash aircraft's nose, just ahead of the cockpit. This arrangement had been previously proposed for use with the B-58; in a prior study it was proposed to use the supersonic Model 25 nuclear powered bomber as the tow plane and the B-58 as the dash aircraft.

The 110A dash aircraft was a three-engined delta-winged design similar to the water-based B-58 derivative. Each delta wing would have a single turbojet suspended beneath a forward-projecting pylon; while on the water, the pylon would tilt upwards, putting the engine, in particular the inlet, well above the water spray. The third engine was in the tail, fed from an inlet located above the fuselage. A single hydroski would be needed to let the otherwise not terribly hydrodynamic configuration lift off from the surface of the water.

The tug and dash aircraft would take off separately and rendezvous; the dash aircraft would then hook up to the tow cable (this seems a non-trivial feat, as there do not seem to be any provisions to actively control the tow cable). Once hooked on, the dash aircraft would shut down its engines and glide behind the tug; the engine inlets would be closed off to reduce drag.

The tug would tow the dash aircraft near to enemy territory; the dash aircraft would restart engines, separate, climb to altitude and accelerate to Mach 3. The tug aircraft would loiter for an hour while the dash aircraft carried out its bombardment mission, turned around and returned to the tow aircraft where it would be recovered. Once again the engines would shut down and the dash aircraft would be towed back to base. It would restart engines, separate and land on its own.

Total mission range could be increased by 300 nautical miles if the dash aircraft took off with just enough fuel to rendezvous with the tug; with a lower wing loading, it would be easier to tow with lower drag. The dash aircraft would be fuelled in flight from the tug just prior to separation.

Even greater range could be had if both aircraft took off fully fuelled; once hooked on, the tow aircraft would draw its fuel from the dash aircraft, using it as an external fuel tank and lowering its weight. Once again the dash aircraft would be fuelled just prior to separation. How this would all be achieved is not a feat described in detail. *Any* detail.

The tug would have a radius while towing the dash aircraft of some 2,590 nautical miles while cruising at Mach 0.9 and 30,000ft. The dash aircraft would have a radius of 670 nautical miles at Mach 3 and 75,000ft. The dash aircraft would have a 10,000lb payload, nominally a single-stage solid propellant rocket standoff missile. This would be loaded into the aircraft through doors on the upper surface of the fuselage, a necessity for servicing while afloat; but for launch it would drop through doors on the underside of the fuselage. Performance data for the missile is currently lacking, but it could be provided with a warhead ranging from 1,000-2,800lb… seemingly a meagre end result for all the bother of a large tug aircraft and a Mach 3 dash aircraft.

Convair was at the time heavily invested in the Atlas ICBM project as well as the WS-125A nuclear powered bomber project. The effort devoted to those programmes was effort that was not devoted to the WS-110A project or derivatives of it; this is at least partially responsible for Convair not seeming to be very interested in WS-110A. There is no evidence that Convair officially submitted its concepts, nor that the designs were carried out to a high level of engineering detail.

The 'three ship formations' had been rejected by LeMay and the Air Force but the Air Force still wanted

Convair Water Based 110A Tug-Tow

SCALE 1/350

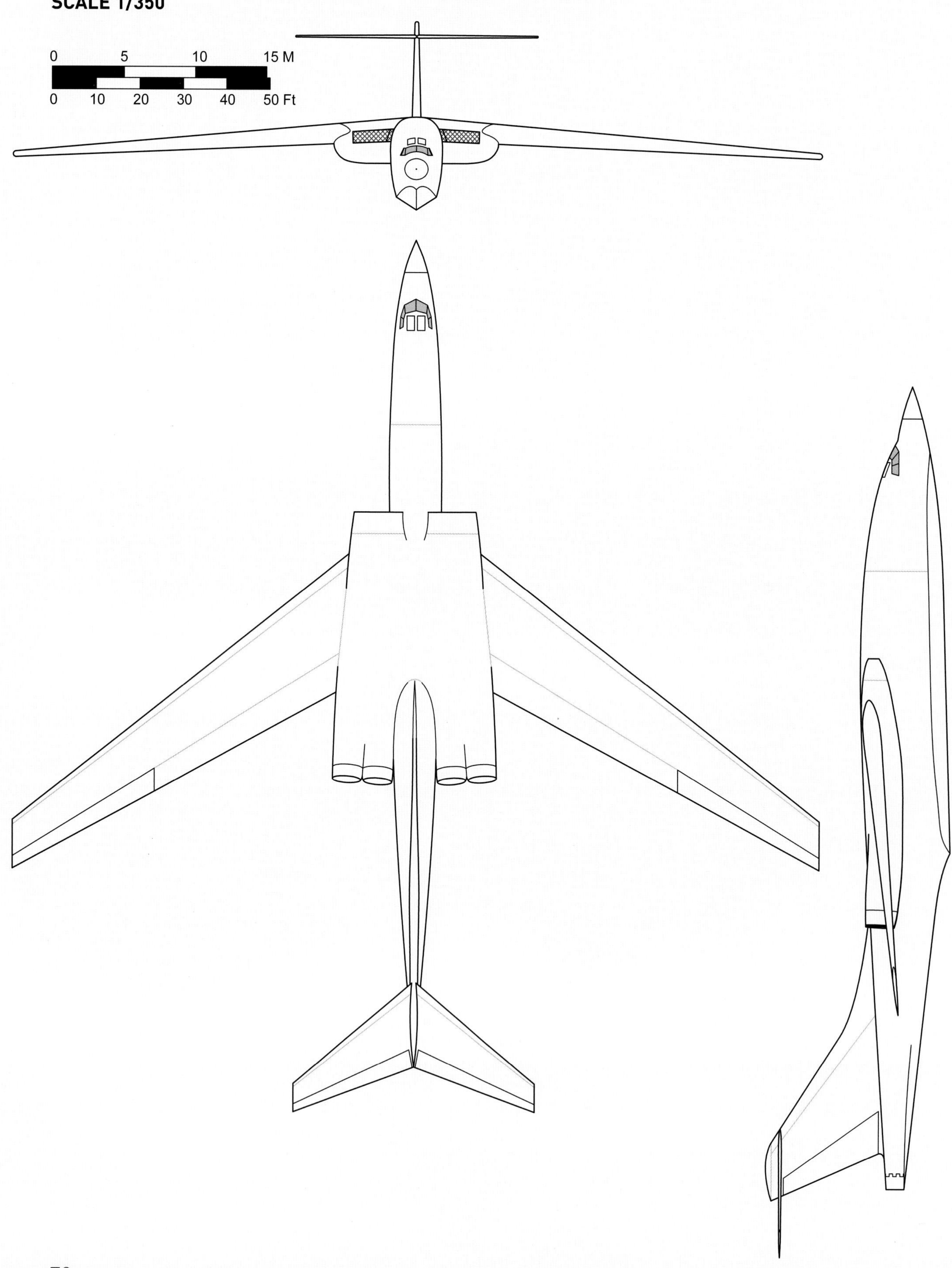

what it wanted. Boeing and North American would have to try again and they did.

Boeing Model 804-1

At Boeing in 1956 a small group – working under the presumably intentionally unenlightening code name of Tea Bag – reviewed existing work to see if anything held promise of meeting the WS-110A specifications. Subsequently a new model designation, 725, was created for a new range of studies.

Aircraft configurations, engines, high energy fuels (including liquid hydrogen, producing some very large and voluminous designs), boundary layer control and staging concepts were examined. Some designs were quite similar to some of the preceding Model 724 concepts, including floating wingtip configurations, but many were wholly – and in some cases, bizarrely – different.

One of the more promising of the designs was Model 724-115, a tailless delta configuration. This was sufficiently promising that it was developed further and granted a new model designation of Model 804-1 in February 1957. This design had six General Electric GE X279E engines and a 24,200lb military load (of which 10,000lb was the actual bomb, the rest being navigation equipment, countermeasures and so on), for a gross takeoff weight of less than 500,000lb.

The engines were located in individual nacelles lined up under the wing; each was fitted with an extendable/retractable inlet spike, resulting in nacelles that bore a substantial similarity to those of the Lockheed SR-71. It had a clean layout with no expendable components and was designed to fly virtually its entire mission supersonically, cruising at Mach 3.0.

The wings were of a slightly unconventional configuration, basically triangles with the tips cut off. This wing geometry was not new, however, being similar to the wings of the IM-99B BOMARC surface-to-air missiles developed by Boeing and the Michigan Aerospace Research Center (hence the name) a few years previously. According to an inboard profile diagram of the Model 804-1, the nose, as with the Model 724-16, would droop to allow the pilot a decent view of the runway for landing. However, the available three-view diagram seems to indicate that the nose was fixed, providing no direct forward vision for the pilots. Presumably in this case they would rely on television for landing. It's unclear if the discrepancy is due to a changing design or to a draftsman's oversight on the three-view.

The Model 804-1 had a unique high and low frequency antenna system in a long, thin 'spike' projecting aft from near the tip of the vertical fin, with a stubby ventral fin directly beneath to assure stability at high angles of attack. The fuselage was something of a rounded rectangle in cross section; the weapons bay was not long at only 252in, but it was also wide enough to accommodate two sizable bombs side by side. Inboard diagrams depict the bomb bay with one bomb and one fuel tank.

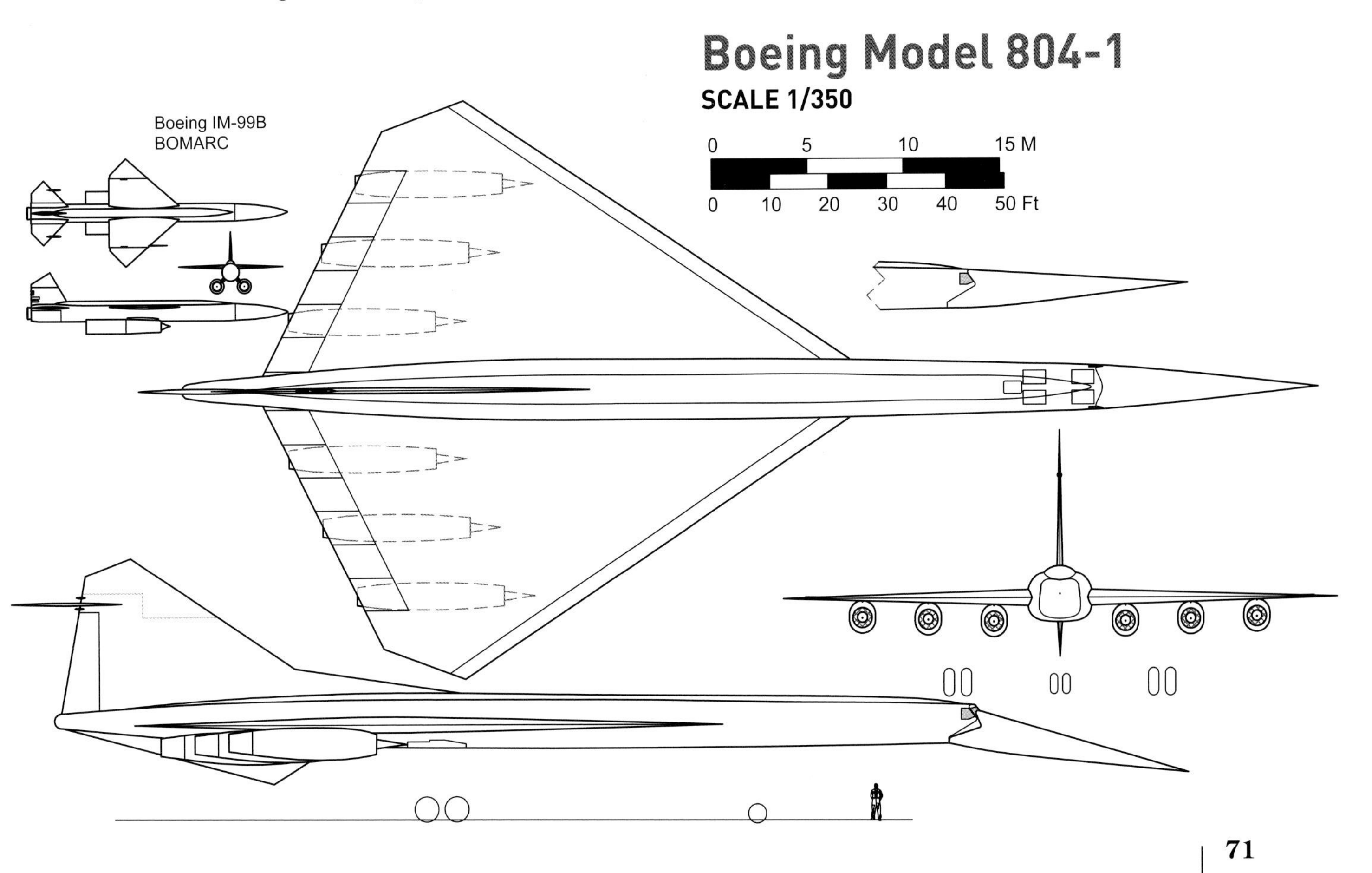

The crew of four each had their own escape capsules; as before, the bombardier-navigator and defence system operator sat 'backwards' behind the pilot and co-pilot.

As aerodynamics was refined, the Model 804-1 was modified into the 804-1A which had a pair of canards. These shared the geometry of the wings, but scaled down. Model 804-2, -3, -5 and –6 tinkered with wing sweep, engines (number and size) fuselage shape and overall size. However, there was one design that seemed best.

Boeing Model 804-4

Model 804-1A was refined further into Model 804-4. It appears to be much the same vehicle, but carried out to a greater level of fidelity. Boeing had enough faith in it to submit it to the Source Selection Board November 4-6, 1957, as its second WS-110A proposal.

The major obvious difference between the 804-4 and the 804-1 was the use of canards, previously included on Model 804-1A. They were stubbier than those of the 804-1A, and incorporated a variable geometry feature: they would fold vertically at low speed. This provided a constant centre of gravity position for the aircraft with minimum trim drag penalties.

The Model 804-4 weighed more than the Model 804-1; it also used slightly different engines, the GE X279J. This engine, which would become the J93, had a maximum thrust with afterburner of 28,500lb and a military thrust of 18,800lb. This would burn more or less conventional JP-6 (a kerosene fuel derived from JP-5, modified for a lower freezing point and improved thermal oxidative stability), though boron-based high energy fuels could also be employed. Fuel capacity was 20,300 gallons in six wing tanks, 18,500 gallons in three forward fuselage tanks and 16,700 gallons in three aft fuselage tanks. High energy fuel could replace JP-6 on a pound-per-pound basis, up to 111,000lb of the dangerous propellant; but the performance boost was surprisingly meager.

Top speed remained the same at 1,725 knots; ceiling was slightly improved, as was range… going from 6,420 nautical miles for a basic mission to 6,835 nautical miles with the use of high energy fuel. The high energy fuel would be injected only into the afterburner; the turbine components would not see the increased temperature or, importantly, the unfortunate physical effects of the gritty exhaust. The inlet spike would translate based on the Mach number, spilling the shock over the edge of the cowl. The cowl itself would translate forward at low speed (below Mach 0.5) to increase inlet area by creating an annular inlet behind the cowl.

The wings were much the same shape as those of the Model 804-1. With a relatively thin thickness-to-chord ratio of 2.375%, the symmetrical-airfoil wings were fitted with elevons and spoilers for longitudinal and roll control, and leading edge flaps for low speed performance. The spoilers alone were used for roll control at high speed.

The nose had the ability to droop for landing, but it also provided small cutouts and small forward-facing windows to give the pilot and co-pilot direct forward vision throughout the flight. These windows likely would have been woefully inadequate for landing, but they would at least have allowed the pilots to see what was ahead of them. During forward flight, forward vision was augmented with X-band radar and infra-red scanners. The nose would also droop during air-to-air refuelling operations.

Landing gear was a conventional tricycle arrangement. Ground run for takeoff was 8,000ft; no use of RATO was planned. Stall speed was 166 knots. At the tail of the fuselage was a fuel vent pipe; below that was provision for a parachute to reduce the landing roll.

The bomb bay was 252in long by 104in wide by 80in deep. It was proposed to carry the same Class A to Class D bombs described for the Model 724-15. The Model 804-4 could carry one Class A weapon, two Class Bs (side by side), four Class Cs or 18 Class Ds. It was casually mentioned that biological or chemical weapons could be carried in dispensers shaped much like those of the Class A-D nukes. It could carry a single air-to-surface missile (designed under WS-130A) in the right-hand side of the bomb bay, with a 10,000lb bomb in the left side. The missile, Boeing Model 812-1, was a hypersonic boost-glider using a solid rocket booster. With a gross weight of 5,450lb (1,000 being the warhead) it would reach a maximum speed of Mach 7.8, slowing to Mach 4 at the end of its flight.

Range of the missile itself would be 510 nautical miles; total range of the Model 804-4 and the 812-1 would be 6,185 nautical miles unrefuelled or 7,565 nautical miles if the bomber tanked from a KC-135. A larger version of the missile (13,600lb gross weight, 2,800lb warhead with a liquid rocket booster) could be carried externally. It would reach a maximum of Mach 7 with a range of 440 nautical miles. Total mission range would be 5,700 nautical miles unrefuelled, 7,050 nautical miles refuelled.

An alternate weapon load would be to have a single 10,000lb Class B nuclear bomb with up to four turbojet powered decoy missiles, similar in concept to the ADM-20 Quail missiles carried by the B-52.

At Mach 3 and cruising altitude, the skin temperature was expected to reach 565°F. To deal with this, the majority of the wing skin was made of brazed honeycomb panels of PH 15-7Mo stainless steel, the main structural elements of the wing made from the same steel. The fuselage in contrast was clad in 6Al-4V titanium alloy directional core sandwich panels, and its main structure was made from the same titanium. The

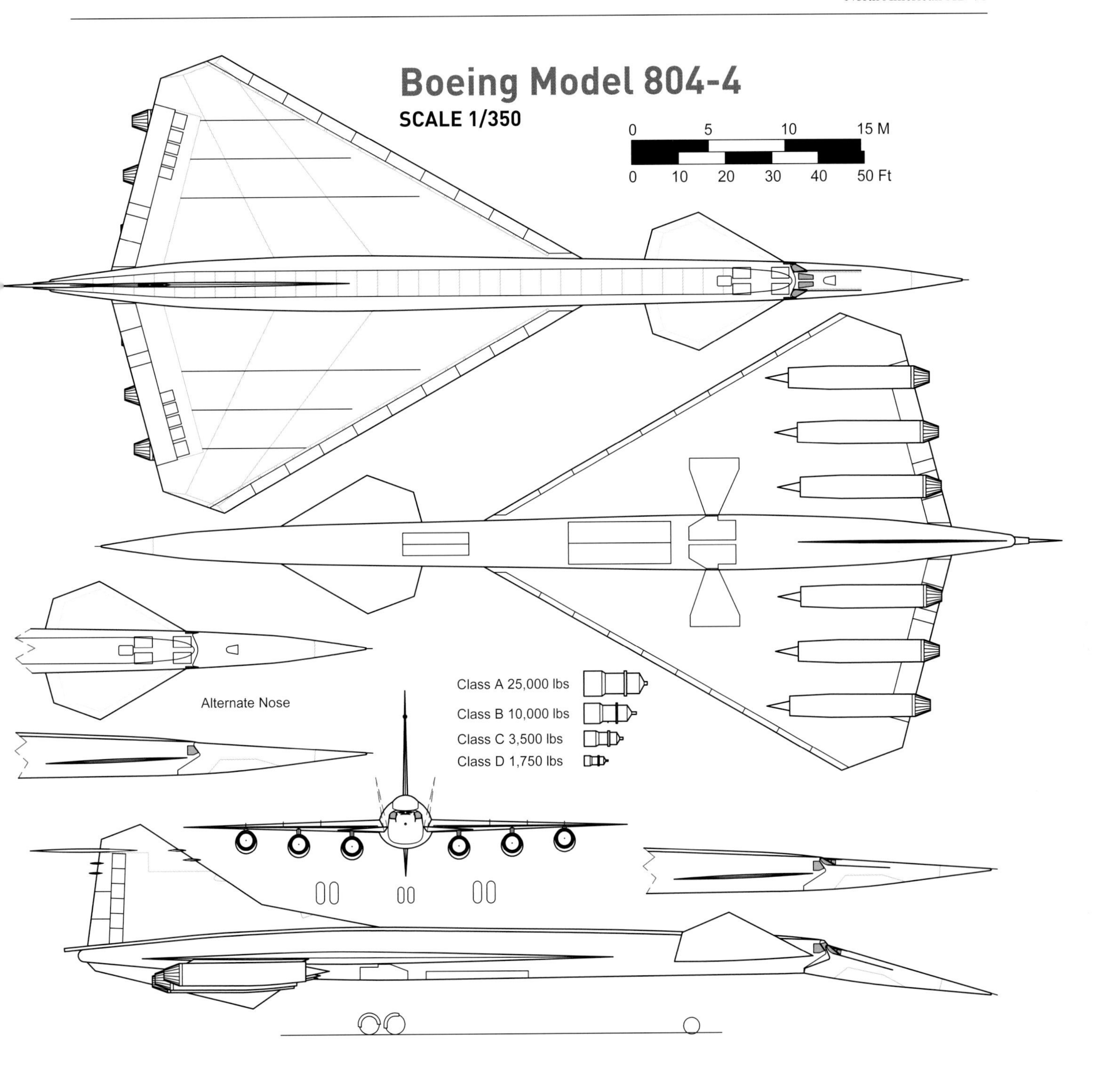

pressurized cockpit was to be made of commercially pure titanium; the canards and vertical fins were made of and clad with the same steel as the wings.

The cockpit had the same crew and escape capsules as the Model 804-1, but the bombardier-navigator and defence system operator ejection capsules were rotated so that they faced forward. There was enough room in the cockpit for the crew to get up and move about, both to stretch and to maintain electronic components.

The design was initiated in January 1957; by November of that year it was estimated that the mockup would be reviewed in January 1959 and the first flight would occur in February 1962.

North American B-70

It's at this point that this author must acknowledge that, to his very great annoyance and frustration, the history of the development of the B-70 is terribly incomplete. There is a fair mountain of information on the Boeing competitor and the designs that led to it… but the North American design seems to have arrived almost fully formed. This is because a great deal of documentation has been lost, or squirreled away in forgotten file cabinets, or slapped with a 'classified' label and put behind lock and key.

There is hope that documentation on what must surely have been a long and convoluted design process will eventually come to light… but it does not seem to have done so quite yet. So there are, at the moment, only a few scraps to work with.

When the floating wingtip concept was rejected by the Air Force, North American still had to come up with a way for the aircraft to fulfill the requirements. The existing aircraft, stripped of external tanks, could not fulfill the range requirement. Even the use of high energy fuels would not do the job. The aircraft needed to either lose a vast amount of structural weight while keeping the payload and the fuel, or it needed to lose a large amount of drag. The designers had already taken weight savings into account as much as possible given the materials technology of the time; it would be many years before carbon fibre composites would become available on an adequate scale to reduce the weight of an aircraft as large as this by a meaningful amount. So attention was given to drag reduction.

An earlier revolution in the reduction of drag at supersonic speeds had been started by NACA studies on the area rule phenomenon. So the North American designers went back to the well of NACA studies and found the 1956 paper Aircraft Configurations Developing High Lift/Drag Ratios at High Supersonic Speeds. This paper examined designs that would today most likely be thought of as 'spaceplanes', highly swept wing-bodies with downwards drooping wings or wingtips. It had been found that with proper shaping, the shockwaves generated off certain aircraft structures – the nose, the wings, etc. – could be engineered to impinge on the underside of the craft. The drag of the vehicle would be basically unchanged, but lift could be increased through the use of 'compression lift'. This would allow a vehicle to fly at a lower angle of attack to generate the same lift… and lower angle of attack means lower drag. So proper aircraft design could substantially reduce supersonic drag and consequently increase range. This, the North American designers decided, was exactly what they needed.

The changes in design from the NA-239 to the NA-259 were substantial, but perhaps the most important was the change in location of the engine inlets. Instead of side inlets, the new vehicle had a single split inlet on the underside, just behind the apex of a highly swept delta wing.

At supersonic speeds the shockwaves shed from this inlet would create a higher pressure region under the wing, increasing lift. This was the 'compression lift' discovered by the NACA researchers, and the inclusion of it into the NA-259 design made the aircraft work. Without it, it would not have had the range to carry out the intended mission without the use of high energy fuels and/or external drop tanks.

A new feature added to the aircraft was the drooping wingtip; these were not initially part of the compression lift system but were a means of increasing directional stability at high speed. At low speed – such as takeoff – the wingtips were held horizontal; this turned them into lift-generating surfaces, maximizing the lift of the aircraft. At low speed, the conventional vertical tails provided adequate stability. But as speed increased into the supersonic, much less wing area was needed to generate enough lift to cruise, (lift is a function not just of wing area, but airspeed) while at the same time the vertical tails began to lose their effectiveness. By angling down the wingtips, the aircraft increased stability without losing necessary lift.

North American NA-259 wind tunnel model

A three-view exists of a wind tunnel model depicting a not-final configuration. Unfortunately the scale of the wind tunnel model is not available, so the intended full-scale dimensions are not available either. However, as the NA-259 configuration is quite like that of the actual B-70, presumably the dimensions are much the same as well. And while the overall configuration is clearly almost that of the final XB-70, there are a few noteworthy details.

Firstly: the wind tunnel model diagram does not indicate that the aircraft had the variable geometry wingtips that would come to be associated with the Valkyrie. This may be because the model simply did not have this feature… or it could be because this feature had not yet been designed into the configuration. If it did have variable wingtips, they would have been notably smaller in area than those of the final design, as it is known that the size of the wingtips grew over time as the design evolved.

The cockpit canopy appears to be a fixed geometry feature; it does not appear to have the variable geometry ramp and windscreen of the final XB-70. The splitter of the inlet is quite different, pushed forward some distance as a forward-projecting structure. The precise layout of the inlet and its role in compression lift would have been an area of considerable study early in the NA-259 development cycle. The canards are larger in area and more highly swept, shaped quite a bit like the main wing.

The diagram shown here includes the North American XF-108 Rapier interceptor's early NA-257 configuration of May 1958 to scale. The XF-108 would have had two of the same J93 engines that the XB-70 had six of; capable of Mach 3, the F-108 would have carried three AIM-47 Falcon air-to-air missiles, predecessors of the AIM-54 Phoenix missiles that armed the F-14 Tomcat. NA-257 and B-70 designs are similar – but which came first?

The NA-257 was derived from the NA-236 of summer/autumn 1955. NA-236 was designed in response to a late 1955 USAF call for designs for a

North American Early B-70 Wind Tunnel Model

SCALE ~1/300

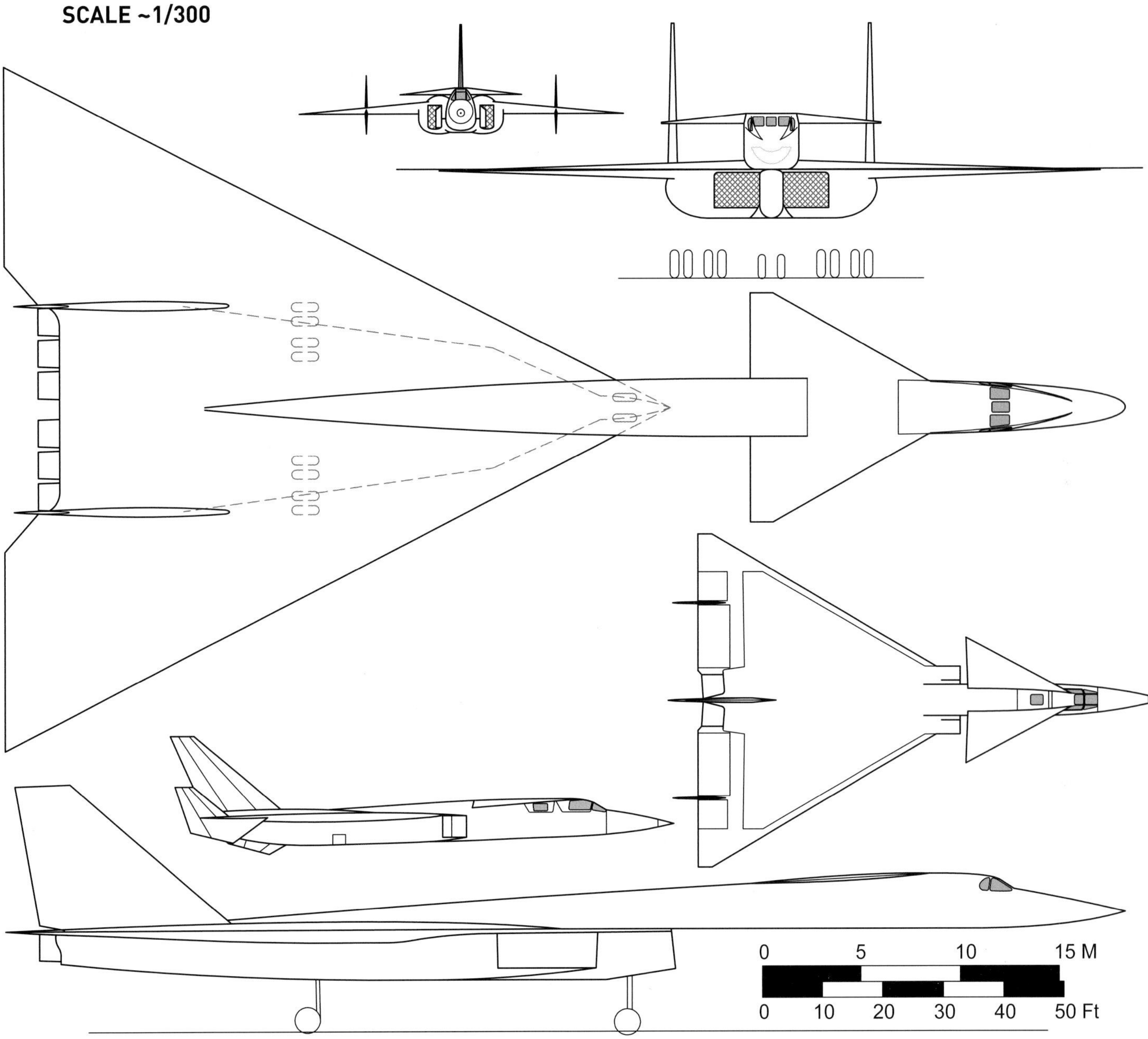

Long Range Interceptor – Experimental (LRI-X). The USAF selected NA-236 for LRI-X in January 1956; it transitioned to the NA-257 configuration, and then on to further configurations that dispensed with the canard.

Since it was designed a year before work started on the B-70 and had an earlier designation (NA-236 and NA-257 for the early XF-108 vs NA-259 for the B-70) it seems likely that the basic shape of the B-70 evolved from the smaller interceptor.

It should perhaps be noted that the F-108 would not have been an escort fighter for the B-70, as attractive a notion as that might have been. The F-108 did not have the same level of effort devoted to compression lift and as such its range was, by comparison, shockingly low. The standard interception mission for the early F-108 was well under 1,000 miles. Even with drop tanks and inflight refuelling, it would not have been able to keep up with the B-70.

The wind tunnel model probably represent a design close to what North American proposed to the USAF for WS-110A. This would be the design that won the contest on December 23, 1957. North American signed the contract for Phase I development of WS-110A on January 24, 1958. WS-110A was officially designated

'B-70' on February 14, 1958. The name 'Valkyrie' was selected for the B-70 by the Strategic Air Command on June 27, 1958, following a six-week contest involving more than 20,000 submissions.

In December of 1958 North American was contracted to build a single XB-70, internally designated NA-264. The mockup review was held from March 30 to April 4, 1959, resulting in more than 700 suggestions for design changes. The design was then given the new internal North American designation of NA-267 in late July, 1959.

Development of the GE J93 engine had been proceeding apace, and the promised performance of the B-70 using compression lift and hydrocarbon fuels was good enough that development of the boron-based zip fuel was cancelled on August 10, 1959.

At the same time the General Electric J93-GE-5 variant engine was also cancelled since it relied upon high energy fuel injection into the afterburner. On the whole this was a net benefit for the B-70; the advantages in terms of range when using high energy fuels were not spectacular, but the weight penalties for developing fuel tanks that could handle both hydrocarbon fuels and pentaborane fuels were substantial... never mind the safety, cost and logistics concerns. The B-70 would rely upon the J93-GE-3 engine, designed specifically for JP-6 fuel. Even though it provided slightly less thrust than the -5 (29,300lb vs 30,200lb), the performance was good enough, especially when coupled with increasingly promising supersonic aerodynamics, to essentially equal the high energy fuel system in terms of range.

The F-108 was cancelled in September of 1959 due largely to cost. This was bad news for the B-70 programme... there had been not only technology-sharing between the programmes but also cost sharing. A sum of about $180m in development cost was suddenly shifted from the now-defunct F-108 to the B-70, already quite an expensive programme.

This began a period of gloom for the B-70. President Eisenhower was not enthusiastic about the project, seeing little value in it and this, coupled with mounting and exorbitant expense, began to cast a pall over the project. At the same time, ICBMs were starting to prove their worth; the Atlas, Titan and Minuteman systems were looking like they would soon be capable of laying waste to the entire Soviet threat all on their own. Still, the B-70 had its supporters; an advantage of a relatively slow manned bomber compared to an ICBM is that it can be recalled. It is a stick that can be shaken at the enemy to get him to come to the table to negotiate. An ICBM, once launched, is a done deal.

Contracts with North American in July and September of 1960 provided funds permitting the completion of three XB-70s and gave hope for a YB-70 and even a possibility of a dozen operational B-70s. Things, however, did not improve with the dawning of 1961. The new President Kennedy was, like Eisenhower, not a fan of the B-70. Worse, his Secretary of Defense Robert McNamara was opposed to manned bombers on general principle, seeing them as obsolete technology.

In April of 1961, the contract was slashed to only three prototypes. The first two ('Air Vehicle' or A/V-1 and A/V-2) were to be XB-70s, not fitted with functional bomb bays or other operational military equipment; they would be purely test aircraft with a crew of two. Air Vehicle 3, though, would be a prototype (likely 'YB-70A') for an operational military aircraft, with the full crew of four, a functional bomb bay and bombing/navigation equipment.

Following that massive reduction in programme scale, a reversal happened in March 1962 when Congress called for the development of the RS-70 'Reconnaissance Strike' vehicle, optimistically expecting 60 RS-70s to enter service in 1969 and 150 more in 1970. Congress authorized funds to see this happen, but Secretary McNamara refused to release the money. So for the following years, aircraft construction moved forward somewhat slowly at the North American plant in Palmdale, California, with little hope of full production. Congress may have wanted full production, but the man who actually wrote the cheques did not.

The XB-70s were built largely of stainless steel. This may seem a little odd since it was developed at the same time as the Lockheed Blackbird series which flew just as fast and was made almost exclusively from titanium. Titanium is lighter than steel and handles the high temperatures of Mach 3 flight better. But the Blackbirds were, compared to the B-70, small aircraft and there were few of them. The B-70 was a giant (the heaviest aircraft in the world when it debuted) and the Air Force had originally intended for there to be hundreds of them. There was not enough titanium in the free world to build the B-70 fleet.

The Blackbird titanium was sourced by the CIA from the Soviet Union, but even the Soviets would have noticed a sudden increase in exports of titanium on a scale adequate to build the B-70 fleet. So the North American designers were restricted to the less 'strategic' material of steel. Still, a not inconsiderable 12,000lb of titanium ended up in the B-70, mostly in the forward fuselage which was the hottest region of the aircraft in high-speed flight.

The fact that the B-70 programme was essentially restricted to three aircraft meant that it did not have a production line manufacturing process. The three aircraft were assembled as unique vehicles without proper manufacturing jigs; this led to many problems. The fuel tank for A/V-1 leaked like a sieve; the welds holding the various metal sheets the tank was made

XB-70 A/V-1 – High speed

SCALE 1/210

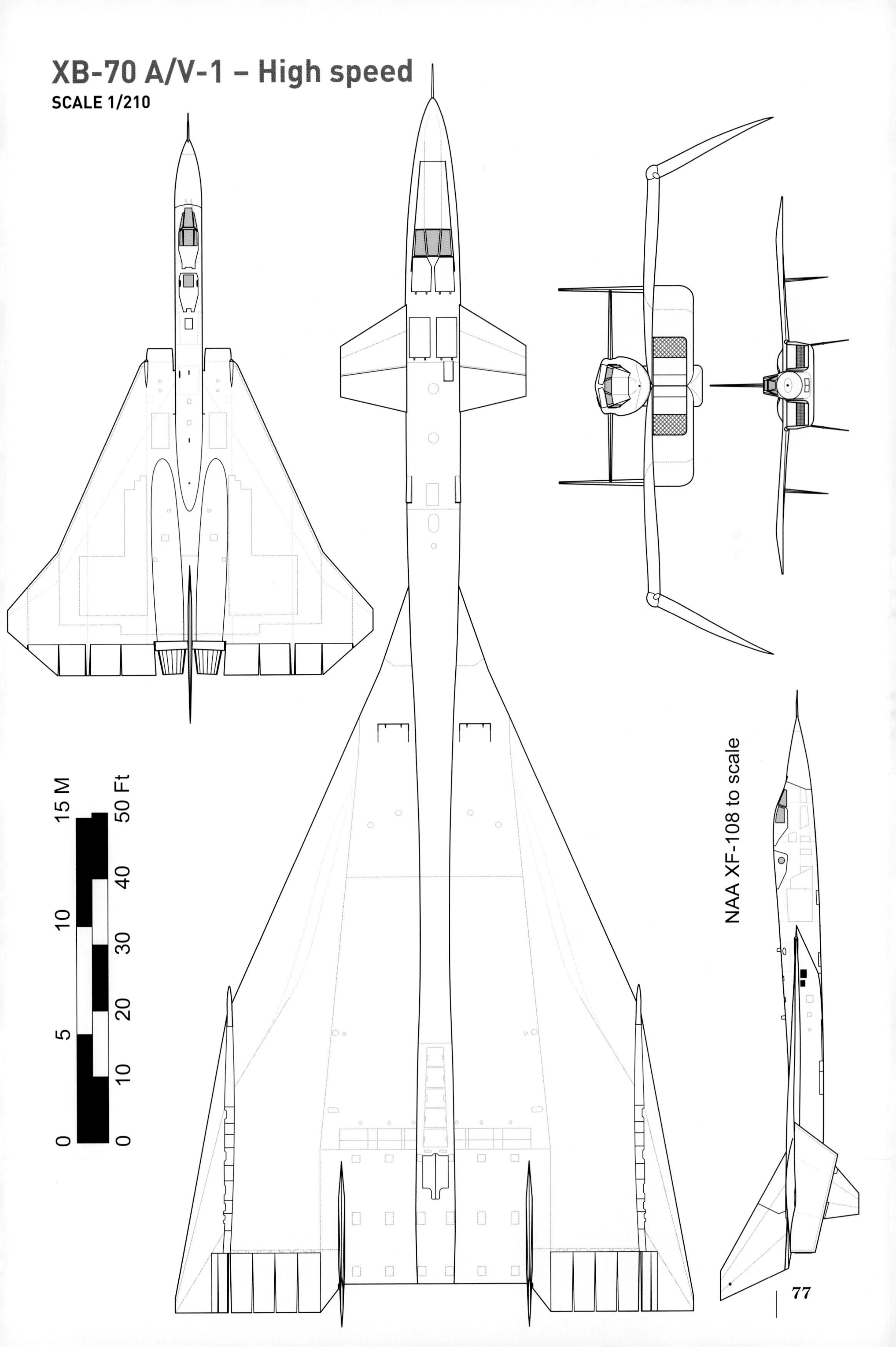

XB-70 A/V-1 – Low speed

SCALE 1/210

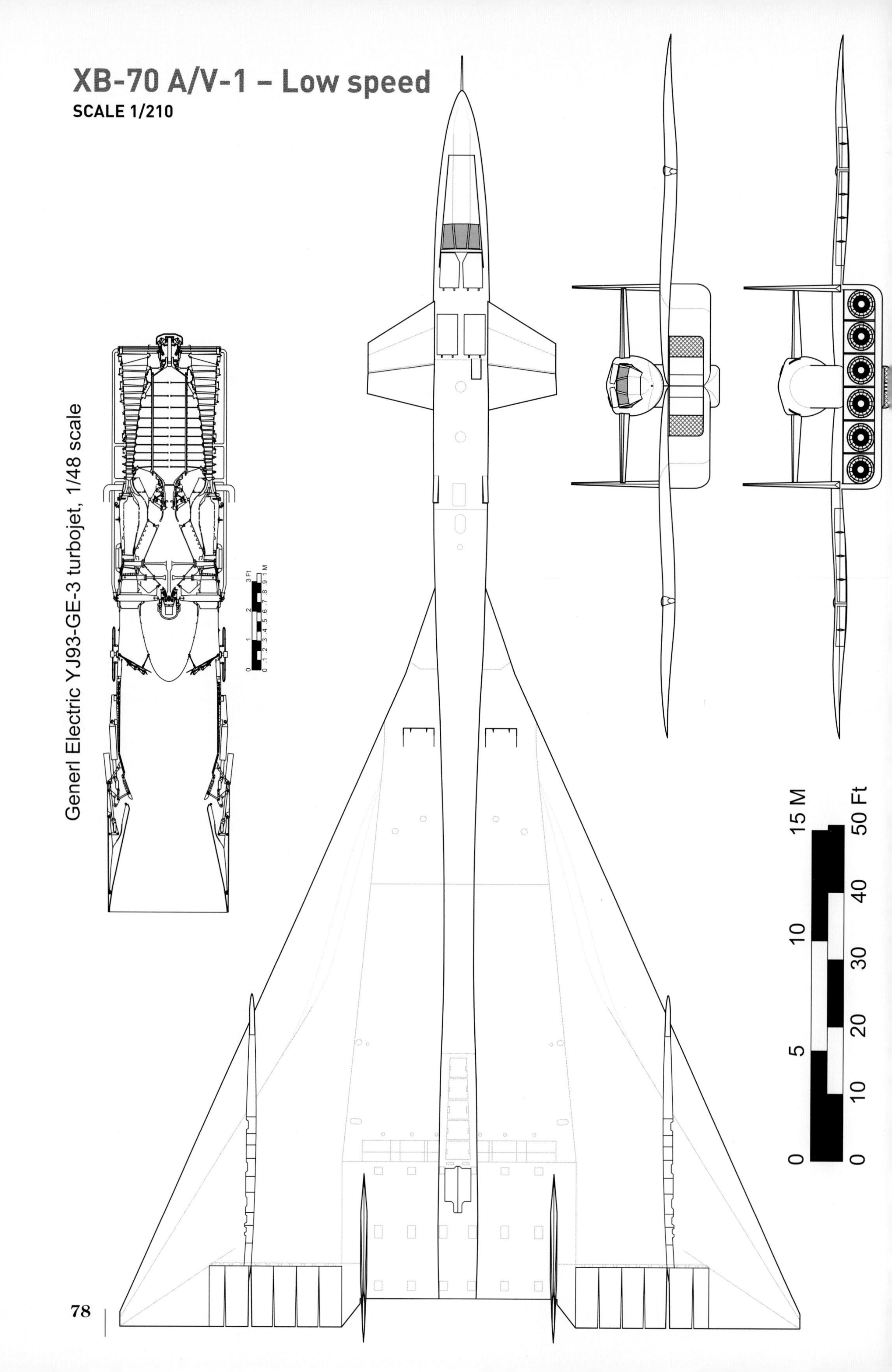

from were filled with pinholes. This was a result of the welds being done by hand in an 'artisan' fashion, rather than a more automated, more repeatable process. Finding the leaks was a challenge; fixing them, more so. The problem was eventually resolved adequately and A/V-2 had fewer issues. But had these tanks been filled with pentaborane, the whole programme would be known largely for one of the most impressive and comprehensive aircraft fires in history.

XB-70 A/V-1

The first B-70 rolled out on May 11, 1964. This was not a secret ceremony but was well publicized and included celebrities such as famed actor (and former Army Air Forces pilot) Jimmy Stewart. From there, the XB-70 underwent a series of tests and adjustments, fixing the many, many problems that sprang up. It finally took to the air on September 21, 1964. It had been planned to go supersonic on that flight; instead, due to a hydraulics fault the landing gear stayed extended and the aircraft made its way, sub-sonically, to Edwards Air Force Base. The hydraulic system fault that had caused the issue also led to the landing gear being damaged upon landing.

The second flight occurred on October 5, 1964. Again the plan included a supersonic portion, with the intention of reaching Mach 1.1... but landing gear problems cut the flight short. The third flight on October 12 finally saw the plane reach Mach 1.11. But a new problem was becoming painfully obvious. Starting on the second flight, structural flexing had caused some of the white paint to flake off, revealing the stainless steel structure underneath. The third flight saw much more of the paint detach, leaving the plane looking spotty and unusual.

Flight tests continued, with problems of all types arising regularly... less a problem of design, more a problem of how the aircraft was built. The first Mach 2 flight occurred on March 24, 1965, reaching Mach 2.14. The first and only time A/V-1 would reach Mach 3 (3.02 in fact) was on October 14, 1965, at an altitude of 70,000ft. The 83rd and final flight of A/V-1 was on February 4, 1969, when it flew from Edwards Air Force Base to Wright Patterson Air Force Base in Ohio in order to be installed at the USAF Museum.

XB-70 A/V-2

The second XB-70 was a bit different from A/V-1, lessons had been learned that were incorporated into the new vehicle's construction. Two items were visible to the casual observer:

1) The radome on the underside of the nose was painted black on A/V-2, where it had been white on A/V-1. The black radome would most likely have been how operational vehicles would have been painted. However, the radome of A/V-2 was, like A/V-1, not equipped with an actual bombardment/navigation radar system. The black paint was not purely cosmetic, however, as it was a new material being tested for its Mach 3 survivability.
2) The main wing of A/V-2 was given 5° of dihedral, where A/V-1 had 0°. Wind tunnel testing during the construction of A/V-1 had shown an issue with roll stability while the wingtips were folded down; bending the wings up slightly cured this, while introducing a sideslip issue at low speed. This could be countered by diligent piloting, and could be cured in operational aircraft with a properly calibrated stability augmentation system. Bending the wings up was not easily, or elegantly, accomplished; as a result, a distinct 'kink' or discontinuity is blatantly visible in the wing leading edge just outboard of the underside inlet ducts.

The maiden flight of A/V-2 on July 17, 1965, was much more successful than A/V-1's thanks to the host of improvements made since A/V-1's debut. The second aircraft had much improved overall construction quality; as a result, it was able to lower its wingtips on that first flight and hit Mach 1.41 on its way to Edwards Air Force Base. It surpassed Mach 2 (reached Mach 2.23) on its sixth flight on September 29, and surpassed Mach 3 (reaching Mach 3.05) on its 17th flight on January 3, 1966. A/V-2 captured the XB-70 speed record on April 12, 1966 by attaining Mach 3.08 (2,025 mph) at 72,800ft... and stayed above Mach 3 for 20 minutes.

On June 8, 1966, during a publicity photo op for General Electric engines, the XB-70 A/V-2 flew in formation with other aircraft that utilized GE turbojets: a Lockheed F-104N, a Northrop F-5A, a Northrop T-38 and a McDonnell F-4B. These were photographed from a Learjet, also powered with GE turbojets. It may have looked impressive to see these aircraft lined up wingtip to wingtip in flight, but it turned out to be an incredibly unfortunate thing to do.

The F-104N was off the slightly drooped right wingtip of the XB-70, when its tail struck the wingtip. The F-104N rolled hard to the left, rolling up the wingtip and going fully over the back of the bomber. In the process it knocked off much of the XB-70's right vertical tail and most of the left. The F-104N was destroyed immediately; the XB-70 continued to fly straight for a moment, but with the loss of the stabilizers and other damage, loss of control was inevitable. It began to roll; attempts to counter that caused a violent yaw. In the process the left wing separated from the aircraft and it began to plummet towards the desert below in a flat spin.

Pilot Al White managed to close his escape capsule – not without difficulty – and eject. Co-pilot Carl Cross, for reasons unknown, never encapsulated, never ejected, and died with his aircraft. The aircraft was utterly destroyed when it hit the desert floor.

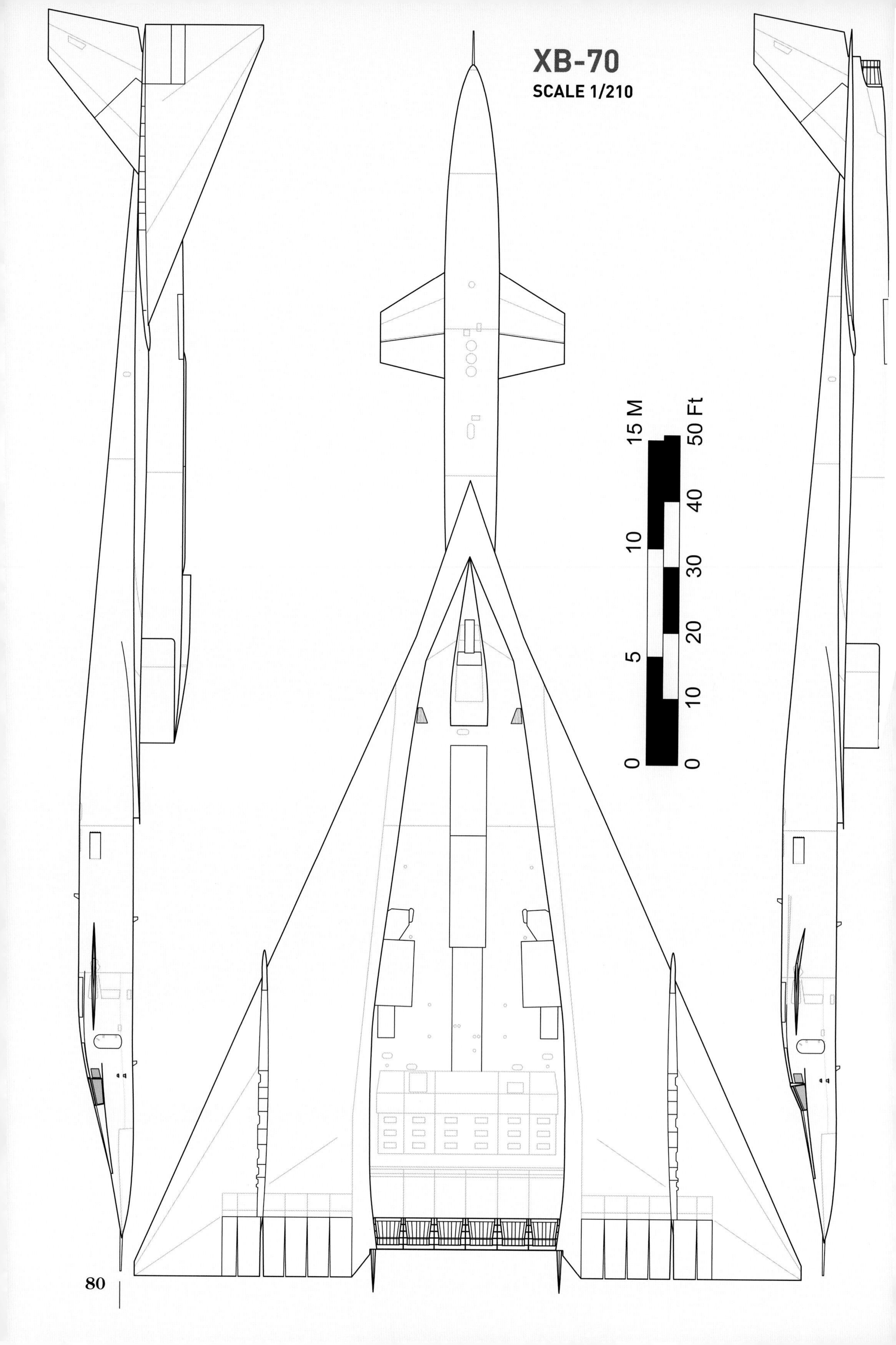
XB-70
SCALE 1/210
0
5
10
15 M
0
10
20
30
40
50 Ft

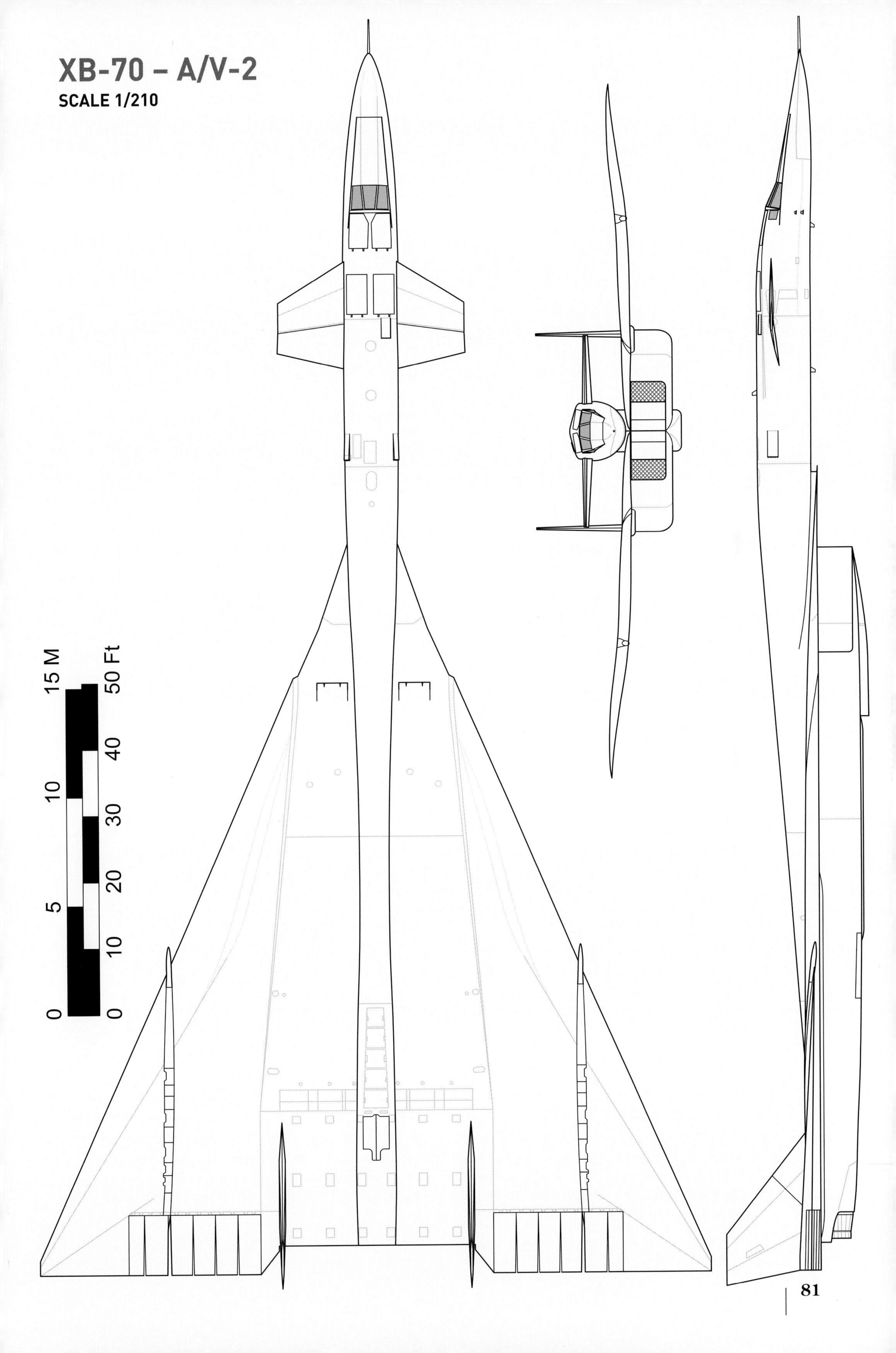
XB-70 – A/V-2
SCALE 1/210
15 M
10
5
0
50 Ft
40
30
20
10
0

The pilot's escape capsule kept White alive, but it did not keep him intact. When he actuated the encapsulation process the doors slammed down and trapped his extended right arm. This set in motion a series of events that resulted in the capsule not living up to expectations, ending with it hitting the ground far harder than it could and should have and doing pilot White extensive injuries.

A few components from A/V-2 were scavenged for use as spares on A/V-1, but the aircraft was basically a total loss.

YB-70A A/V-3

The third B-70 airframe was to be the more operationally-representative YB-70A, but sadly it was cancelled on March 5, 1964. By that point many components were under construction or actually finished; many would serve as spare parts.

Since the YB-70A was never finished, just exactly what it would have looked like is unknown. It's unclear whether it would have had the dihedral of A/V-2; almost certainly it would have had that aircraft's black radome. More interesting is the possibility of an overall change in appearance. The mid-1960s was a decade before the Air Force got serious about 'stealth', but signature reduction was a well-known and desired concept. There was little that could be done at the time to reduce the sizable radar return of the B-70; it was covered in unfortunate 90° reflectors, such as the vertical stabilizer and the upper fuselage, the canards and forward fuselage, the side walls of the engine module and the lower surface of the wings.

To make the B-70 in any way radar-stealthy would have taken a massive effort. But the B-70 was also a sizable target in infra-red. There was, again, little that could be done to reduce the blinding IR illumination from the engines when seen from the rear, but plans were in progress to duct cooling air underneath the engines. At full afterburner the effect might be minimal, but A/V-3 was reportedly going to have this modification.

Additionally the structure of the aircraft itself was also an impressive emitter from all aspects when flying at Mach 3 and generating substantial aerothermal loads. Tests were made on alternative coatings that would reduce thermal emissivity; one idea was to coat the aircraft in somewhere north of 31lb of gold. This idea also featured on the Pluto nuclear ramjet (see Volume 2), and for the same reason. A less gaudy and expensive approach was to coat the structure largely in silver, with nickel in some higher-temperature regions. When cleaned and polished, a silver-plated B-70 would have been a sight to behold. After a rough flight, with long durations at Mach 3 and transits through snow and rain and dust and bugs… it would have been a somewhat less shiny sight.

B-70 derivatives

A fair number of proposals were made for derivatives of the B-70, or for alternate uses of the two XB-70 airframes. But curiously, the great majority of the proposals that are currently known are not for bombers. The B-70 as a supersonic transport demonstrator, or to test advanced materials or engines, or to carry high speed research aircraft, or to launch satellites, satellite interceptors or even manned vehicles into orbit… these are known in some abundance. But they are not bombers, and so fall outside the scope of this work. However, there are a few known bomber projects based on the B-70.

RSB-70

The B-70 is rarely depicted carrying weapons. The bomb bay, though, was well defined, a rectangular bay some 347in long tucked within the inlet diverter section in the lower fuselage. The bomb bay doors would not hinge open as was normally done on bombers such as the B-52. Instead, the doors were two flat rectangular panels that would slide aft to expose the bomb bay. This would reduce drag at Mach 3 as compared to conventionally hinged doors. As to what the bomb load of the operational B-70 would be, that was often left rather vague.

A Standard Aircraft Characteristic document from June 1960 is one of the few to show the B-70 carrying a bomb. In this case, the bomb is a single large device of unknown characteristics. It is entirely possible that the shape shown is purely speculative on the part of the North American draftsmen or engineers, but it might have been an actual configuration.

While considerably 'pointier', the bomb is suspiciously close in size and general configuration to the Mk-36 thermonuclear weapon. The Mk-36 was designed to be dropped from subsonic aircraft such as the B-36 and the B-52, weighed around 17,700lb and developed a yield of about 10 megatons. The shape of the Mk-36, designed to be dropped from very subsonic aircraft, would probably have been unstable at Mach 3; the pointier bomb may have been a new casing for the Mk-36 device to allow it to deploy properly from the B-70.

Alternatively, the bomb might have been a repackaged B-41. The Mk-36 was an update of the Mk-21, developed all the way back in 1955; by 1960, a full five years later, this was clearly approaching obsolescence. The B-41 was a much more advanced weapon based on a three-stage fusion warhead; it would develop a zesty 25 megaton yield, generally considered acceptable for most likely targets (Kaiju, Lovecraftian elder gods and alien motherships being the rare possible exceptions). Due to advances in technology, the B-41 was slightly smaller and notably lighter (at 10,670lb) than the Mk-36. However, the B-41 did not enter service until 1961, the year after the mystery bomb was illustrated.

RSB-70

SCALE 1/210

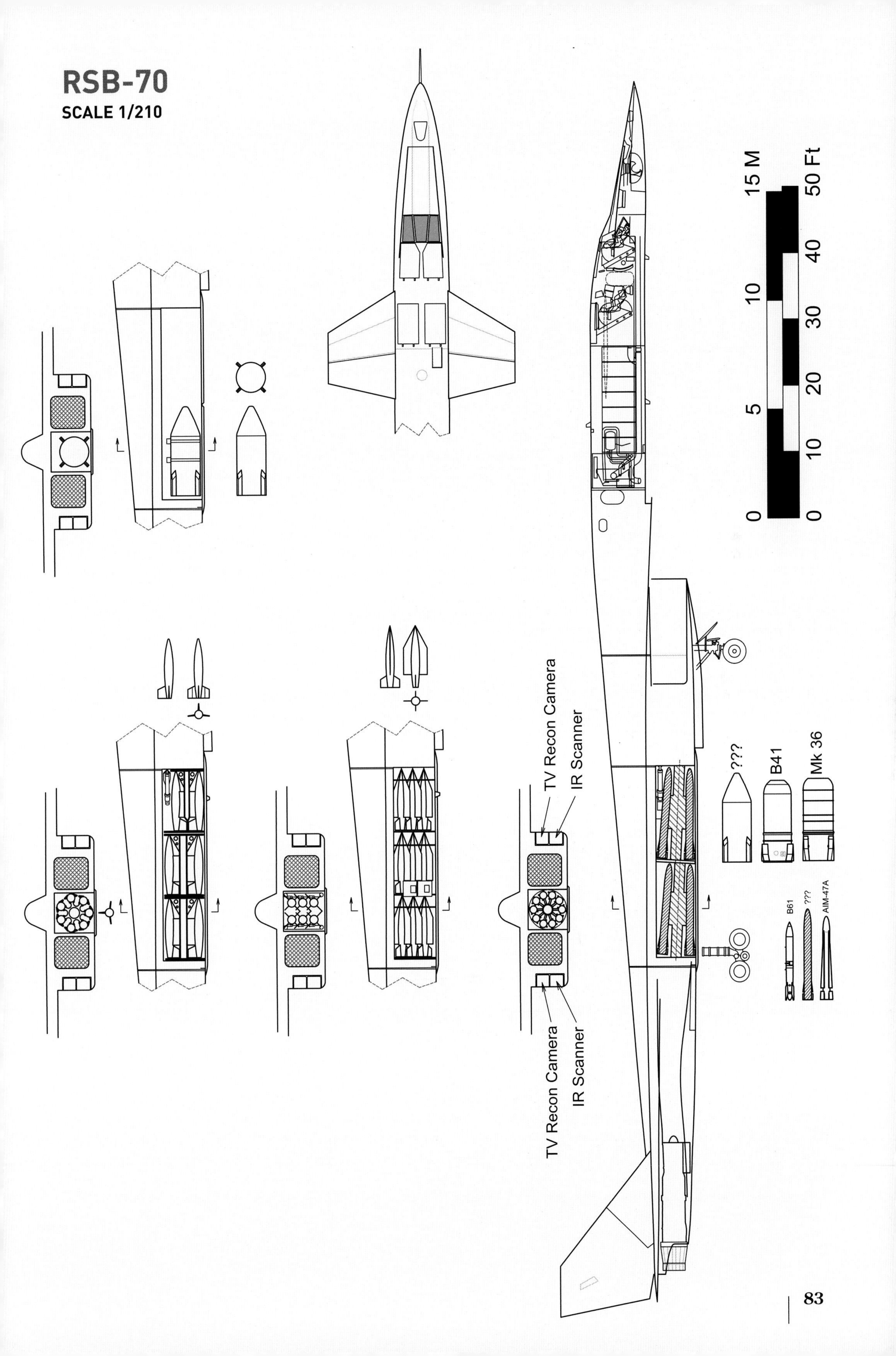

Regardless of what the mystery bomb was based on, it seems likely that the parachute package included in the subsonically dropped version was omitted on the supersonic version. The B-70 would fly high and fast enough that even without parachute retarding, it would likely escape the blast radius of even 25 megatons of canned sunshine.

In any event, the operational B-70 could carry a maximum bomb load of 25,000lb. This could be made up of:

1 Class A weapon weighing 25,000lb.
2 Class B weapons weighing 20,000lb.
1 Class B FUFO weapon weighing 15,000lb (full fusing option or 'Dial-A-Yield').
2 Class C FUFO weapons at 17,000lb.
4 Class D weapons at 8,000lb.
Alternate loadouts included:
2 air-to-surface missiles carried externally and 1 Class B weapon
2 air-to-surface missiles carried externally and 4 Class D weapons

These ASMs likely would have been GAM-87 Skybolt missiles or something similar. Unfortunately, diagrams and detailed descriptions of how and where such missiles were to be carried have not yet come to light. When carrying external air-to-surface missiles, the B-70 would most likely have been restricted to subsonic speeds, only able to dash after the missiles had been launched and the pylons (probably) dropped.

Something that the author did happen across were a trio of large diagrams dated September of 1960 that depict inboard profiles of the operational Recon Strike B-70 with planned payloads. The first shows the bomb bay split in two with two rotary launchers, each launcher loaded with ten 'guided missiles'. These missiles are not well defined, but seem like they might be modified versions of the AIM-47 Falcon. This is unlikely to have been an interceptor variant of the B-70, but rather a ground-attack variant of the AIM-47, which at one point was planned to have the W42 nuclear warhead (replaced with a large conventional explosive warhead by the time the missile flew).

In 1967 there was an attempt to convert existing AIM-47 missiles into the AGM-76 anti-radiation missile which would seek out and attack ground-based radar transmitters. It may be that the guided missiles depicted for the RSB-70 were similarly modified AIM-47s, guided to the target via transmitters on the underside of the B-70.

The second diagram shows the bomb bay split into three compartments (but without a visible bulkhead between them, in essence one long bay), each with two stacks of three winged guided missiles, again using command guidance from the RSB-70. The third diagram shows an RSB-70 with the bomb bay split into three compartments with a bulkhead between, each with a rotary launcher with eight folding-fin guided missiles. These three types of missiles were likely of the kind that would later be brought to life by the AGM-69 Short Range Attack Missile which entered service in 1972.

The warheads would have been miniscule compared to the B-61 (the SRAM's W69 warhead topped out at 200 kilotons), but the sheer number would have allowed the RSB-70 to lay waste to considerable Soviet acreage. All three diagrams shared common reconnaissance equipment – on the side walls of the lower fuselage straddling the bomb bay were infrared scanners and TV cameras looking both port and starboard. This would have permitted recording, and likely real-time, bomb damage assessment.

The operational B-70 would have had a crew of four. The additional two crew (bombardier-navigator and defence system operator) would have sat behind the pilot and co-pilot; all would have been secured within their individual escape capsules. The escape hatches for the second two crewmen were built into the two XB-70s though the additional crew stations were never fitted. The operational B-70 would have also been equipped for in-flight refuelling using a receptacle on the upper side of the nose ahead of the variable geometry ramp.

The defence system operator would not have had systems like guns or air-to-air missiles, as it was felt that the high altitude and high speed of the B-70 would have put it out of reach of fighters or interceptors. All that could threaten a B-70 were missiles, susceptible to various countermeasures. So the defence system operator would have systems such as chaff, flares and electronic countermeasures to use in order to confuse incoming missiles. There had been some thought to using guided missiles for a more active defence, but in the end these ideas came to nothing.

B-70 with General Purpose Missiles

One of the more absurd looking proposals was a North American concept for using the B-70 as a carrier for a 'General Purpose Missile'. Sadly, little information is available about the missile; performance, weight data and warhead are lacking. All that is available is a single illustration showing how a B-70 could be used to carry 18 of the missiles at once. The General Purpose Missile was depicted as a delta-winged configuration with a single ramjet engine in a separate nacelle, with downward-drooping wingtips. This was clearly a standoff weapon, presumably with a small nuclear warhead. By calling it a 'general purpose' missile, it may be that it was intended to not only strike ground targets, but possibly serve an air-to-air role as well.

The diagram here shows where the missiles were supposed to be gathered about across the great expanse of the B-70, suspended beneath the wings with pylons, attached to the tips of both the canards and the vertical stabilizers, perched atop and underneath the fuselage. The source sketch does not depict all of the necessary pylons, explaining why some of the missiles in this reconstruction are not attached to the aircraft.

Another diagram presents an alternate design for the General Purpose Missile. This missile was similar in size with a similar looking ramjet engine… but otherwise the configuration was quite different, looking more like a catamaran boat with a jet engine than a normal sort of missile. This version of the GPM weighed 698lb, would fly at Mach 3 to Mach 4 at 70,000 to 90,000ft and had a range of 975 nautical miles. The B-70 would be able to carry 19 of this version of the GPM.

B-70 w/General Purpose Missile

SCALE 1/300

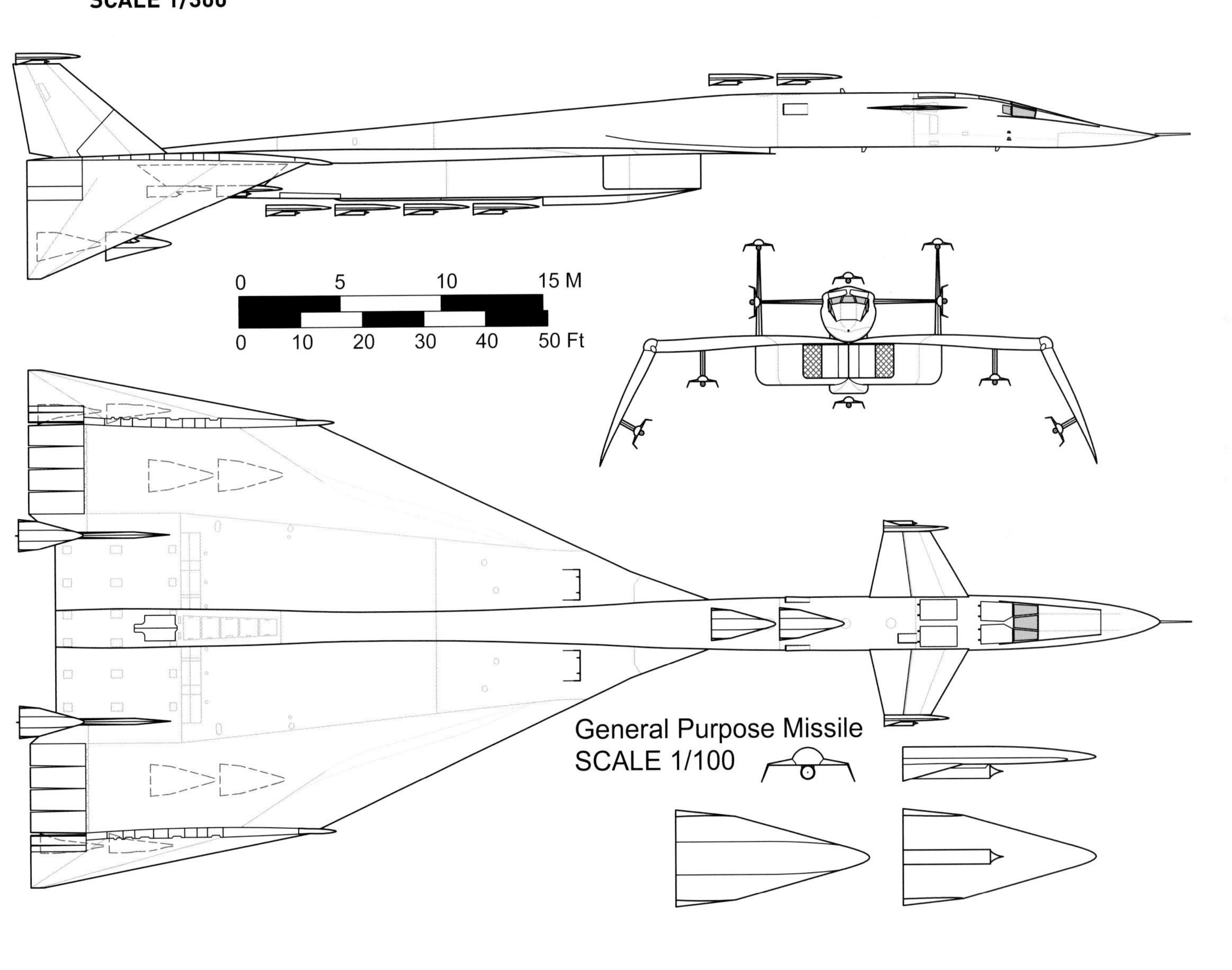

6 CHAPTER General Dynamics F-111

The history of the United States Air Force is replete with fighters that were used to drop bombs. From the First World War to the present day, virtually anything that could fly and stood a chance of surviving a combat environment had bombs strapped to it. That, however, does not make those aircraft bombers. Some aircraft, though, straddled the line. And the General Dynamics F-111 stepped well over it. It was designed to be both a fighter and a bomber but it spent far more time equipped as a bomber.

As described in the A3J-1 chapter, the late 1950s saw growing interest in variable geometry wings as the solution to all problems for high speed aircraft. The United States had proven that the concept was at least feasible with the Bell X-5 and the Grumman XF10F-1 aircraft in the early 1950s, but those had been subsonic designs.

It had been hoped these two could be developed into practical fighters… the F10F came closest, compared to somewhat less refined ideas of armed X-5s. Technical problems, cost and lack of interest doomed them both. However, as the 1950s rolled on, variable sweep wings only gained panache in the minds of designers and planners, including those of the Air Force.

As the 1960s approached, the USAF looked forward to a strike fighter faster and more capable than the Republic F-105. Introduced in 1958, the F-105 Thunderchief gained notoriety when it started getting knocked out of the skies of Vietnam; but those problems were not yet known in 1959. Still, a replacement was looked forward to; after all, it was already flying, which meant that obsolescence would soon arrive. (*A note: the F-105 was more a bomber than a fighter, and thus should fit in this book... but this author has no information on early concepts or unbuilt derivatives, so that's that.*)

System Development Requirement 17 from February 5, 1960, called for a Mach 2.3 to 2.5 all-weather high-altitude (70,000ft) fighter. This replaced General Operational Requirement 169 from March of 1958, which called for the same aircraft… except VTOL. SDR-17 went with the technically less aggressive and risky STOL rather than VTOL, with a takeoff run of 3,000ft from austere landing strips, the ability to ferry 3,000 nautical miles and a mission radius of 800 nautical miles. It was to be able to carry not only air-to-air missiles but also nuclear weapons. There were to be two crew and two engines.

On June 14, 1960, the USAF issued Specific Operational Requirement 183, replacing SDR-17. This basically refined SDR-17, slightly reducing requirements… a max altitude of 60,000ft (70,000 being desired), a max speed of Mach 2.2 (2.5 being desired), a takeoff run on austere airstrip raised to 3,300ft. SOR-183 led to a Request For Proposals on October 12, 1960, for Weapon System No. 324A, which was given the name Tactical Fighter Experimental, or TFX.

At the same time, the Navy was interested in a new fleet defence fighter. In normal times, the Navy and the Air Force would have avoided each other and their separate requirements like the plague, but late 1960 was not a normal time. The Kennedy administration was about to take office; WS-324A was put on hold until the new administration could get in and set policy.

Many thought that Kennedy and Secretary of Defense McNamara would simply cancel the fighter in favour of strategic bombing. Instead, McNamara did something almost as inconceivable: in February of 1961 he directed that the Air Force and the Navy work together to design one aircraft that could fulfill both their needs. Even stranger, the Army was brought in to the project with the goal of making sure that the TFX would serve Army (and Marine Corps) needs for a close air support ground-attack aircraft too.

This was one of those brilliant ideas that was never going to work: the requirements were simply incompatible. The Air Force needed a long, sleek, fast aircraft to penetrate enemy airspace; the Navy needed a lightweight aircraft of short length that could loiter at subsonic speed for long duration. The Air Force wanted to haul nuclear bombs; the Navy wanted to carry a multitude of air-to-air missiles. The Air Force needed a relatively small radar; the Navy needed a large radar dish in order to detect and track enemy aircraft at long range. Neither of those types of aircraft are appropriate for a low, slow heavily armoured bomb-and-gun truck for close air support. In short, these wildly divergent requirements were not a good fit for each other.

So, naturally, McNamara ordered the project to forge ahead.

By the summer of 1961, the Army had withdrawn from the project; there was no squeezing the TFX into the close air support role. But the Navy and the Air Force continued to try to maximize commonality between the aircraft that they wanted and needed. In September 1961, the TFX request for proposals officially went out, calling for an aircraft that could be built in Air Force and Navy versions.

The RFP went to Boeing, Chance-Vought, General Dynamics, Grumman, Lockheed, McDonnell, North American, Northrop and Republic. Northrop declined to participate; the other companies responded in early December. At that time the TFX programme was renamed: F-111A for the Air Force, F-111B for the Navy.

In mid-January of 1962, the Source Selection Board concluded that none of the responding designs were acceptable, but that the Boeing and General Dynamics designs merited more study. With million-dollar contracts to produce more data, the two contractors went back to work; in June 1962 the Air Force endorsed the Boeing design, but the Navy did not, preferring to wait for more data.

In September, Boeing and General Dynamics submitted their fourth round of proposals. Once again the Air Force preferred the Boeing design, and even the Navy gave the Boeing design preference… but on November 24, Defense Secretary McNamara selected the General Dynamics design anyway.

This was, unsurprisingly, a controversial decision, one that resulted in Congressional hearings. McNamara's reasoning for choosing the General Dynamics design over the Boeing concept was that Boeing's vehicle required more and larger differences between Air Force and Navy versions.

There were rumours that perhaps something more than pure technical merit helped sway the decision. Boeing at the time was still busy with B-52 production, while the Fort Worth, Texas, General Dynamics plant was ending work on the B-58 and would soon be otherwise idle. Further, Vice President Lyndon Johnson, a man not exactly renowned for his strict and unbending sense of ethics, was from the area and had considerable business interests there. The investigations dragged on for years, in the end not concluding that the decision was made for political reasons.

General Dynamics was contracted to start full development of the F-111A and F-111B in December 1962. Mockup inspection was completed in September 1963, and the first of two test F-111As rolled out on October 15, 1964. The first flight was on December 21, 1964; this proved short, but successful.

Much has been written about the F-111A and B, but much less so about the designs that competed against them to become the F-111. A great deal of this is due to the fact that there is, so far, not a whole lot of information out there about the competitors, and what is known is often scattered across NASA wind tunnel reports. However, the origins of the concept do not lie in the TFX programme itself, but earlier in SDR-17.

General Dynamics Super Hustler 'TAC Bombers'

The only known (to this author) responses to SDR-17 came from the Air Force itself and General Dynamics, who responded in April of 1960 with four aircraft given the Super Hustler and 'TAC Bomber' monikers. The relationship to the Mach 4 parasite bomber described in the B-58 chapter seems tenuous; all that seems to link them is a general resemblance of shape in the first of the SDR-17 'Super Hustlers'.

This did indeed look like the earlier concept, but grown up some. It was no longer a parasite aircraft, and no longer had a booster stage: it was a conventional solitary aircraft, though shaped much like the Super Hustler bomber stage. Gone were the Marquardt ramjets, replaced with a pair of turbojets in the tail, fed through an underslung inlet considerably simpler than that of the ramjet vehicle. It retained the flat-bottomed fuselage and long, low nose, as well as the sharply swept wings and vertical stabilizers.

Much of the wacky complexity of the ramjet vehicle was gone: no longer did it bend itself for landing, no longer were the cockpit windscreens hidden behind deployable heat shields. It was a much simpler design, but one that seems like it would have had some difficulty getting off the ground due to relatively small and extremely swept wings. It was apparently capable of carrying only a single TX43 nuclear bomb, attached to a pylon beneath the underslung engine module. This necessitated long landing gear legs.

The second design saw numerous modifications. The cockpit canopy moved away from the flush design of the Super Hustler, and presented a more conventional stepped profile. The wings were much the same except that the tips were cut off and replaced with reduced-sweep triangular extensions capable of folding down 90°, much like the wingtips of the B-70 and presumably for the same reason (see Chapter 5). The vertical stabilizers were removed from the wing and replaced with a single conventional body-mounted fin; a pair of horizontal stabilizers were added to the rear fuselage. The engine, inlet and weapons arrangement remained much the same.

The third design took the fuselage of the second and replaced the wings with 'diamond' wings similar in outline to those of the F-104 Starfighter. Again the wingtips had triangular, foldable extensions. The depth of the fuselage was decreased by moving the inlets to the sides, rather than below; this allowed the landing gear to be somewhat shorter, though it had a distinctly

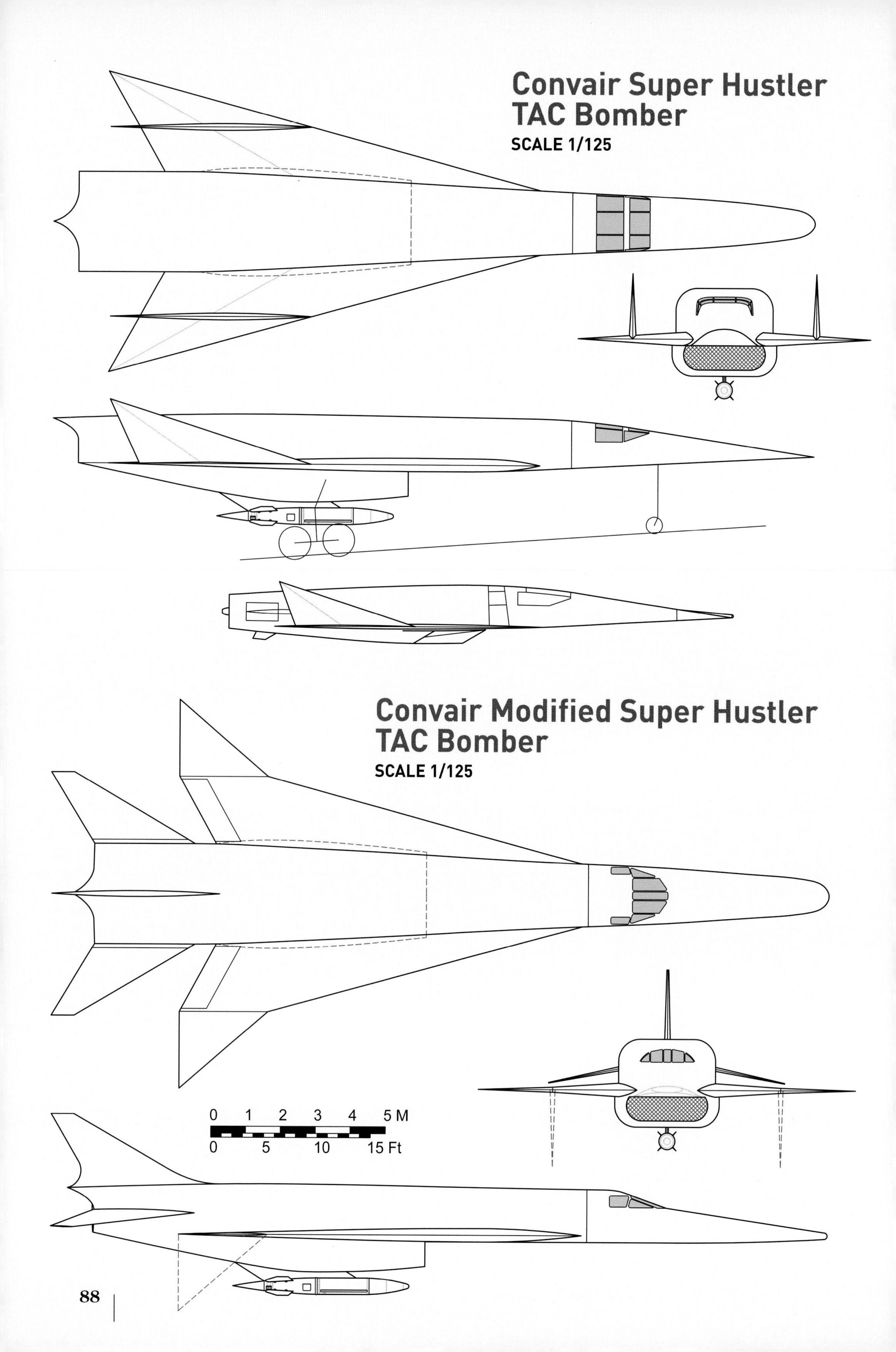
Convair Super Hustler
TAC Bomber
SCALE 1/125
Convair Modified Super Hustler
TAC Bomber
SCALE 1/125
0 1 2 3 4 5 M
0 5 10 15 Ft

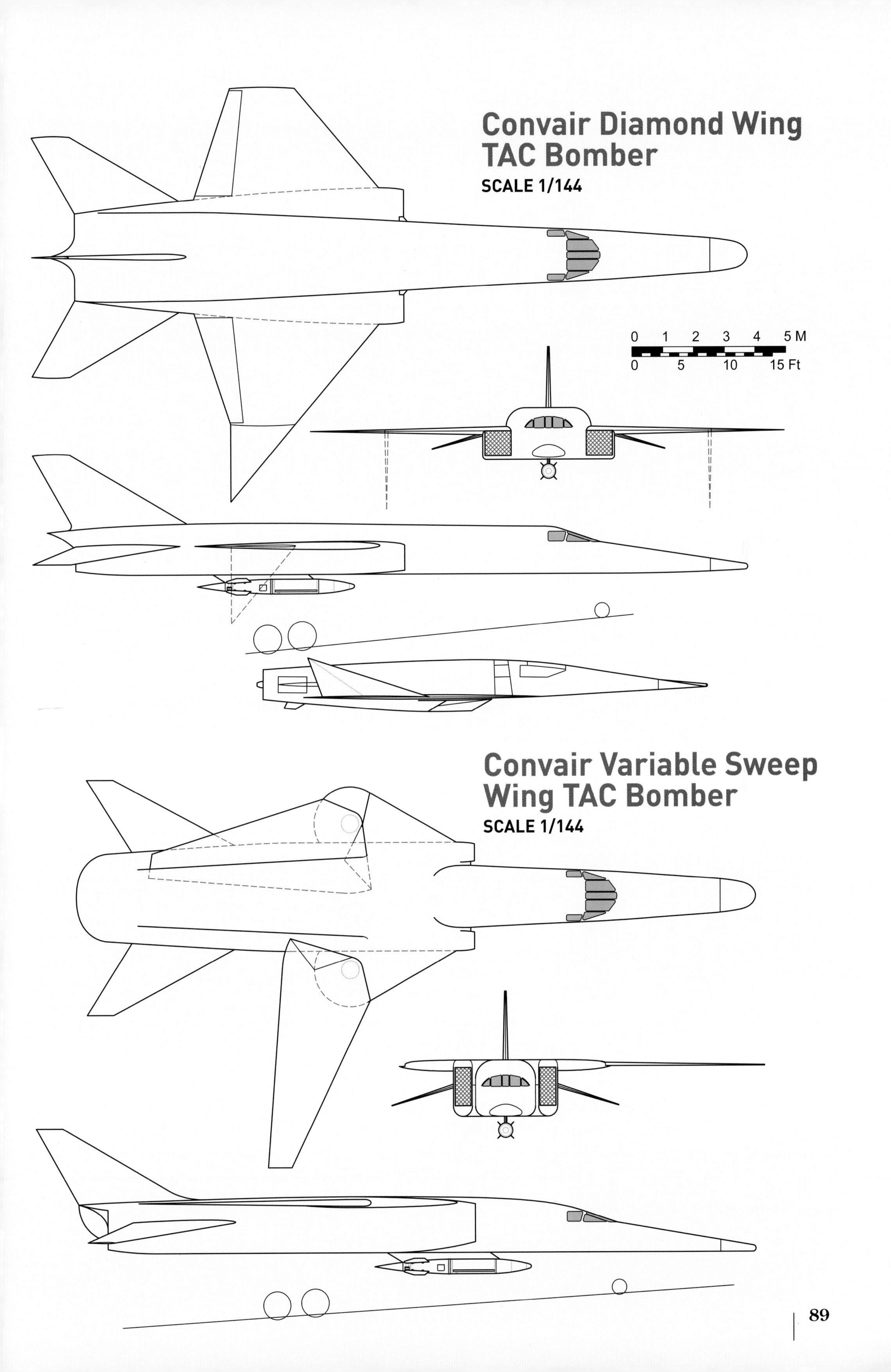
Convair Diamond Wing
TAC Bomber
SCALE 1/144
0 1 2 3 4 5 M
0 5 10 15 Ft
Convair Variable Sweep
Wing TAC Bomber
SCALE 1/144

nose-down stance. The single nuclear weapon remained suspended beneath the aft fuselage.

The fourth and final Super Hustler TAC Bomber basically took the third configuration and replaced the 'diamond' wings with variable geometry wings. These were 'outboard pivot' wings that folded more than 90° back, stowing themselves in slots in the upper side of the rear fuselage. The arrangement was very much like that of the NASA-tested 'Configuration 3' North American A3J-1 Vigilante model tested in 1959, and doubtless derived some if not much of its concept from the NASA work.

The end result was something that bore little relation to the Mach 4 Super Hustler of a few years before... but greatly resembled the F-111 that would come in a few years. Apart from the single nuclear bomb hanging beneath the fuselage (in a position distinctly further forward than any of the other three configurations), the final Super Hustler could be easily mistaken for an F-111 drawn from a verbal description.

WADD46

The Air Force Wright Air Development Division also took it upon themselves to respond to SDR-17 with two of their own designs, WADD46 and WADD63. These were basic concepts, also completed in April of 1960. The two aircraft were generally similar except that WADD63 was larger than WADD46 (76,000lb gross takeoff weight compared to 60,000lb; overall length of WADD63 was 85ft compared to 73ft for WADD46).

WADD46 was a somewhat generic looking craft using inboard pivoted variable sweep wings. These wings were fairly high aspect ratio and nearly rectangular; at full aft sweep (94°) they folded over the fuselage. The WADD46 would then fly at high speed (Mach 1.2) and low altitude (500ft), relying largely on lift from the fuselage. The aircraft could dash to Mach 2.5 at 40,000ft. Two thousand pounds of nuclear weaponry could be carried in an internal bay; additional conventional weapons could be carried externally. The wings at full spread would allow a takeoff run of only 1,682ft without the assistance of catapults or rockets.

NASA wind tunnel testing of the WADD63 configuration showed a large variation in the aerodynamic centre as the wings swept back and forth, requiring large values of trim changes during transonic flight and large supersonic trim drag penalties.

General Dynamics was not the only company to respond to the September, 1961, RFP. Sadly, the Grumman response is unknown to this author, but the others can be described. All, of course, featured variable sweep wings. None apparently included guns as standard equipment; the age of the dogfighter was, it was thought, at an end. Guided missiles would do the job of taking out the enemy. This decision that would be overturned with the lessons of Vietnam.

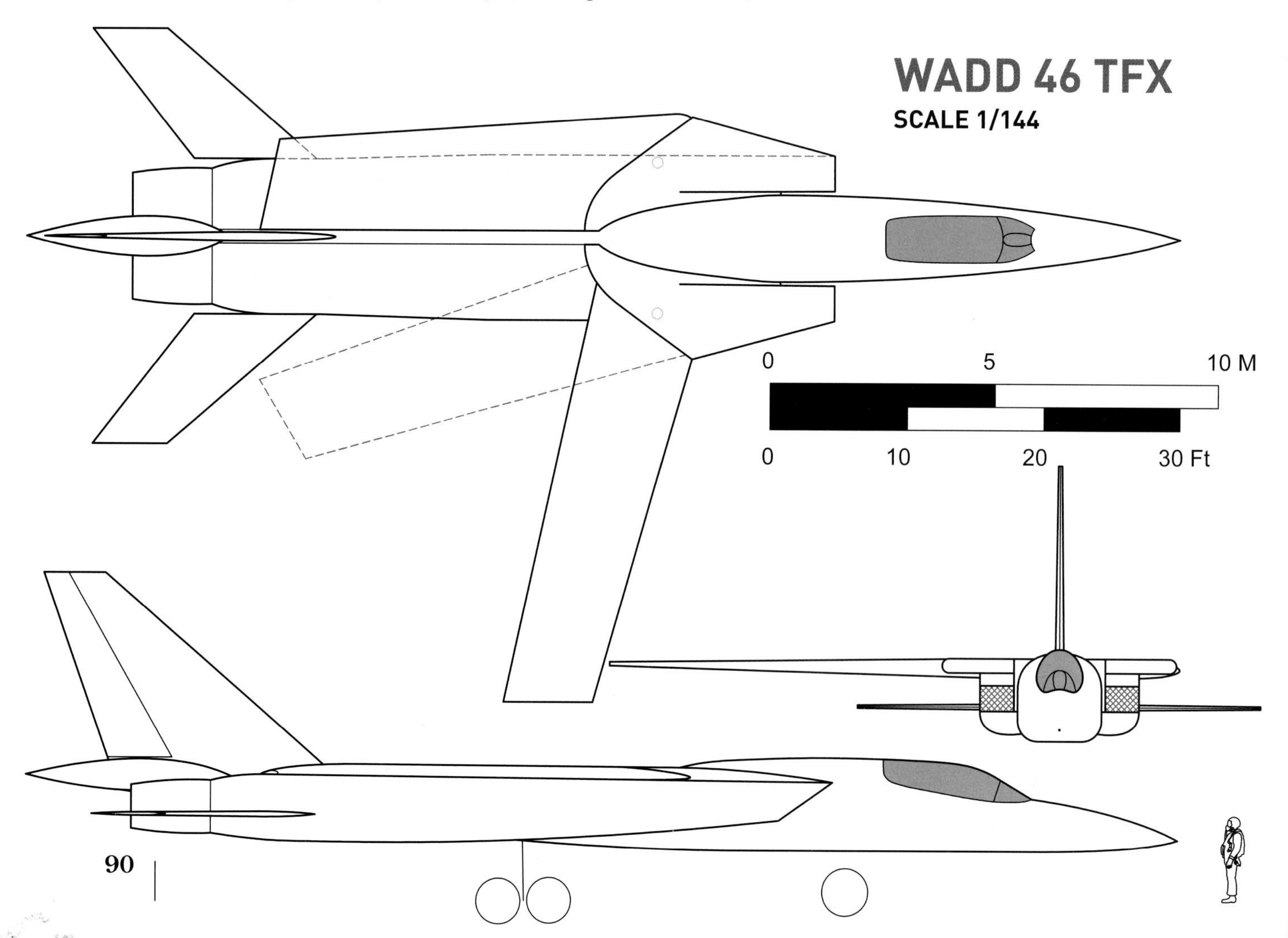

Lockheed CL-590

Lockheed responded with the CL-590, a handsome design with a slim fuselage of rounded triangular cross-section and externally podded engines. It had both an internal weapons bay and the ability to carry ordnance on a pylon under each wing. The pylon would rotate as the wing swept back and forth, maintaining a low drag orientation. The Lockheed diagram shows two Bullpup missiles attached to each pylon, with an internal bay sized for two more. The missiles in the internal bay would be lowered via a 'trapeze' system so that weapons release occurred outside of the bomb bay, in the reasonably undisturbed air flow below the fuselage.

The engine pods were mounted well aft on the sides of the fuselage and had spike inlets similar to those of the SR-71 along with plug nozzles. The wingtips were articulated as control surfaces. The diagram shown here represents the Air Force version; the Navy version would have apparently differed only in having a slightly shorter, blunter nose. An attractive full-scale mockup of the CL-590 was built and displayed alongside an array of possible missiles and bombs that it could carry, including along with the Bullpups Sidewinder air-to-air missiles, iron bombs and TX43 nuclear bombs.

The CL-590 was clearly the result of a great deal of work, but it seems all the documentation Lockheed had on the project was destroyed when Lockheed lost the contest. This, sadly and irritatingly, is entirely too common in the aerospace industry; losing programmes are often utterly memory-holed. Part of this is a way to save money on archiving all that documentation; part of it is a way to keep contracts rolling in. If the documentation on a project evaporates, and if at some future date the Air Force decides that the very same thing is needed… they'll have to pay to generate that information all over again.

McDonnell Model 156

The McDonnell Model 156 design is known from display models and wind tunnel reports, and is a rather unusual vehicle. It is configured similarly to the Lockheed CL-590, but has a seemingly very long forward fuselage. Like the CL-590 it has podded engines attached to the rear fuselage, but where the CL-590's horizontal stabilizers attached to the rear fuselage at the base of the vertical tail, those of the Model 156 attached to the outboard surfaces of the engine pods themselves. The wing pivots were fairly well inboard, but the wings themselves were relatively small.

Two different cockpit seating arrangements were designed – tandem and side-by-side. Display models depict the side-by-side variant along with USAF

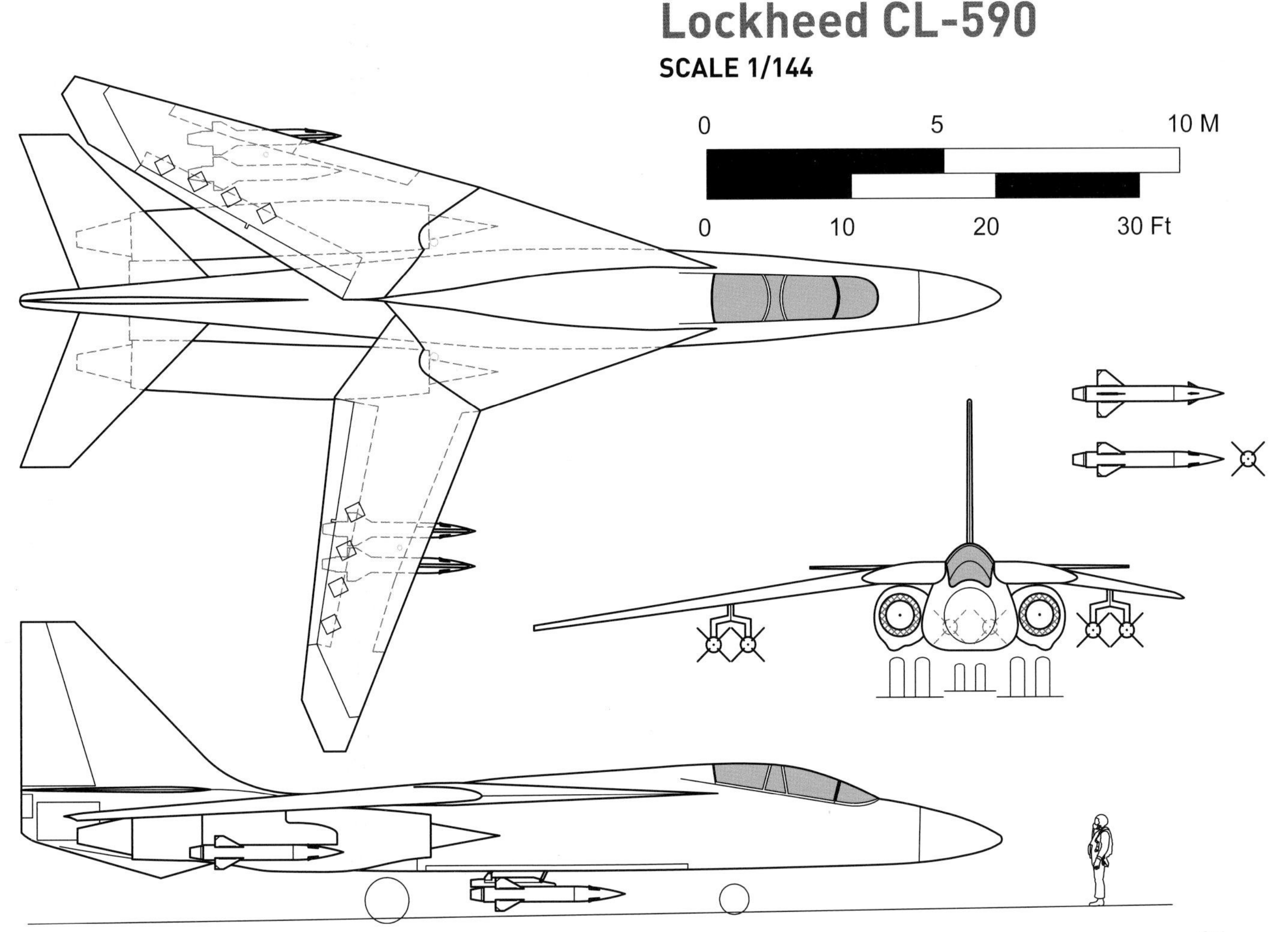

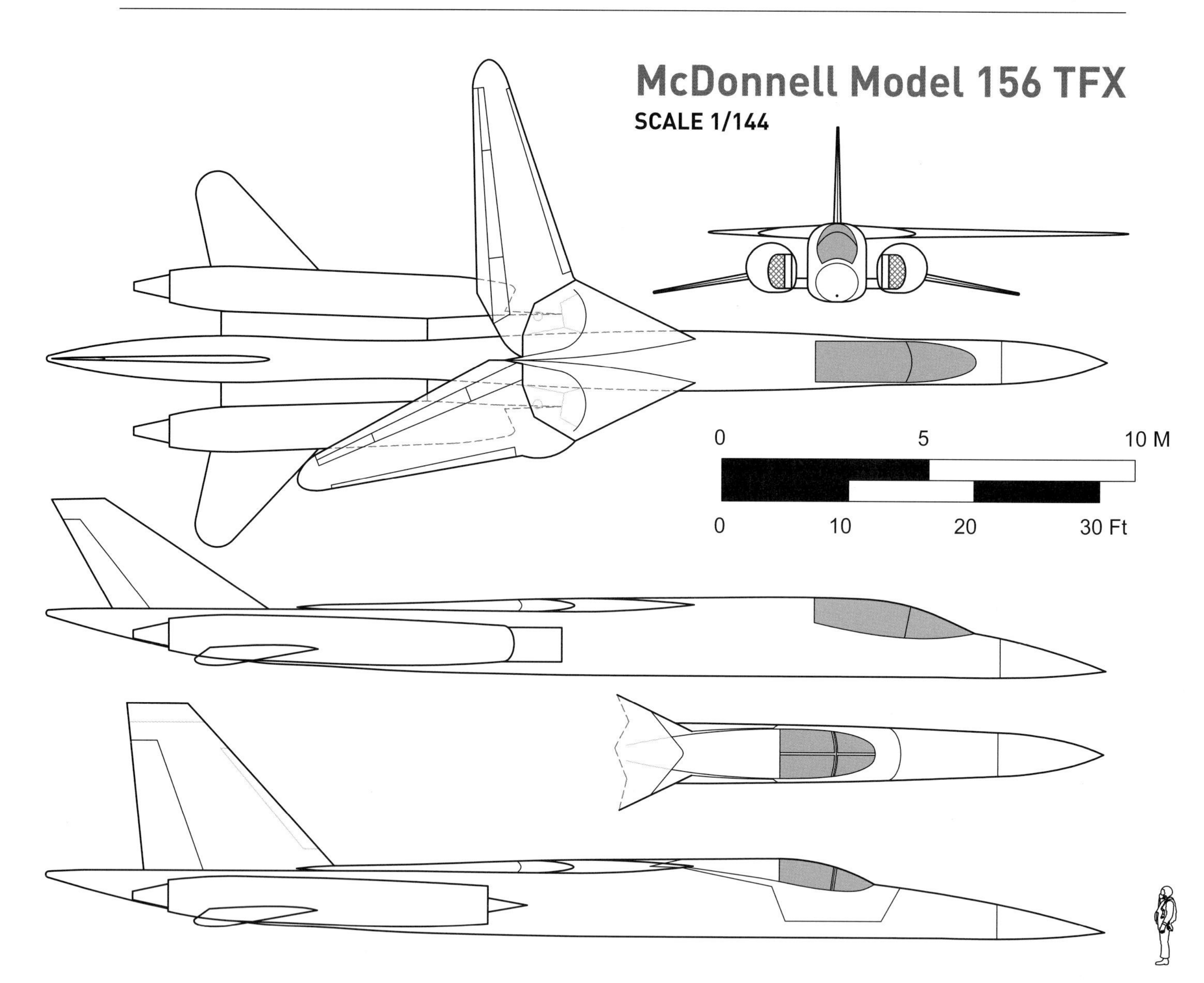

markings; the tandem version comes from a NASA wind tunnel test report and has no markings, so it may or may not depict a Navy variant. Or it may depict an earlier or later design iteration. The tandem seat version had 2D ramp inlets on the fronts of the engine nacelles, while the side-by-side seater had spike inlets.

Republic/Vought

While most designs resembled the winning General Dynamics design to some large degree, the Republic design was a stand-out. Republic teamed with Chance-Vought on the TFX submission, though the extent of Vought's efforts is unclear and seems to have been restricted to last minute design revisions to make the basic aircraft meet Navy standards.

The aircraft used a configuration that Republic tried out on several other aircraft concepts… a supersonic transport, a VTOL strike-fighter and eventually a strategic bomber. It was a twin-engined design with a long-chord, sharply swept (83.5°) wing, optimized for extreme speed rather than loiter or manoeuvring. But like all the other TFX designs, it included variable geometry. In this case, the swing-wings were not wholly separate features, but panels that blended into the upper surface of the fixed swept wing when fully aft-swept. These panels were relatively small but substantially increased wing area when fully deployed.

An impressive sheet metal-clad full-scale mockup was constructed. It had movable wings (the port one, at any rate) and main landing gear that could retract. It also showed multiple weapons bays, including side bay like those of the modern F-22 or F-35 from which Sidewinders could be deployed. When needed, the bay door would open, the missile would project outwards attached to an extendable launch rail, then the main door would close again, leaving the Sidewinder and its rail exposed. The bay would be closed and aerodynamically clean. The main weapons bay was in the central fuselage.

Two TF30 jet engines occupied the rear fuselage, fed by separate side-mounted ramp inlets. The two crewmen sat in a tandem cockpit. No evidence has yet

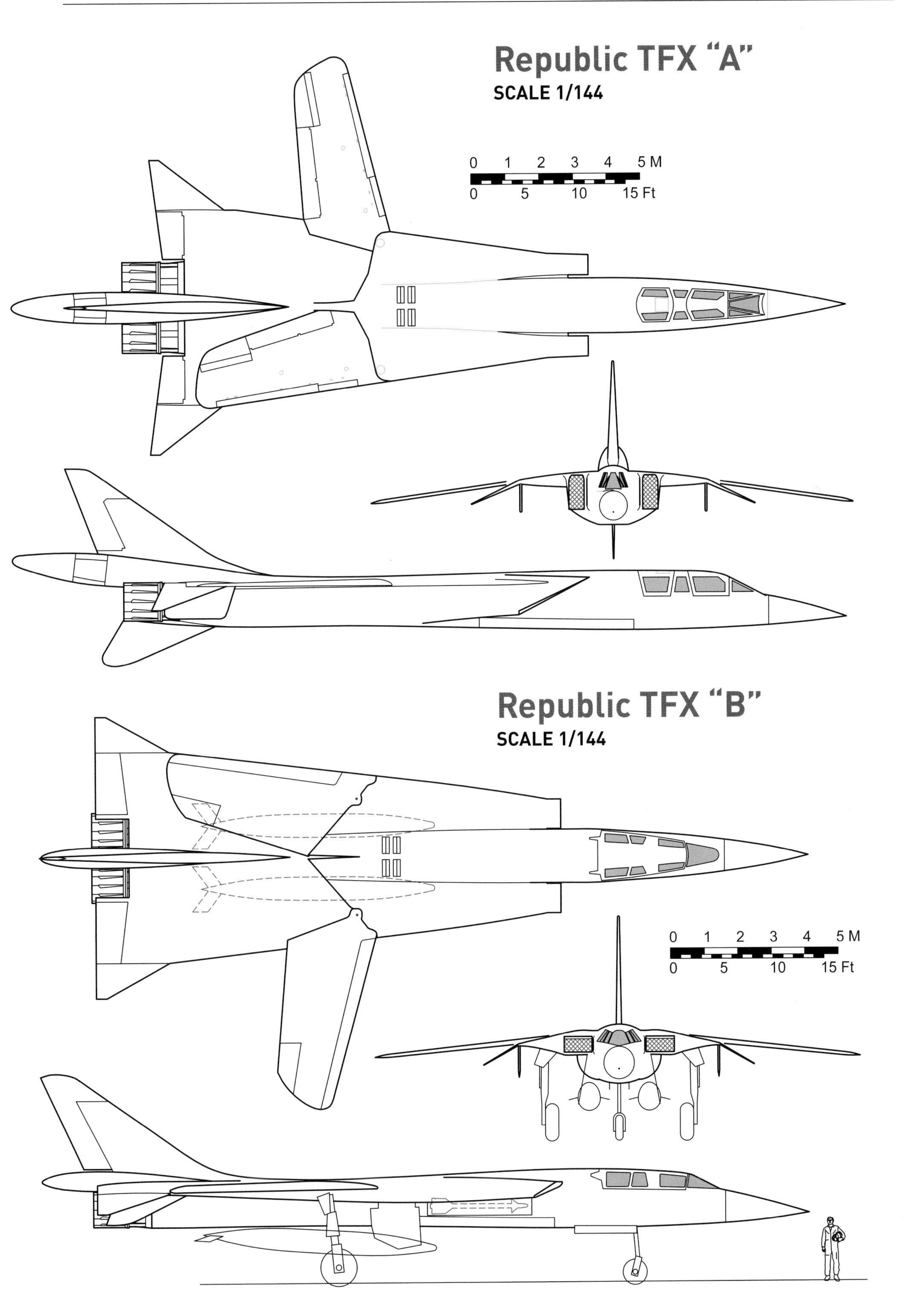
Republic TFX "A"
SCALE 1/144
0 1 2 3 4 5 M
0 5 10 15 Ft
Republic TFX "B"
SCALE 1/144
0 1 2 3 4 5 M
0 5 10 15 Ft

come to light of a side-by-side seating version, nor is it obvious how that might have been possible except through a major redesign and fuselage widening. The tailcone was raised above and projected behind the engine exhausts; a drag chute could be deployed from it to aid in landing.

The Republic design was of impressive size and appearance; it looked fast standing still. Sadly, the only available verifiable data on this design comes from NASA wind-tunnel reports, illustrations from a design patent, photos of display models and film of the full-scale mockup. So while drawings and dimensional data are available, most other data – such as weights and performance – are not.

Since the reports were published often several years after the designs were originally produced, it's difficult to say when these date from. However, the first design (arbitrarily listed as 'design A') was more than 80ft long, and the second ('design B') a bit short of 75ft. Unfortunately, neither of the designs closely matches the full scale mockup nor the patented configuration. Somewhere out there almost certainly exists a report that lays out the officially submitted design in great and exacting detail… but this author has not yet found it.

Photos are available which show a display model of a dedicated Navy version of the Republic TFX concept. This configuration was reportedly developed by Chance-Vought as Republic's collaborator; Vought had far more experience with Navy programmes than Republic, and the company's experience was apparently considered necessary.

Republic's TFX was an excellent aircraft for Air Force needs, but would not have fitted on aircraft carriers, nor would it likely have been able to even land on one. While largely similar to the other known configurations, the Navy version shows a larger diameter radome nose, a shortened tailcone (a notable feature on the other designs… probably containing a braking chute for carrier landings), and four or five external missile stations with Bendix AAM-N-10 Eagle air-to-air missiles. It was on the whole a different aircraft from the Air Force versions in a multitude of ways, other than a general similarity in configuration.

North American D326-49

North American Aviation designed a number of aircraft for the TFX role, but this author only has reliable information on one iteration, the D326-49. As with all the other designs it was variable geometry, but here the movable wing panels were relatively large in span and area, which deep chord. When fully swept the wings blended in with the tail surfaces, making the aircraft basically a highly swept delta.

The single central vertical fin was long and narrow, projecting well above and behind the fuselage. However, artwork and sketches depicted variants of

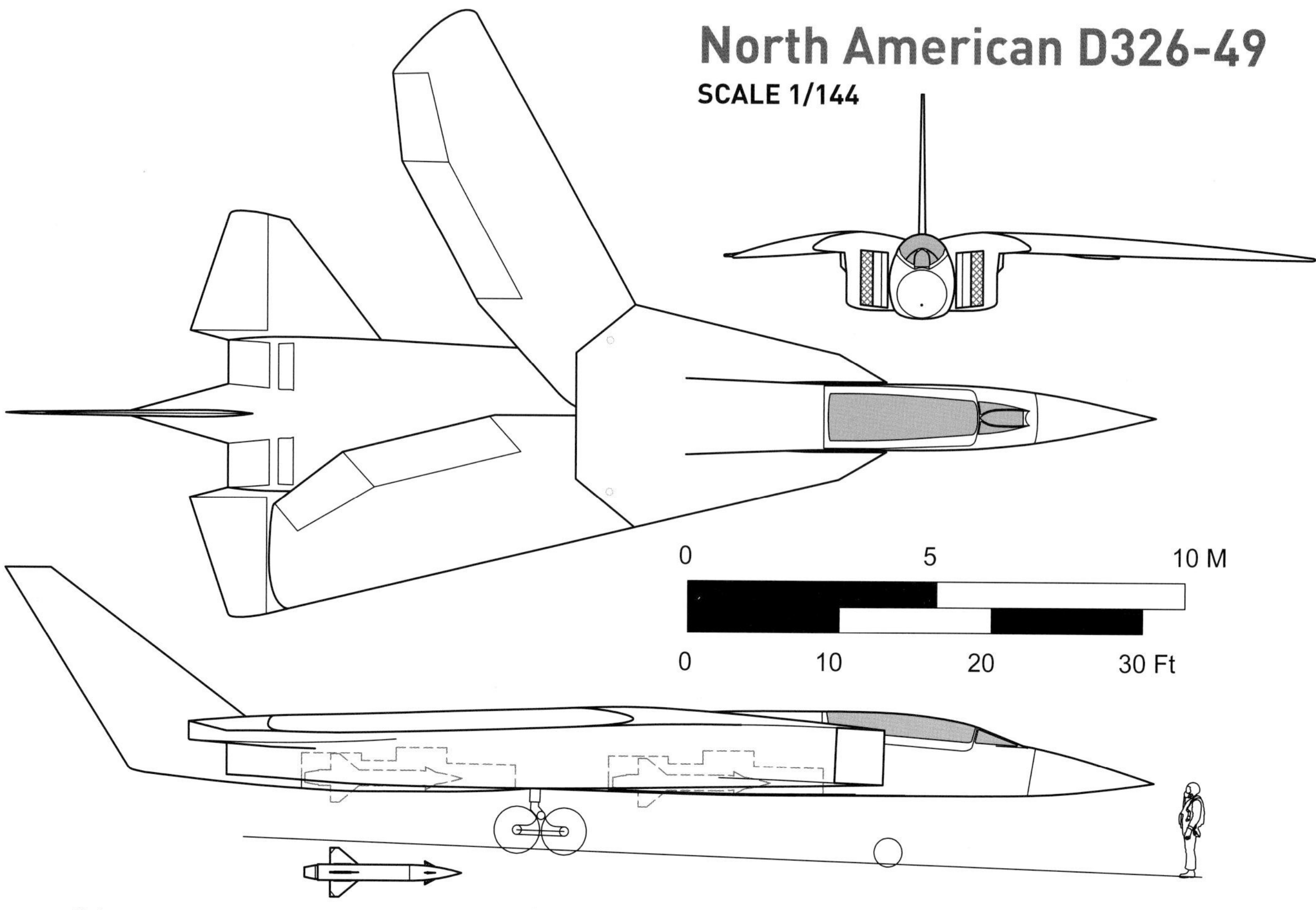

this design with twin fins, smaller with less height and length. While this would have made the aircraft more carrier-suitable, various paintings depict the twin-fin version in both Navy and Air Force markings. The crew sat in tandem underneath a single large fighter-style canopy, flanked by the inlets. Here again illustrations show multiple variations on the inlet. While all known versions feature 2D ramp inlets, the diagram shows the inlet as 'sideways' as on the B-70 (with the right and left inlets separated by the fuselage), with the swept upper edge of the inlet matching up with the leading edge of the wing. In other versions the inlets were recessed behind the leading edge of the wing; yet other versions flipped the left and right inlets so that they were scoops similar in planform to the F-105 inlets.

Somewhat unusually, the D326-49 had two weapons bays, one forward and one aft. The weapons bays are depicted containing a single Bullpup missile or ill-defined bomb (presumably nuclear). Curiously they are not large enough to fully contain the missiles: the tips of the aft fins project through the outer surface of the aircraft, necessitating holes in the bay doors.

Given the '-49' dash number, it's reasonable to assume that North American had many designs for TFX.

Boeing designs

It is unlikely that Boeing did far more work on the TFX programme than, say, North American and Lockheed. But more information is available about various Boeing designs; consequently, there's more to say and more to show.

Boeing's work on TFX evolved through the Model 818 designation. However, not every Model 818 was a TFX design; some Model 818s were subsonic battlefield surveillance platforms, appearing like the offspring of an OV-1 Mohawk and a Learjet; there were Mach 2+ VTOL strike fighters as well, utilising up to a dozen afterburning turbojets in vectoring pods. While these doubtless had some role in at least influencing TFX thinking, the Model 818 designs started at least as far back as 1958, well before TFX existed.

Boeing Model 818-192 & -193

Verifiably TFX-related design work was underway by the time of Model 818-192, date uncertain. This was configured much like North American's D326-49, with sizable swing-wings that at full retraction blended in with the horizontal stabilizers.

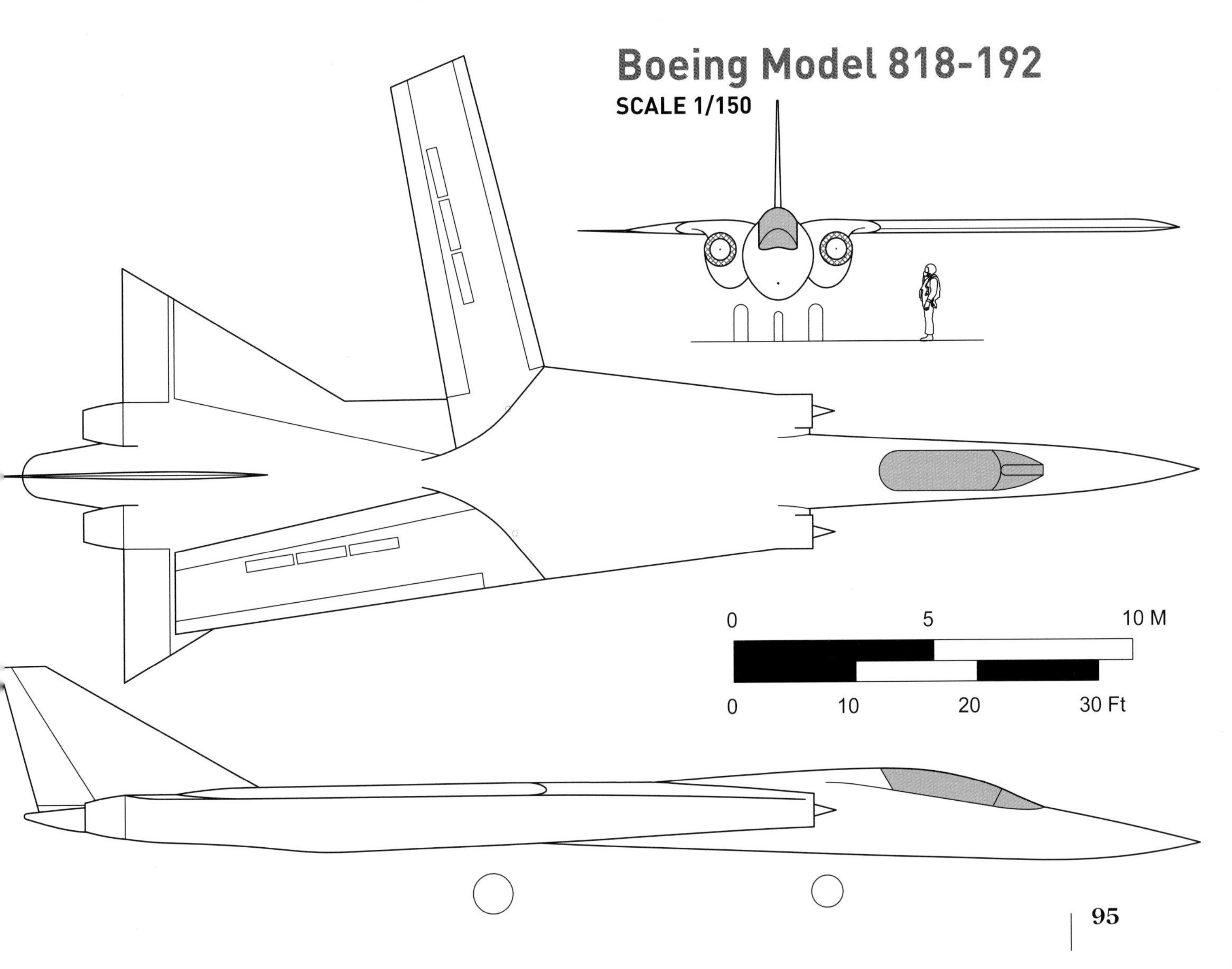

Instead of ramp inlets like the North American design, Model 818-192 used circular inlets with central spikes. The turbojet engines, as with most of the TFX designs, sat side by side in the rear fuselage with some distance between them. No indication of the location or configuration of the weapons bay or bays is available in the known diagram, but the width of the rear fuselage indicated the possibility of bays between the engines in the rear fuselage.

The following design, Model 818-193, was broadly similar. Noticeable differences include the use of ramp inlets and a narrower rear fuselage, the engines mounted close together. A single weapons bay was located in the central fuselage behind the cockpit and between the engine inlets. The 818-193 was a slim and elegant design, but no performance or weapons load data is currently available. Given the narrowness of the design, and the limited real estate under the wings when fully swept, it's unclear if the aircraft could carry any payload except for whatever would fit in the weapons bay. Additionally, the 818-193 and related designs were substantially longer than Navy requirements; these designs were undoubtedly meant solely for the Air Force. A full-scale mockup of Model 818-193 – or a configuration very similar to it – was built and displayed by Boeing.

The following design, Model 818-194, was broadly similar to the 818-193, with only a few minor geometrical changes. The 818-194 would use J79MJ254C engines rather than TF30s.

The full history of the Model 818 is sadly lacking at this time. However, it ultimately resulted in the Model 818-255. This June 1962 design was Boeing's fulfillment of the TFX requirements, with versions for both the Air Force and Navy (dubbed simply '818' and '818N', respectively). Its resemblance to earlier Model 818 studies was limited only to the twin-engines and swing wings; it was otherwise a very different beast.

Much shorter in length in deference to Navy requirements, with less sharply swept wings, this aircraft was somewhat less impressive looking. It had side-by-side seating rather than tandem; the entire forward fuselage would, in an emergency, break off to become an escape capsule.

The two variable geometry horizontal ramp inlets were moved to an unconventional above-fuselage position; this was doubtless a result of the desire to operate from unimproved dirt airstrips, but it would

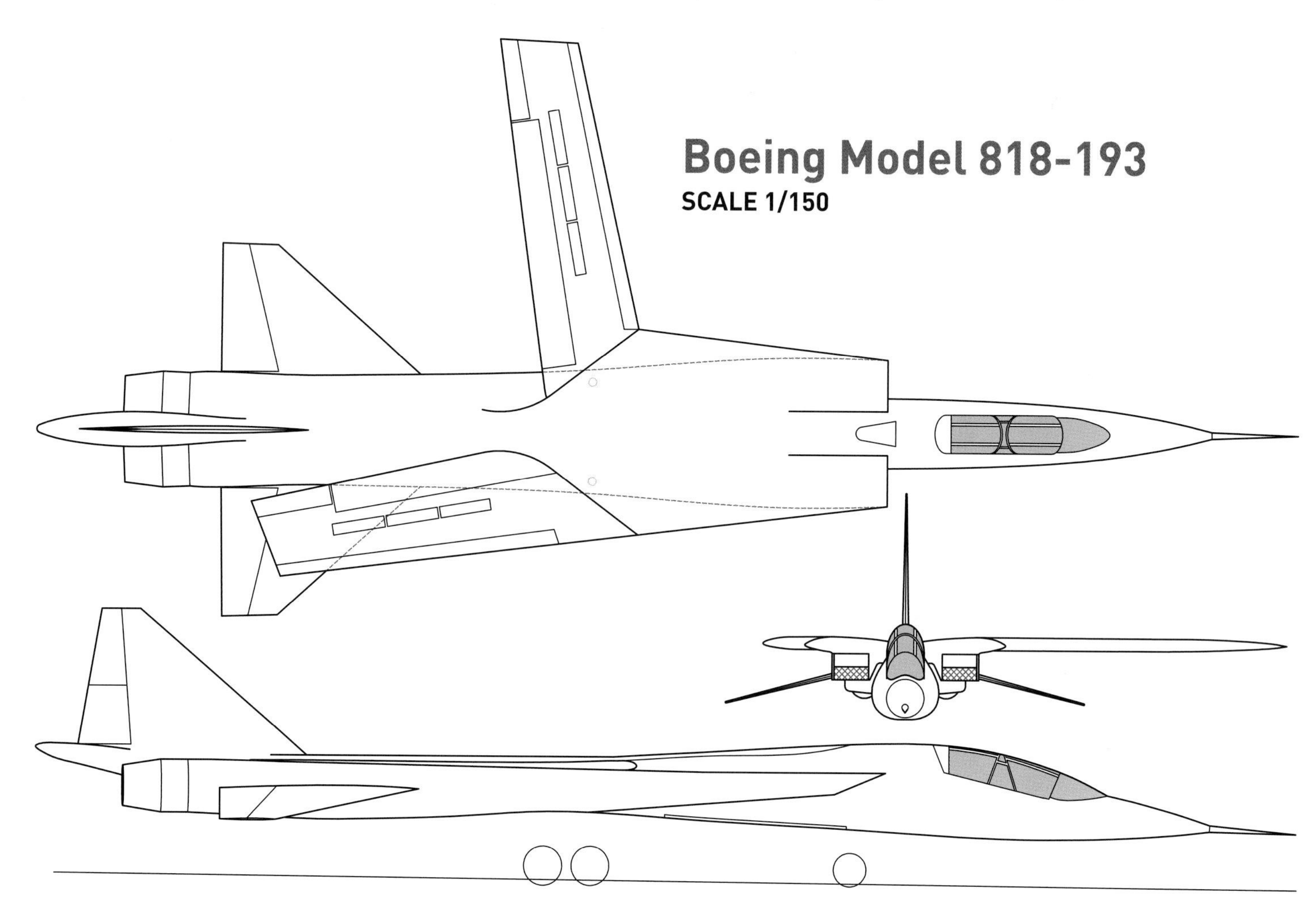

play havoc with pressure recovery at low speed and high angles of attack. The TF30 turbofan engines – common in type and arrangement to both the Air Force and Navy – were equipped with afterburners and thrust reversers. The nose of the 818N was broader and more voluminous than the Air Force version; this was in order to contain the much larger radar system needed to detect and track distant enemy aircraft. The Air Force 818 was longer, slimmer and faster than the Navy 818N.

The Air Force 818 and the Navy 818N were reported to share 60.4% identical parts, 19.7% 'similar' parts and 19.9% 'uncommon' parts. They shared 89.6% major and subassembly common tooling, and 72.2% common fabrication tooling. The differences between the 818 and 818N were many; apart from the obvious changes to the nose and tail, the cockpit instrument panels were to be entirely different. This makes sense when you consider that the Air Force version was to be primarily a bomber, while the Navy version would have been a missile-armed interceptor. Different weapons, used differently, aimed differently.

The Air Force aircraft would have spent much of its time flying low and fast; the Navy version would have loitered at high latitude and low speed, flying slow orbits at some distance from the carrier to provide missile cover. Further, the 818 would have had an internal weapons bay that could fit two Bullpups or two nuclear bombs, with many pivoting attachment points under the wings to carry pylons for additional conventional bombs, while the 818N would have carried two AIM-54 Phoenix air-to-air missiles in the internal weapons bay and two missiles semi-submerged within the exterior of the bay doors, with one more missile under each fixed wing root. Initial versions of the 818N had had two somewhat generic long range air-to-air missiles within the bay, and one more semi-submerged between the doors. The leading edge of the 818N wing root would have been pulled forward to provide adequate mounting attachments, as well as to provide mounting points for infra-red sensors.

The Model 818 Air Force version was littered with internal fuel tanks: 6,250lb of jet fuel within wing tanks, 12,000lb within the forward body tank and 12,000lb in the aft body tank. With all tanks split into numerous sub-tanks in order to maximize available volume, total internal fuel load was 30,250lb. Model 818N, though, had much less internal fuel, with no fuel at all in the wings, 8,190lb in the forward body tank and 8,190lb in the aft tank, totalling 16,380lb. Both versions were capable of inflight refuelling, but they used different means: the 818 had a refuelling boom receptacle in the left hand wing strake, while the 818N used a retractable probe, deployed from the left forward fuselage.

Model 818 could carry two GAM-83A Bullpup missiles internally, or it could fill the bay with six Sidewinders, with two more carried externally on forward fuselage pylons. Under wing root pylons could carry one additional Bullpup each, as could pivoting pylons beneath the inboard portion of the wings. Three further pivoting pylons along the length of the wings could carry four M117 750lb bombs or three CBU-1A cluster munitions dispensers. The three outboard pivoting pylons, and the fixed wing root pylon, could alternatively carry a single 450 gallon fuel tank each. The basic mission, however, called for only 2,330lb of ordnance.

As of October 1962, Boeing estimated that the development engineering inspection could be held in the fourth quarter of 1963, with first 818 flight in early 1965, with first operational deliveries in the first half of 1967. A mockup of at least the forward fuselage – the complete cockpit from nose to the ejection capsule separation plane, along with the left-hand fuselage back well past the inlets – was constructed and displayed alongside a series of related cockpits. It's unknown if these other cockpits, which included both side-by-side seating as well as tandem, were meant to represent earlier designs such as the 818-193, or if they were alternate studies for the final 818... or if they were meant to represent possible variants that could be built on the final 818 airframe.

As previously mentioned, the Air Force Source Selection Board found the Boeing 818 to be the best design of the TFX contest, but that decision was overruled by the Secretary of Defense. The General Dynamics design was found to not only have higher commonality between Air Force and Navy versions, the Boeing 818, with its dorsal inlets, was seen as unlikely to be able to sustain Mach 2+ flight. As a result, General Dynamics got the opportunity to build the F-111.

General Dynamics Configuration 430

The evolution of the General Dynamics design is partially known, with the available designs reconstructed largely from display models and NASA wind tunnel model diagrams. After the Super Hustler TAC bombers for SDR-17, the earliest available GD TFX concept is the 'Configuration 430'. This is a fairly remarkable design, showing some evidence of having originated from the final Super Hustler configuration.

Like the Super Hustler, it had a flattened underside to the nose with a definite similarity in plan and profile back past the cockpit. And like the Super Hustler, its wings could sweep back well past 90°, stowing over the rear fuselage. In the case of Configuration 430, the wings were sharply tapered, coming almost to points. Unlike the Super Hustler – or any other design – the rear fuselage was topped with a 'shelf' that closely matched the planform of the fully stowed wings. For high speed flight the aircraft became an almost wingless

General Dynamics Configuration 430

SCALE 1/144

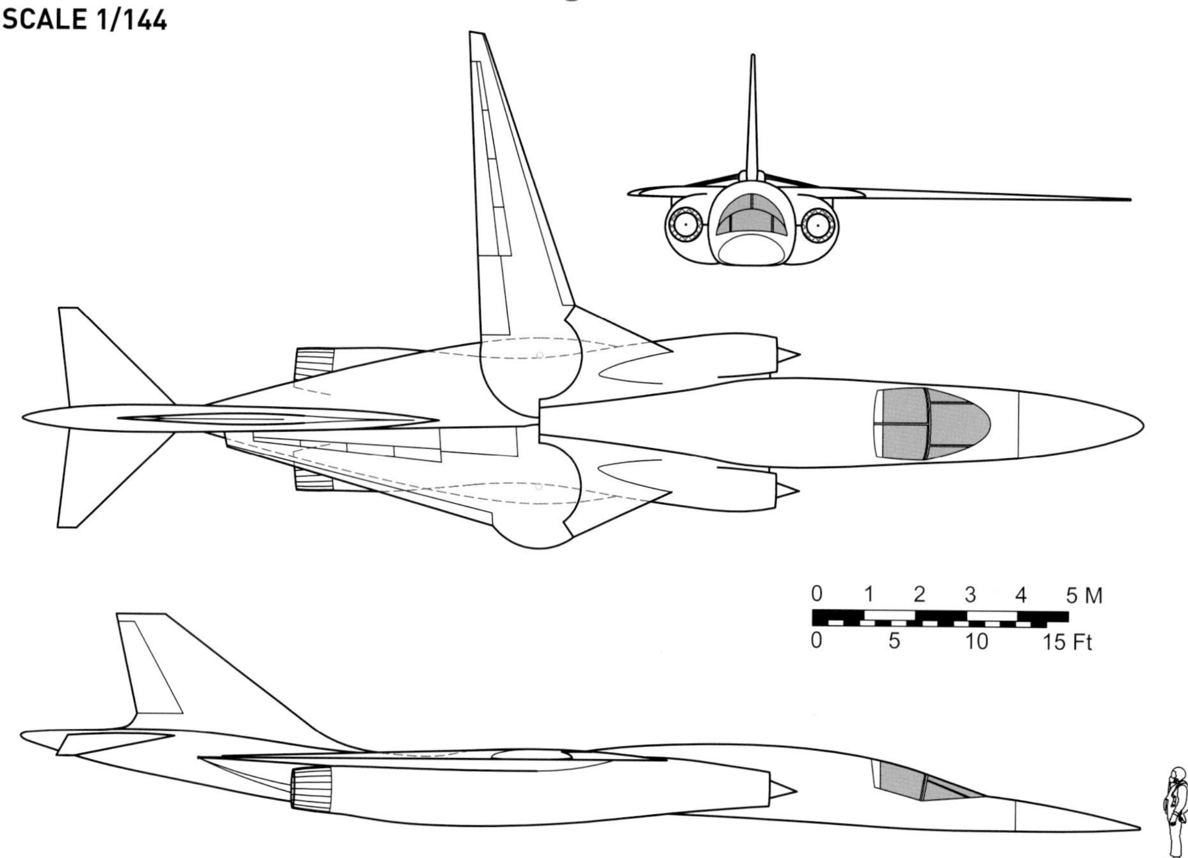

dart, relying almost exclusively on body lift. The wings were equipped with both leading and trailing edge flaps as well as numerous spoilers on the upper surface.

Configuration 430 had side-by-side seating. Seen from the side the fuselage was sinuous… downward drooping at the nose, with an arched back that went down then back up again at the tail. The drafters job of lofting, not to mention the work of the aerodynamicists, must have been entertaining and challenging.

Performance and payload details are not currently available. However, the payload bay was most likely located in the central fuselage somewhere between the cockpit and aft of the side-mounted circular inlets; that regions seems to be designed just for that sort of rectangular volume. As with many early TFX designs, this was clearly put together with USAF goals in mind.

Configuration 1000

The subsequent Configuration 1000 (circa May 1961) was less exotic by far and much closer to the final product. It is clearly the result of later TFX studies, taking into account revisions needed to suit the Navy – in particular, shorter length. Gone was any resemblance to the Super Hustler; the forward fuselage was squarish in cross section and pointed in plan view.

The two crewmen sat side-by-side behind a sloping multi-paned canopy. The main fuselage was, compared to Configuration 430, squat and rectangular, aerodynamically, structurally and artistically unaggressive. The wings swept aft, but to a less radical degree; while much of the wing area ended up over the fuselage, the wings remained important lift generators when fully aft swept.

The upper surfaces of the wings were equipped with spoilers which seem to have been the main roll control mechanism, and full-span flaps for low speed lift. The horizontal stabilizers remained aerodynamically and mechanically separated from the wings at all times.

The inlets were translating spike external-internal compression types, roughly half-circles on either side of the forward fuselage just ahead of the wing roots. They were fitted with movable half-spikes to generate the shock waves needed to properly control air flow into the inlets at supersonic speeds. Available illustrations do not show the weapons bay.

GD TFX: December 1961

General Dynamics' proposal to the Air Force in December of 1961 was a midpoint between Configuration 1000 and eventual F-111 designs. At this stage ejection seats were still specified for crew safety, though the general outline of the cockpit is much like that of the F-111. A mockup of this configuration was built.

General Dynamics Configuration 1000

SCALE 1/144

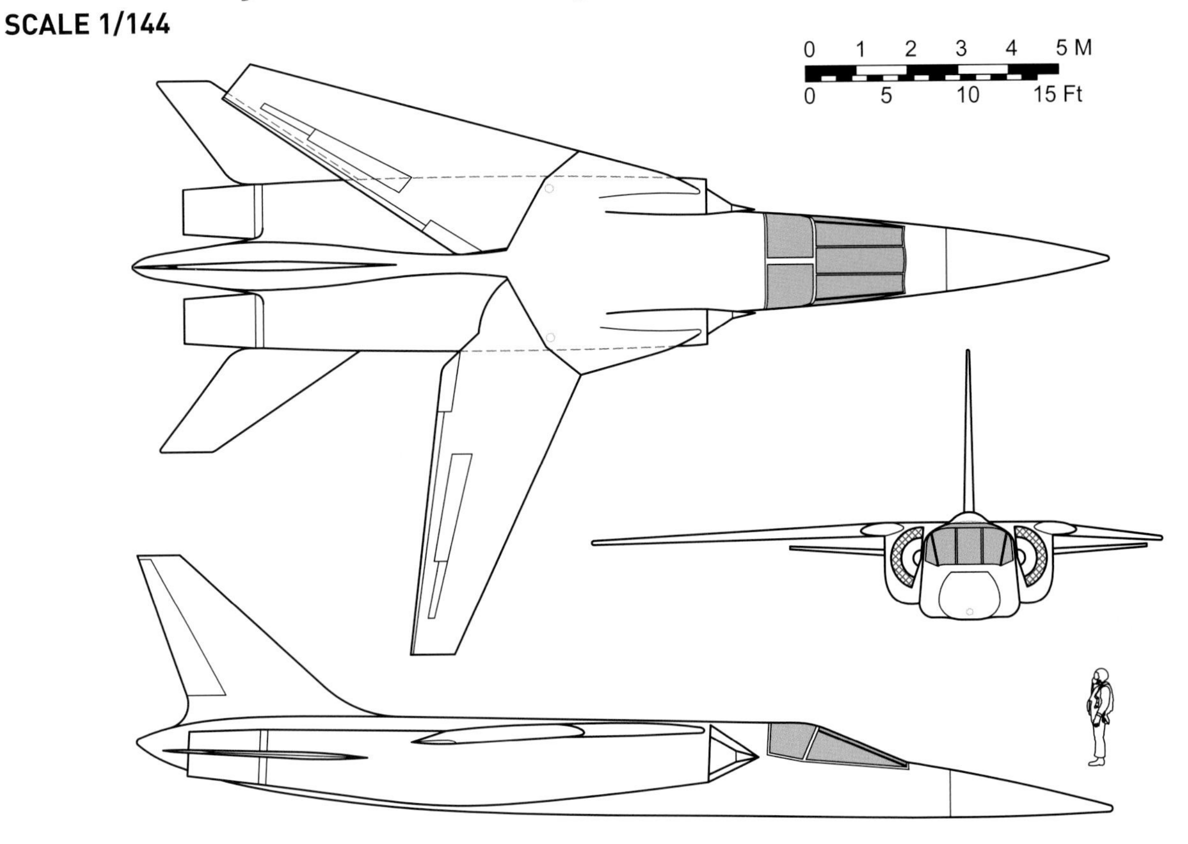

The wings actually overlap when fully stowed. A movable flap covered part of the wings when stowed, and folded fully down to the upper surface of the fuselage when the wings were swept full forward. The engines were set fairly fair apart, though the weapons bay was in the forward fuselage, behind the cockpit and between the inlets.

The weapons bay of the Navy version was to hold three long range air-to-air missiles internally, with another one or two (it's unclear in available documentation) carried semi-submerged beneath the aft fuselage. The Air Force version had a baseline payload of one TX-43 nuclear bomb and two Sidewinders.

The inlets were much like those of the Configuration 1000, with a somewhat simplified translating cone. The aircraft had an extended tail. This was in the form of a 'paddle' that could split into left and right halves to serve as a speed brake. At this stage thrust reversers were not incorporated into the design due to weight issues.

Additionally, within the speed brake was a ventral fin which would deploy at speeds above Mach 2. All of these would disappear on the final F-111; instead of a deployable fin, the F-111 would have a pair of strakes along the underside of the rear fuselage for additional stability.

The design was found to have a number of deficiencies, including carrier takeoff and landing performance; single engine rate of climb (Navy version); high drag for Lo-Lo-Hi mission; ECM and radar cross section; inlet sensitivity to angle of attack and yaw; carrier blast deflector interference; down vision; Navy loiter altitude; crew escape system; altitude manoeuvrability, and landing gear.

GD TFX: April 1962

General Dynamics, working with Grumman and McDonnell, spent several months correcting the deficiencies identified. This included 475 hours of wind tunnel testing. Resubmitted in April 1962, the new design was closer still to the eventual F-111. A mockup of this configuration was built.

A number of changes were made to the design to correct the problems that the December 1961 configuration was found to have. These included:

- Increased horizontal tail area for better manoeuvrability, trim drag and increased high lift.
- Inlets moved under the wing and after past the maximum cross section station, shortening the duct, reducing drag and saving some weight; it also used the leading edge of the wing for precompression at high speed.
- Aspect ratio of the wings increased.
- Full span leading edge slats and double slotted flaps on the trailing edge.

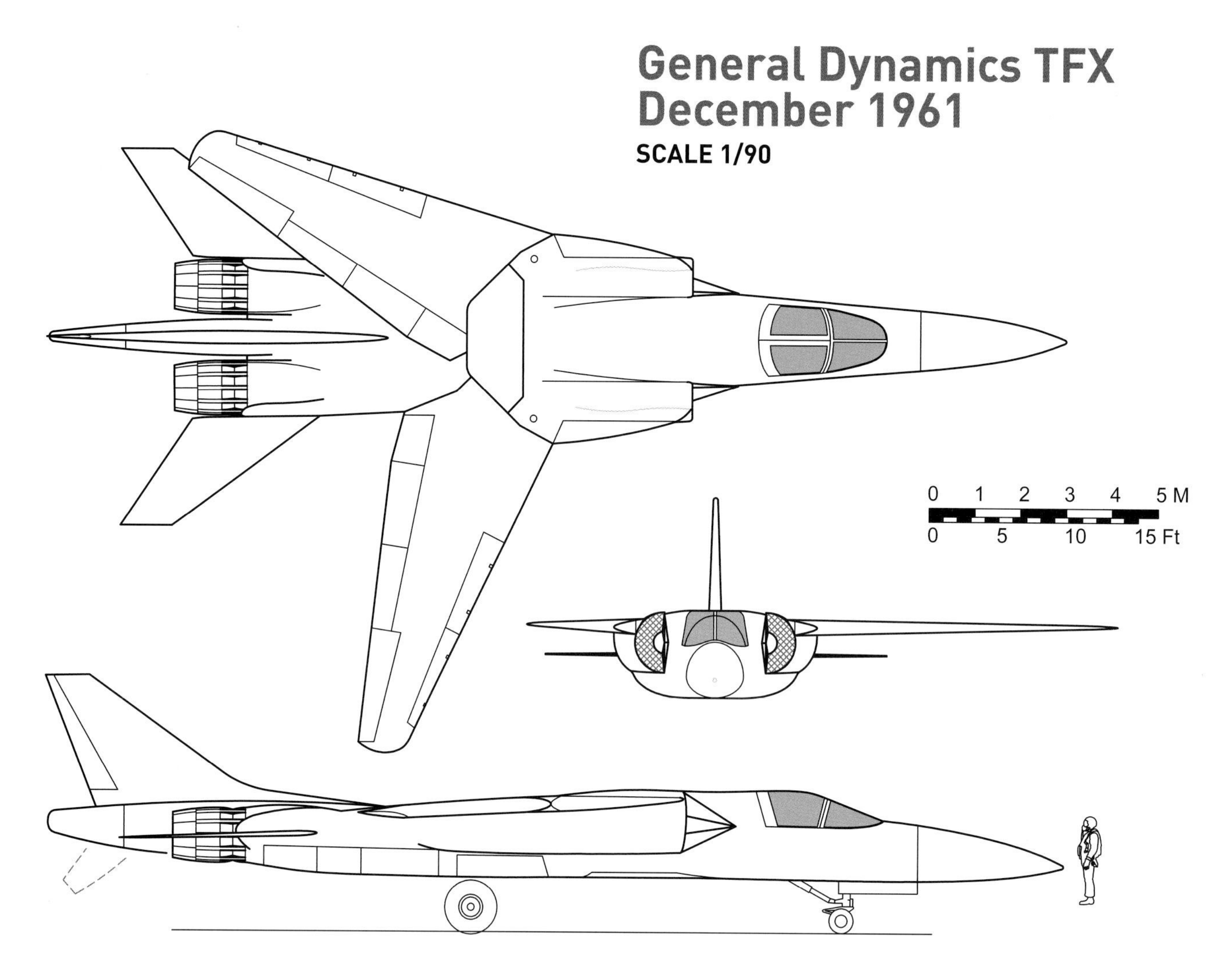

- Maximum cross sectional area reduced.
- Landing gear UCI (Unit Construction Index, a measure of relative floatation characteristics of comparative aircraft) reduced to 30. This meant a runway somewhere between 'minimum operation runways' using landing mats (UCI of 40) and 'emergency runways' using landing mats (UCI of 25). A graded bare soil runway has a UCI of 20, and an unprepared bare soil runway has a UCI of less than 15.
- Radar cross section reduced and supplemented with electronic countermeasures.
- Crew escape pod added.
- Navy version reduced in length, both folded and total.

Changes led to improved high and low speed performance, improved carrier suitability, increased crew survivability and greater penetration capability. Enlarging the all-moving horizontal tail meant that the tail and wing overlapped when fully swept; wind tunnel testing showed that this resulted in favourable aerodynamic interference. Even though the tails were larger, this resulted in lower drag.

The increased aspect ratio wings were moved forward; sweep in fully forward position was reduced from 26° to 16°. The nose wheel was moved aft; modifying the main landing gear system helped reduce fuselage cross section. The USAF version of the April '62 TFX had the extended tail with deployable ventral stabilizer and side-opening air brakes.

The April 1962 TFX aircraft was capable of lifting off in 1,800ft at an airspeed of 131 knots, and could clear a 50ft obstacle in 2,630ft. The landing distance over a 50ft obstacle would be 4,040ft with a touchdown airspeed of 139 knots. The baseline tactical strike mission called for the aircraft to be armed with a single Mk 43 nuclear bomb and two Sidewinders, and added two 400 gallon drop tanks under the wings. The weapons bay for the Navy version would carry only two long range air-to-air missiles internally, and the aft semi-submerged missiles carried by the December 1961 version were now deleted.

The aircraft would have an 800 nautical mile radius, of which just short of 300 nautical miles would be a target dash conducted at Mach 1.2. The flight towards the target would be at low altitude; after dropping the bomb the aircraft would climb to more than 60,000ft and Mach 2.2. Ferry range purely on internal fuel would be 3,300 nautical miles; with external fuel a 4,740 nautical mile range could be reached.

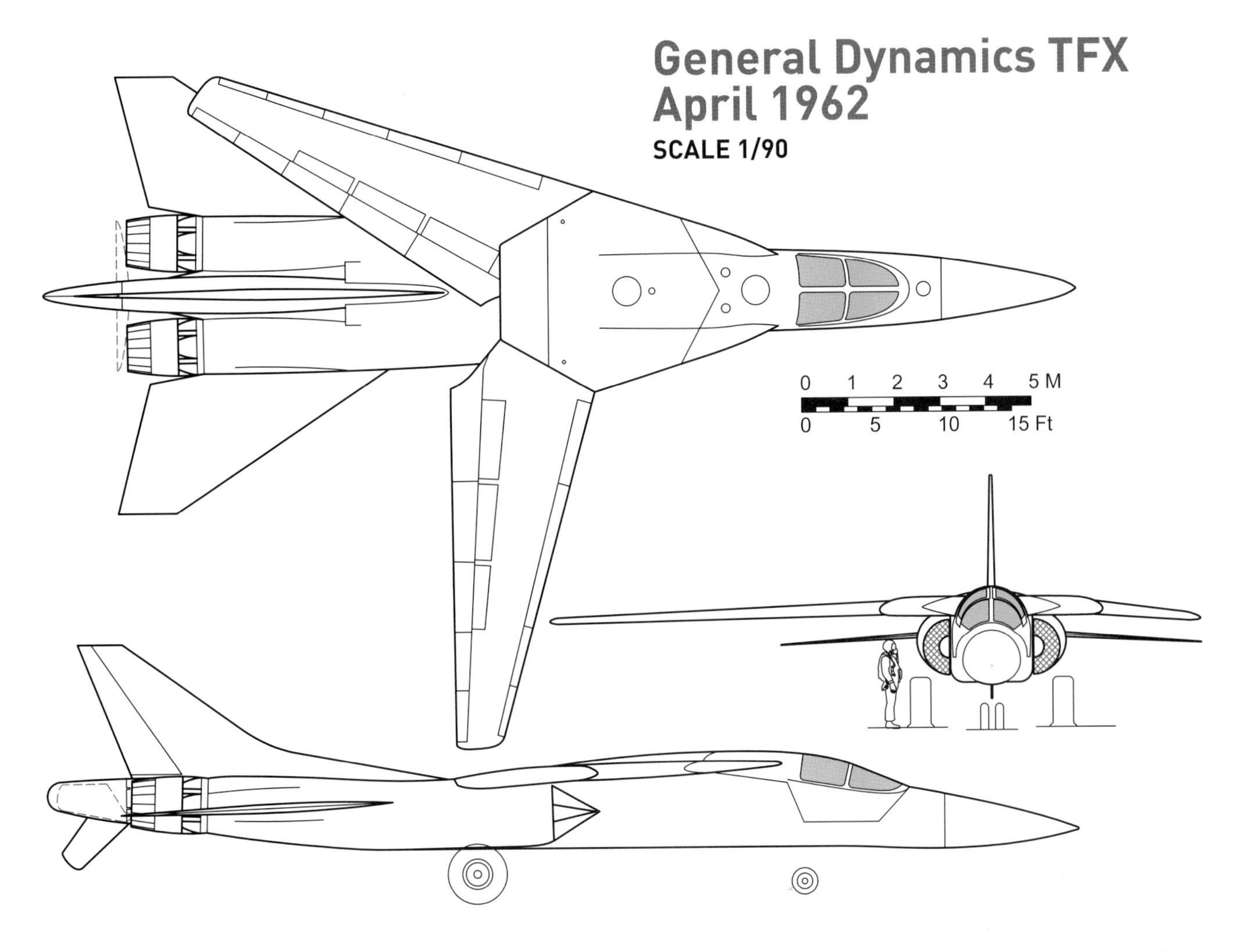

The crew ejection capsule was an important addition. The whole cockpit would, in an emergency, pop off with the aid of a sizable solid rocket motor. It would take the wing root leading edges with it and these would serve as stabilizing fins until a drogue chute was deployed, followed by a main chute. The capsule, containing all provisions deemed necessary for the crew to survive until rescued, would then descend at a rate of 29ft per second, with airbags to cushion the eventual impact. Touching down on land, it would provide a safe enclosure; on water a seaworthy boat.

Even though more than a decade would pass before 'stealth' would be a major goal of Air Force aircraft design, radar cross section reduction was deemed worthy of study and incorporation. This would come in the form of a few changes. The forward bulkhead behind the radar-transparent nose cone was canted upwards so that radar from ahead would be deflected partially upwards. The engine inlets were tilted a little upwards for the same reason, and the interior lined with a radar absorbent material. The canopy would be made from an electrically conductive glass, making it a smooth, angled reflector and blocking radar from entering – and reflecting from – the jumbled interior. The radar support structure and forward bulkhead would also be covered in radar absorbent materials. Tests indicated that a radar cross section of one-half of a square metre in the forward +/- 50° was achievable.

This may have been the configuration that lost to the Boeing Model 818 in the Air Force and Navy… but won in the office of the Secretary of Defense. However, this design was from April 1962 and the submission was in September of that year. The months between probably saw further revisions to the design; in all likelihood the September 1962 General Dynamics TFX was closer still to the F-111 that would come.

FB-111A

Construction of the F-111 was primarily of aluminium, with steel in higher stress and higher temperature regions. The wing pivot structures were largely steel due to the very high loads they would encounter. The escape capsule changed only slightly from the April 1962 configuration. It was capable of separation from the aircraft at any condition from high altitude and high speed down to sitting still on the runway. It could even safely jettison while underwater, floating to the surface and remaining stable there.

The F-111 had a conventional tricycle landing gear layout but the main gear was of an unusual and complex arrangement. Instead of being two separate units on either side of the fuselage, it was a single mechanism... complex, but surprisingly rugged, giving the aircraft a low stance on the ground for easy ordnance loading and maintenance. The main gear central door doubled up as an air brake, and could be deployed in flight without deploying the landing gear. The tyres were relatively low pressure to aid in operations from less than pristine runways.

The F-111 was the first American production aircraft with variable geometry wings. These could be swept from 16° to 72.5° by means of two mechanically interconnected hydraulic motor driven linear actuators. They were equipped with full span double slotted Fowler flaps and four- or five-section leading edge slats. Spoilers were used for lateral control at low speed; these were gradually locked out as the wings were retracted aft, with lateral control turned over to the all-moving horizontal stabilizers. At the junction of the wings and the wing roots were a callback to the A3J-1 studies performed by NASA: rotating gloves. These provided the maximum lift at low speed and could deflect 40°.

The F-111 was a pioneer and as such problems were inevitably encountered. Several years into flight, microscopic cracks began to appear in the wing pivot forgings, requiring costly and time consuming repairs.

The Pratt & Whitney TF30 was the first production engine that married an afterburner to a turbofan; all prior afterburner equipped production engines had been turbojets. This promised greater fuel efficiency in cruise along with bursts of high speed. Perhaps unsurprisingly, this first of its kind system encountered some serious issues including engine stalls at high angles of attack. The problem was resolved with engine upgrades and changes to the inlet and duct to improve airflow.

March 1968 saw six F-111s begin bombing operations in Vietnam. Unfortunately, in the end three of the aircraft crashed; only one crew survived. This quickly led to the end of the bombing missions. Nine F-111s in total crashed in 1967-1968. An examination of the fleet led to repairs to the horizontal stabilizer actuator rods; the determination that the terrain following radar became unreliable in the rain (something of a problem in Vietnam); fixes to the forged wing pivot fittings; discoveries that M61 Vulcan cannon added to the craft were mounted poorly and the perennial favorite: pilot error. The fixes for these – not to mention the lost aircraft and crew – were expensive and led to the public perception that the F-111 was a widow-maker.

The Navy experience with F-111B test aircraft was underwhelming. It started off overweight, and only grew worse as problems were encountered and fixed. As the aircraft was modified for carrier operations based on actual experience, the F-111B's design diverged further from the F-111A, reducing commonality – the whole reason why the General Dynamics design was selected over Boeing's. The Air Force wanted to keep the Navy involved; with the Navy buying airframes, economies of scale would reduce the per-airframe cost for the Air Force. But the Navy, which had never been truly interested in the F-111B in the first place, cancelled its side of the programme in early July 1968.

The F-111A returned to south east Asia in 1972, and by September two squadrons were in action, attacking sites in North Vietnam and Laos. The F-111A proved a useful bomb truck, each aircraft able to carry the bomb load of five F-4 Phantom IIs. But problems and losses persisted. Of the 52 aircraft sent to south east Asia, seven were lost by the time of the Paris Peace Accords of January 1973. A total of 159 F-111As were accepted by the Air Force, including 30 development airframes.

Along with five development aircraft, the Navy accepted only two pre-production F-111Bs, neither of which entered service. Twenty-four F-111C aircraft were manufactured as a bomber for the Royal Australian Air Force, modified from the F-111A design with longer span wings and ruggedized landing gear for better performance on unimproved airfields. The F-111D was a more dedicated fighter, equipped with an improved engine and updated avionics and instruments focussed on air-to-air interdiction.

A total of 96 F-111Ds were accepted by the Air Force. The F-111E actually preceded the F-111D and incorporated some of the same updates including the new Triple Plow II inlets which moved the inlet a little further outboard, reducing the ingestion of boundary layer air. The F-111D should have come before the F-111E, but it was a more complex development; the F-111E was essentially an updated F-111A. Ninety-four F-111Es were delivered to the Air Force. The final model of F-111 to use the same basic airframe was the F-111F, distinguished by the use of the most powerful engine of the breed. It incorporated all of the lessons learned in previous models, with structural changes to reduce or eliminate the problems that had plagued earlier versions, and all the latest avionics and instruments. A total of 106 were manufactured.

Of greatest interest here is the FB-111A, Weapon System 129A. This was most definitively a bomber, with modifications to the airframe to turn it into a practical, if small, strategic bomber.

With the end of the B-70 programme, the Air Force needed another strategic bomber. This resulted in the AMSA programme (see the next chapter), but this proved to be a terribly protracted and contentious development. In the meantime, the Air Force needed something that could fly low and fast carrying a meaningful payload of nuclear weapons. The B-52 was already more than a decade old; and back then,

General Dynamics FB-111A

SCALE 1/110

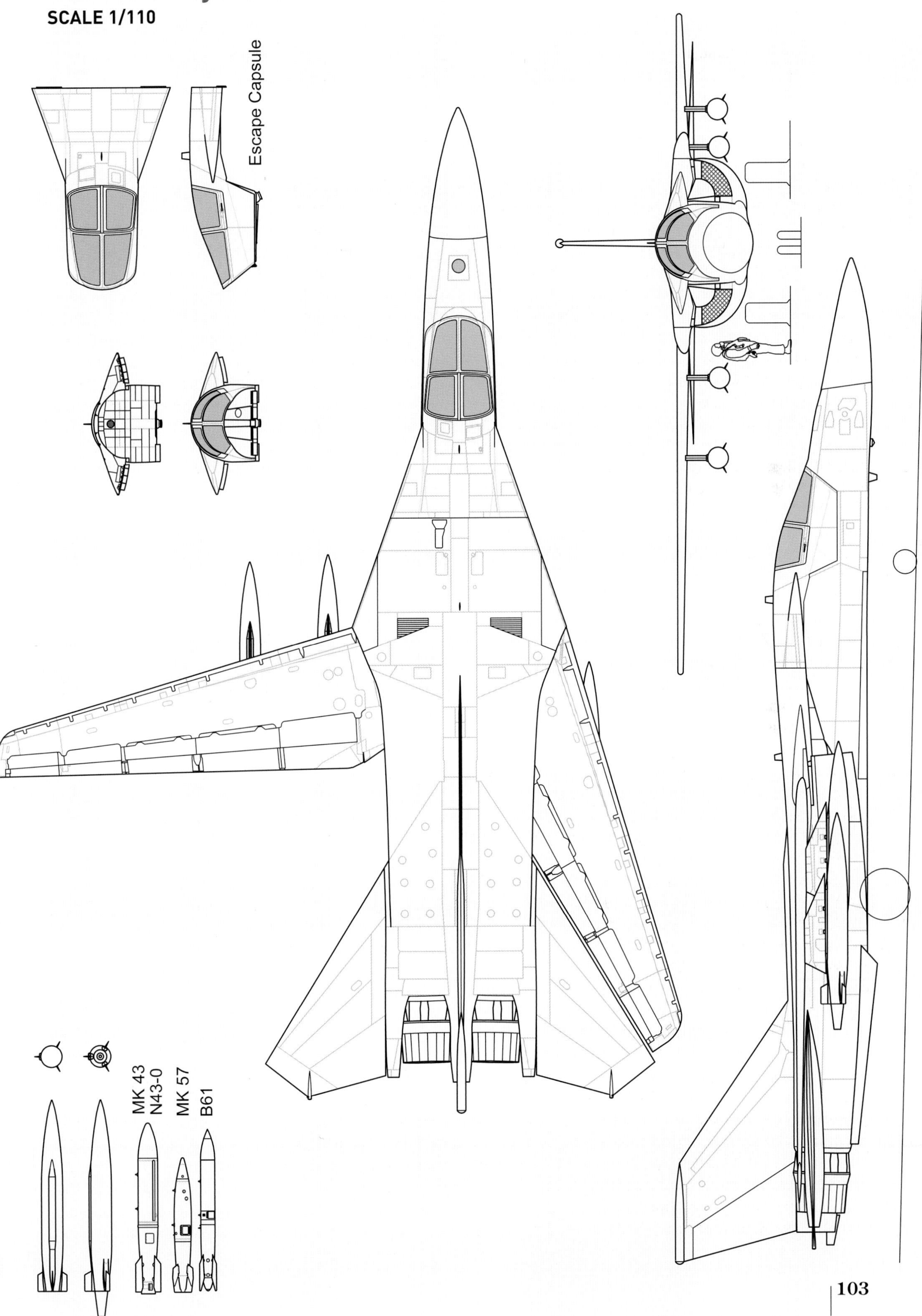

that meant something. It was a huge radar target and creakingly slow. Little could be done to convert the B-52 into the nimble, fast bomber of the future.

The F-111, though, could be converted into an interim bomber, to fill the gaps until AMSA came along. To that end, the FB-111A was designed and contracted for by the Air Force in June 1965. Changes to the basic F-111 were not extravagant... the fuselage was largely unchanged (claims that the FB-111A fuselages were stretched a little over 2ft from the basic F-111A are incorrect, coming from confusion over the length of the aircraft from nose to tail versus the length of the aircraft including the pitot tube on the nose), the wingspan was increased by 7ft (using the extended wing of the F-111B, increasing lift for takeoff and for added payload), increased capacity fuel tanks were added, improved TF-30-P-7 engines and updated attack radar, avionics and controls.

The avionics system was derived from that of the F-111D, but with further augmentations, including hardening against EMP to protect the aircraft from nuclear blasts. An astronavigation system was added, using a circular window located atop the nose just ahead of the cockpit. The landing gear was given sturdier brakes to handle the added weight. The FB-111A's systems were updated to accept the new AGM-69A Short Range Attack Missile.

The FB-111A was equipped with an internal weapons bay and four pylon stations under each wing. The two inboard pylons could rotate as the wing swept fore and aft, but the outboard two pylon stations were fixed. If the aircraft carried something under the outboard two stations, it would have to fly with the wings fully outstretched until those payloads, and the pylons that held them, were jettisoned. However, it seems that the furthest outboard pylon station was not used. The only payload that the next-most-outboard pylon seemed to carry was a 600 gallon drop tank; the two inboard pylons could also carry a single 600 gallon tank each.

The weapons bay could carry two nuclear bombs of the B43, B57 or B61 variety, or two AGM-69A SRAMs. Each of the two inboard pylons could each carry one additional nuclear bomb or SRAM. Conventional bombs could of course also be carried under the two inboard pylons. Each of the pylons could carry four M-117 750lb bombs, or six Mk 82 500lb Snakeye retarded bombs, or 1 Mk-84 2,000lb bomb or six Mk-36 (four on the inboardmost pylon) 500lb retarded bombs.

The Secretary of Defense announced the FB-111A programme in December 1965, shortly after announcing the retirement of the B-58 fleet and all B-52s prior to the G-model. This meant that the Strategic Air Command would soon see a drastic drop in the number of strategic bombers; the need for the FB-111A to fill part of that gap until the AMSA arrived was clear.

The first prototype's maiden flight on July 31, 1967, proved successful; lasting 45 minutes, it reached Mach 2. The maiden flight of the first production aircraft was on July 13, 1968, but a year of testing followed prior to the model entering service in October 1969. Seventy-six FB-111As were accepted by June 1971.

The FB-111A was only supposed to serve as a temporary measure until the AMSA/B-1 became available. But delays in developing the larger aircraft were compounded when President Carter cancelled the programme; by the time President Reagan revived the B-1 and production models of the B-1B entered service, yet more years had passed. But as the B-1B began to prove itself and took up the mantle of fast strategic penetrator, the FB-111A became obsolete and was withdrawn from SAC service and turned over to TAC.

Thirty-four FB-111As were modified for tactical bombing and redesignated F-111G; eventually 15 were sold to the Royal Australian Air Force. The last FB-111A/F-111Gs were retired by the USAF in 1991, by which point the B-1B was fully in operation... and the Soviet Union wasn't.

F-111 derivatives

Doubtless many derivatives were designed of the F-111 over its lifespan, both as fighter and as bomber. Only a few, though, have become public.

F-111 'B-X'

General Dynamics designed the 'B-X', Configuration 122-1, in June 1970. Documentation on this is lean, restricted so far to a few general arrangement, structural and weapons bay diagrams. But the B-X was a dedicated bomber variant, with a stretched fuselage, a greatly enlarged 'belly' weapons bay, and a much expanded internal weapons load. The fuselage was stretched some 14ft over that of the FB-111A, but the wings – and wingspan – remained the same. The engines were upgraded to the TF30-P-100.

The main focus of the B-X was the weapons bay. The FB-111A had a weapons bay that occupied the lower portion of the fuselage behind the cockpit, fitting two SRAMs side-by-side. The B-X, however, had a weapons bay that filled the entire fuselage, justifying the substantial fuselage stretch. The weapons were no longer carried side-by-side, but instead on a rotary launcher.

The cross-section of the bay was not circular but D-shaped, flat side down; as a result, the rotary launcher could not fit weapons all the way around itself. As the launcher rotated, weapons were projected outside of the aircraft. The bay door was a single piece, attached to the launcher; it rotated into the bay as the launcher turned. The launcher could hold four AGM-69A SRAMs or five B-61 nuclear gravity bombs. The bay itself bulged downwards, giving the aircraft

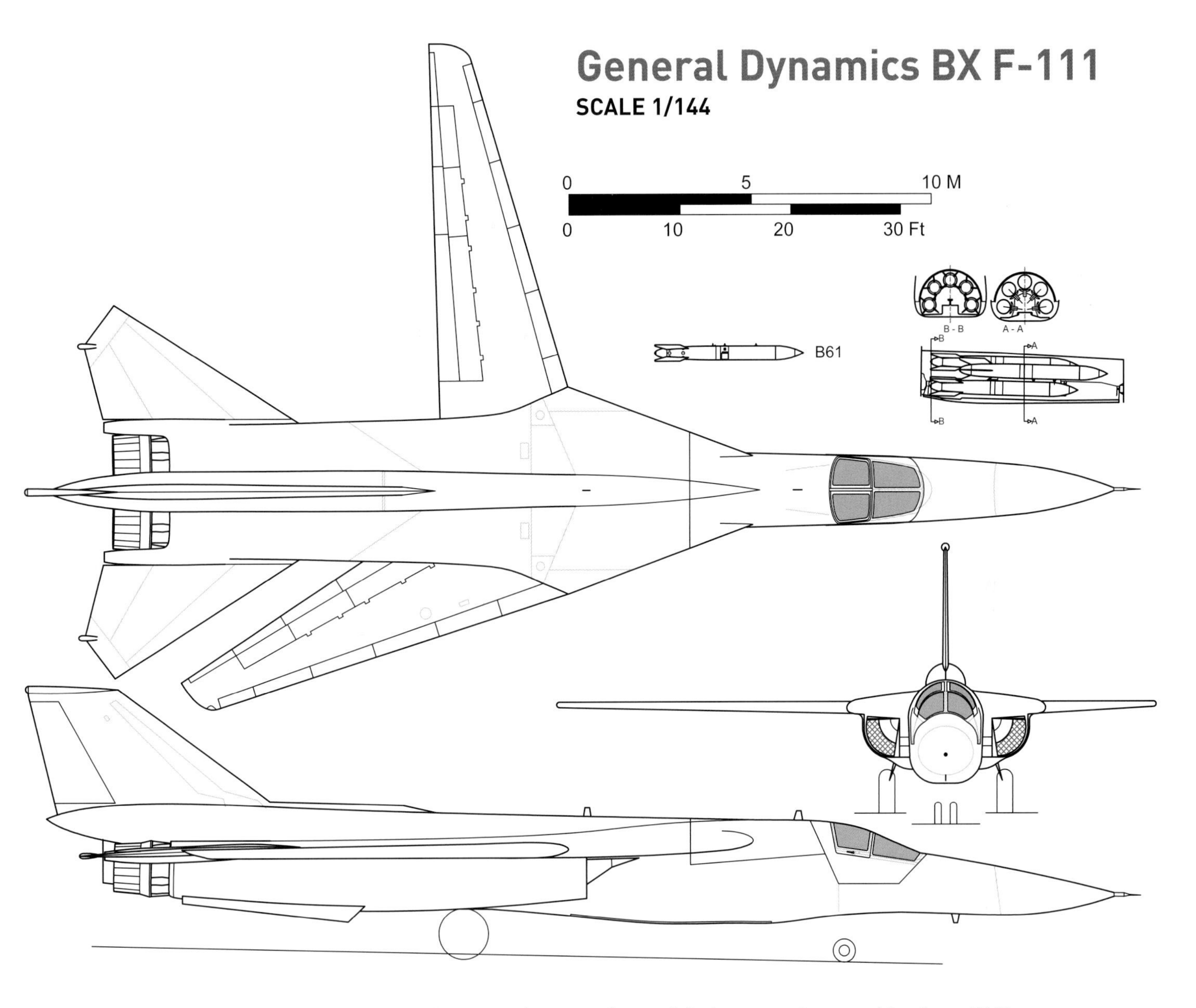

a distinctive 'belly'. The available diagrams do not show whether or not ordnance or fuel tanks could be carried under the wings, nor do they provide range or speed performance.

A raised spine was added to the airframe, lifting the tail up. The spine was doubtless volume for fuel storage. With the forward fuselage being stretched, the cockpit was moved further from the wings. Consequently, the ejection capsule was modified, the 'tail' extended further back so that it still included the leading edges of the wing roots to serve as post-ejection stabilizers.

FB-111G

Less than a year after the F-111 B-X, General Dynamics produced the FB-111G. Like the B-X, it was a stretched FB-111A and shared its overall configuration with an interceptor variant dubbed the F-111X-7. That configuration added a 64in stretch to the forward fuselage, a 40in stretch to the rear fuselage and a raised spine 'saddle tank' for an additional 23,000lb of internal fuel storage. It was said to have 81% common structure with the FB-111A.

The FB-111G had an increased capacity weapons bay quite similar to that of the B-X, but wholly contained within the aircrafts outer mold line… no protruding belly. Like the B-X it was to use TF30-P-100 engines and the weapons bay could carry five B61 nuclear bombs; alternatively it could carry six 'potential' bluff nuclear weapons similar in yield to the B43. Further, it could carry four additional AGM-69A (or other penetration aids) under the wings on pivoting pylons.

The F-111X version would have different radar and avionics in order to serve as an interceptor or a bomber escort (presumably escorting FB-111Gs). It would carry nine AIM-47B air-to-air missiles or six AIM-54, or eight AIM-7F, using both the weapons bay and under-wing pylons. Performance data for neither version is currently available, other than the range of the FB-111G was said to be 4,100 miles at high altitude or 2,200 miles at low altitude. It was, of course, capable of in-flight refuelling.

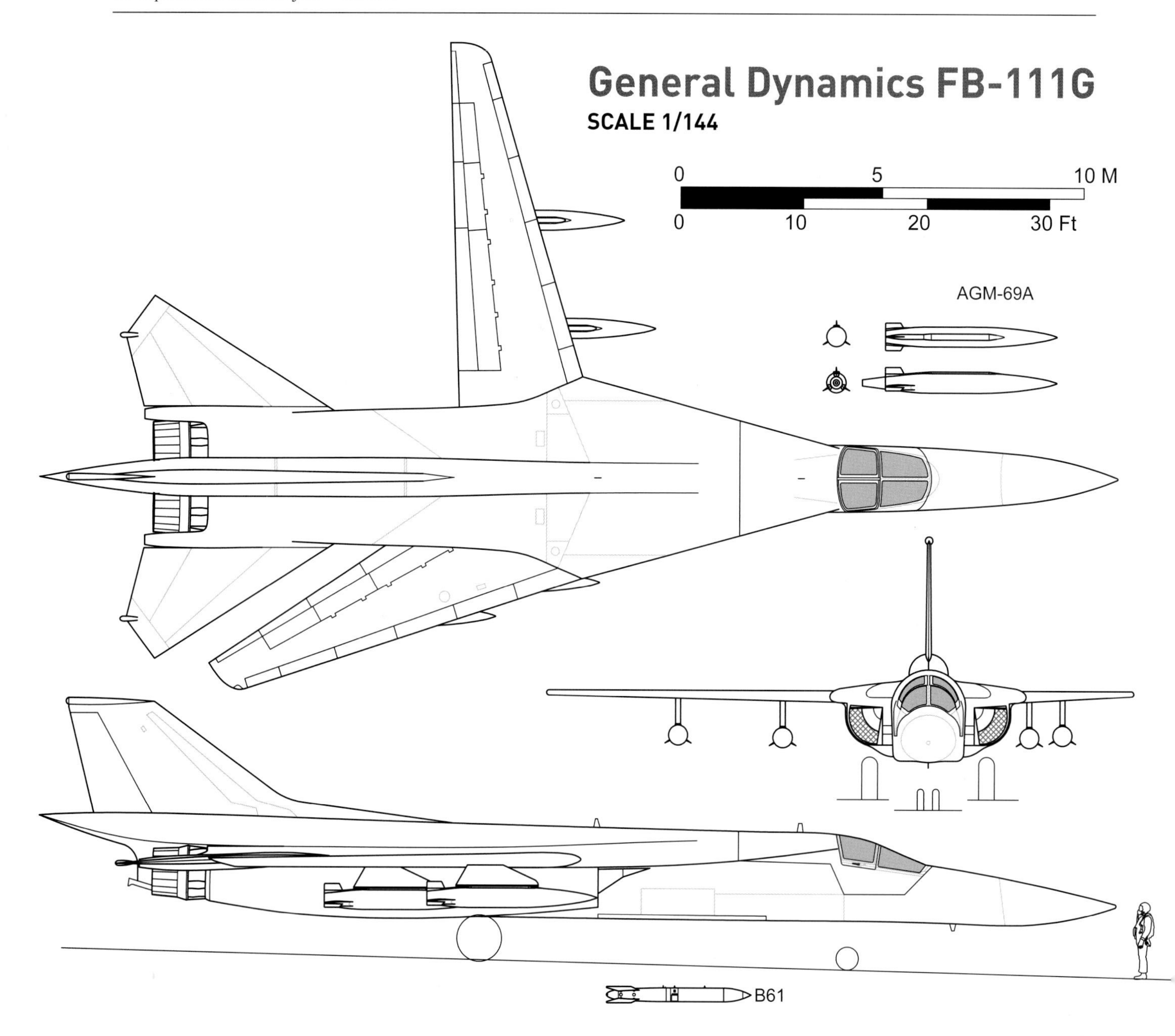

FB-111H

A much more modified aircraft was proposed in the form of the FB-111H. While the FB-111A, B-X and FB-111G were all seemingly designed based on the presumption that the AMSA – then the B-1 – would be delayed and overly expensive, the FB-111H was designed with the prospect that the B-1 would be outright cancelled. It seems to have originated around 1975, but was described in 1977.

It used parts of the FB-111A – 43% structural commonality, including the forward fuselage and cockpit, the wings and carry-through structure, the horizontal and vertical stabilizers, and reportedly 75% of the subsystems – but married them to an otherwise quite different aircraft. The rear fuselage was noticeably larger, a necessity given that the TF30 engines were to be replaced with a pair of the same engines meant for the B-1... General Electric F101-GE-100 turbofans. These would provide greater thrust and improved fuel efficiency.

The inlets would be wholly replaced. Instead of the complex movable spike inlets, the new inlets – which were reportedly wind tunnel tested and shown to be much less troublesome – were fixed, no translating spike. They were of a somewhat teardrop shape; reportedly, earlier FB-111H designs had used 2D ramp inlets of the kind used on the F-14 and F-15. There was again a large fuel-filled raised spine. The nose gear was to have been that of the FB-111A, but the main gear was entirely new, a more conventional setup with two wheels on either side.

The weapons bay appears to be much the same as had appeared on the B-X and the FB-111G, again capable of carrying five B61 bombs or four SRAMs. It could carry four more SRAMs under four pivoting underwing pylons, and six more attached to individual pylons under and alongside the rear fuselage. This would give a maximum load of 14 SRAMs, or ten SRAMs and five B61s… certainly a thermonuclear punch worthy of note. No fighter or interceptor variant seems to have been contemplated.

While the wings and folding mechanisms were the same as those on the FB-111A, the wings did not sweep back as far… only 60°. Curiously, this shallower wing sweep was married to a higher top speed… Mach 2.5. In order to have a hope of penetrating Soviet airspace, some consideration was given to radar cross section; two years of testing with a quarter-scale RCS model showed that the aircraft was reasonably stealthy (2.15m²).

The FB-111H did not succeed with the Air Force. Nevertheless, General Dynamics persisted, and in 1979 (by which point the B-1 programme had been cancelled and was seemingly dead) tried again. The aircraft GD proposed seems to have been little different from the FB-111H… same basic data, same artwork, same diagrams. But now it was called the FB-111B/C; the actual differences from the FB-111H were mostly wrapped up in simplified systems in the hopes of cutting costs.

The FB-111Bs were to be built from modified FB-111A airframes while the FB-111Cs were to be built from modified F-111D airframes. And this time, there was an interceptor option proposed, or at least mentioned… the FB-111B/C could carry up to 18 AIM-54 Phoenix air-to-air long range missiles. The F-14, in contrast, could only carry four of them. But in 1981, President Reagan revived the B-1 programme, and all the arguments for a stretched strategic bomber variant of the FB-111A evaporated.

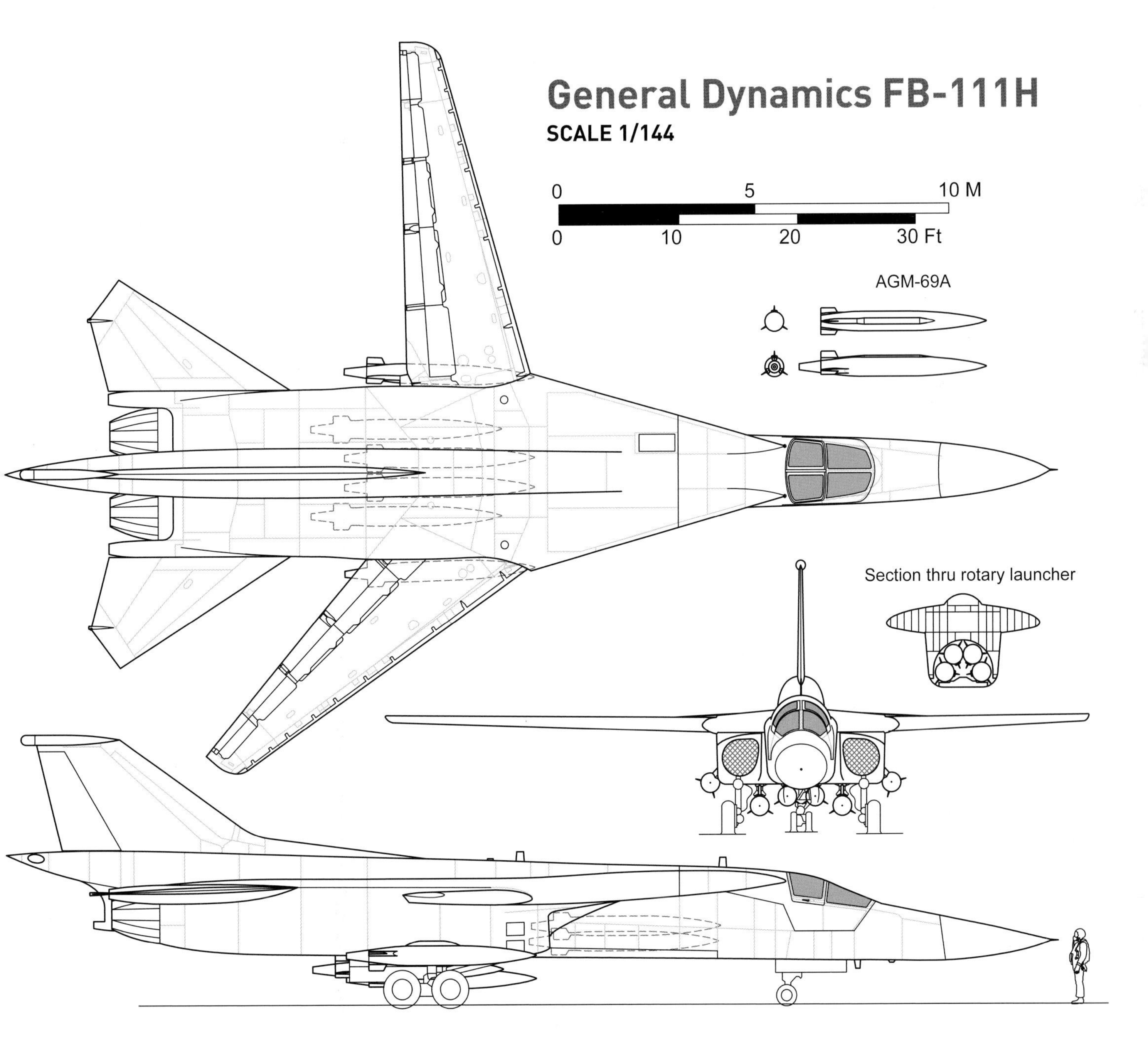

7 CHAPTER Rockwell B-1

With the premature termination of the B-70 programme, the Air Force was left without a strategic bomber to replace the B-52 and B-58. This suited many in the Air Force and the civilian government just fine: missiles were, to them, obviously the way of the future. Manned aircraft would soon be obsolete. However, that view was not universally held.

Whatever replaced the B-52, it would have to be survivable in the new era of Soviet anti-aircraft missile capability. The B-70 had been designed with the assumption that high speed and high altitude would keep it safe; by the early 1960s that was clearly no longer the most secure way to fly. So the new assumption was that the bomber of the future would continue to need to fly at a high speed, probably supersonic, but at low altitude.

Radar and infrared detection ranges would be greatly reduced near the ground. And even when visible to radar systems, chances were fair that the aircraft would be lost in the clutter of background, and would very quickly be over the horizon. In the time before effective digital computers integrated into advanced airborne radar systems, even look-down radar from aircraft flying overhead would have difficulty making out a fast aircraft against the ground below.

Starting in the early 1960s, the USAF cast about for a new programme. Many were started, many designs proposed… but this era is marked by the distinct dearth of good information on these designs. Years passed and many millions were spent, yet most of the resulting designs have been lost or remain classified; a time filled with doubtless hundred or thousands of well-considered designs has been reduced to a mere handful, often known from little more than an out of context diagram.

Programme followed after programme in rapid succession. The SLAB (Subsonic Low Altitude Bomber) study dated from 1961 and looked at a direct B-52 replacement. This aircraft was to weigh up to 500,000lb, have a 12,000lb payload and have an 11,000 nautical miles range, of which 4,300 nautical miles were to be at low altitude. This was followed by ERSA (Extended Range Strike Aircraft), a variable-sweep 600,000lb aircraft with a 10,000lb payload capable of 8,750 nautical miles range, of which 2,500 nautical miles were to be at an altitude of 500ft. Then came LAMP (Low Altitude Manned Penetrator) in August 1963, calling for a 350,000lb aircraft with a 20,000lb payload flying 6,200 nautical miles, 2,000 of which at low altitude. Around the same time AMP (Advanced Manned Penetrator) was put forward.

In November of 1963 the Air Force sent a Request for Proposals to Boeing, General Dynamics and North American for the AMPSS (Advanced Manned Precision Strike System). Proposals came in by mid-1964, but by then AMPSS was replaced with AMSA (Advanced Manned Strategic Aircraft). This, at last, was a programme that would last. And last, and last.

Secretary of Defense McNamara remained opposed to developing new manned strategic bombers but not to advancing the state of the art in avionics and propulsion. As a result, for several years the AMSA programmed crept by on relatively low funding for aircraft design, but better funding for developing the subsystems the eventual bomber would need. This led to what was at the time a very protracted period of concept study, evolution and development.

Conceptual designers and wind tunnel technicians were kept busy with a constant stream of changing configurations; thousands of variants were looked at to diverse degrees. This had been the case in the very early days leading to the B-58 Hustler… but where those studies of nearly two decades earlier had been looking at a kind of aircraft that had never been imagined before, now the goal was perfecting designs to fit evolving requirements. This seemingly interminable analysis and rethinking led to the Advanced Manned Strategic Aircraft being referred to jokingly as America's Most Studied Aircraft, an accurate if not knee-slappingly hilarious description.

The first proposals for AMSA came from Boeing, General Dynamics and North American in late 1964, while at the same time Curtiss-Wright, General Electric and Pratt & Whitney proposed new engines. IBM and Hughes Aircraft proposed avionics systems for the new bomber.

Studies continued. The FB-111A interim bomber began development, with the goal of replacing B-52s starting in the early 1970s. The FB-111A was of course incapable of reaching the same range or carrying the same payload as the B-52; the Air Force wanted something that could actually do better than what it already had. But McNamara remained dubious of the

AMSA, convinced that the FB-111A would do the job – especially if it could be improved with avionics and propulsion systems being developed for AMSA. This further delayed final decisions.

Secretary McNamara's position was not permanent, of course. In November 1968 Richard Nixon won the Presidential election, and when he took office in January 1969, McNamara was replaced with Melvin Laird. Laird and the new Administration took a different view of the utility of manned strategic bombers. The order for FB-111As was cut and the AMSA programme was accelerated. As perhaps a symbol of this new interest, in April 1969 the AMSA was officially granted a new designation: B-1A.

The B-1 was the first new bomber approved since the Tri-Service aircraft designation system was introduced in 1962. Had the aircraft designation systems in use prior to that been continued, it is possible that the B-1 would have instead been designated B-72, as there were bomber variants planned for the SR-71 (the B-71). While the B-1A designation was made official in 1969, it had been used unofficially for some years prior to that, as the new designation system made an eventual 'B-1' inevitable.

In November 1969 a final Request for Proposals was put out for the B-1A. A Source Selection Evaluation Board was put together by the Air Force in December and they began the job of evaluating proposals for engines and airframes early in 1970. In contrast to the McNamara years, things moved quickly and somewhat decisively and in early June 1970 North American Rockwell was selected to build the airframe and General Electric to build the new turbofan engine.

All of the proposed programmes, from SLAB through AMSA, doubtless produced a wealth of designs. Sadly… most are not available, especially from the early days when requirements changed rapidly. What is available is a smattering of diverse aircraft, ranging from designs with fairly substantial documentation to designs known only from isolated illustrations.

Lockheed CL-820-8

Little information is available on this design. It was one of a large number of designs studied in 1963 for the LAMP (Low Altitude Manned Penetrator) role, but so far a few Lockheed designs are the only LAMP concepts known with any certainty. Most of the designs Lockheed studied under the CL-820 designation were

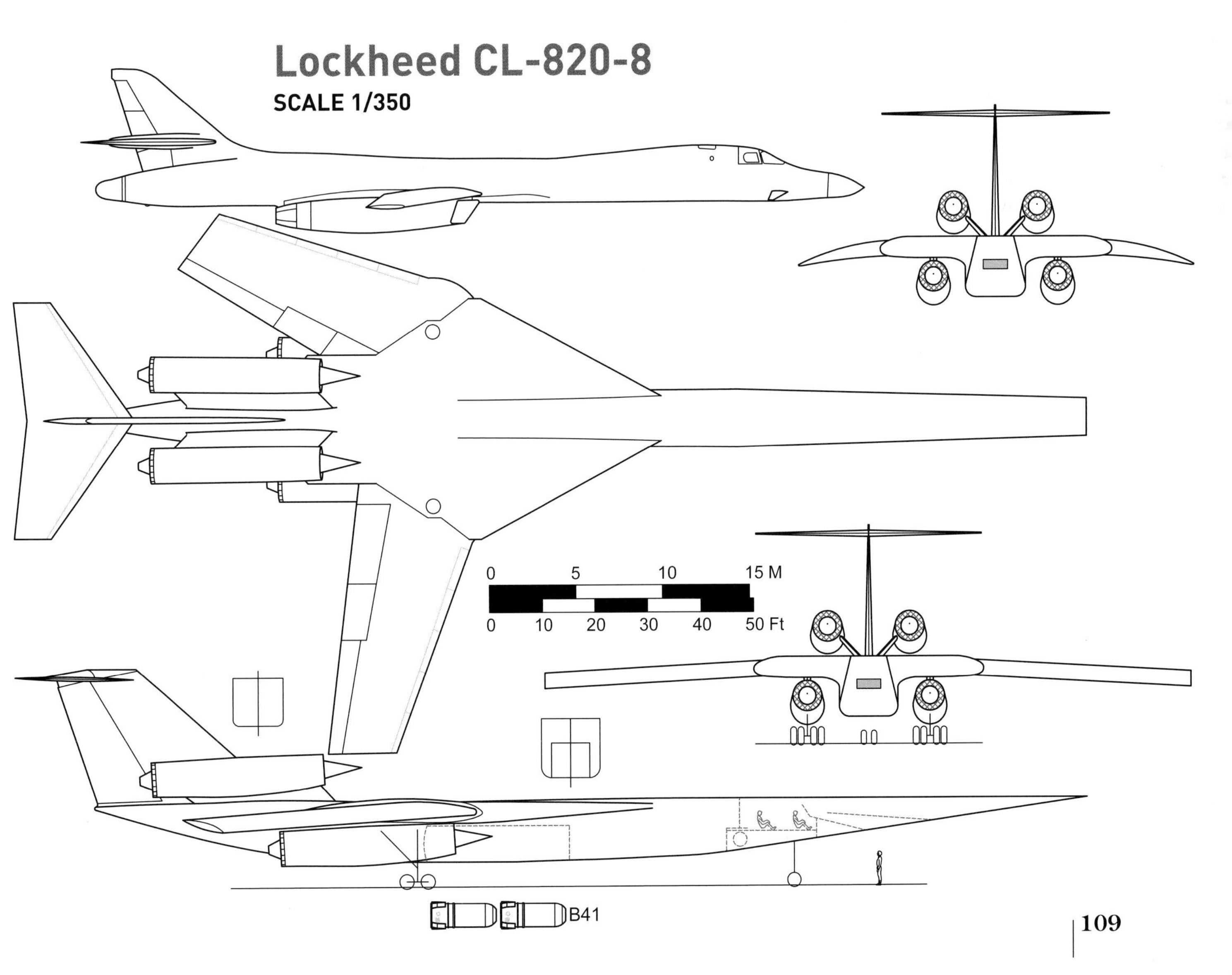

subsonic, but many featured variable geometry wings. They appeared to be wholly conventional subsonic cargo or passenger jets, but with variable sweep wings. This would help them both cruise long range at high altitude and dash at high subsonic speeds at sea level.

The CL-820-8 was a supersonic configuration with an unusual spatula-nosed fuselage, a feature used before on the CL-805-503 strategic reconnaissance aircraft. Such a fuselage geometry would be appropriate for a hypersonic cruise vehicle which would use the flat underside of the fuselage as a giant inlet ramp for the scramjet engines, but here the reasoning is rather more obscure.

The podded engines would not benefit from the fuselage shaped as an inlet ramp. The available side-view diagram seems to indicate that the pilot would have had a sizable window on the underside of the fuselage, certainly a novel arrangement, but one which would have been quite handy during landings. Payload is unknown, but the size of the payload bay would permit the loading of two B41 thermonuclear gravity bombs. Top speed was likely Mach 3.

Republic AMPSS

One of the earliest known designs to fulfil the changing requirements was a Republic concept for the Advanced Manned Precision Strike System. Republic was not apparently asked to respond to the AMPSS RFP, and the design certainly does not indicate that they did: it is known from a single incomplete two-view diagram, devoid of any information beyond the configuration and dimensions.

This configuration was clearly related to the Republic TFX entry (see Chapter 6), with a highly swept arrow wing with extended wingtips and deployable variable-sweep wing panels. These wing panels were more substantial compared to the size of the aircraft than their equivalents on the TFX design, but filled the same function and stowed fully over the main wing for high speed flight. The fuselage was bent upwards like a snake readying to strike, resulting in an unusual profile and a more unusual forward view.

The same general configuration was employed not only on Republic's idea for an SST (Rep-10, dated September, 1963), which was virtually the same size and shape save for a wider and straighter fuselage, but also on the VTOL Republic-Fokker D-24 Alliance strike fighter (see Volume 2). Unfortunately, not only does the original diagram provide no performance or weight data, it is incomplete and vague in some areas, such as the details about the engine type and arrangement. Consequently, the diagram presented here should be viewed a being accurate in the overall size and shape, but somewhat provisional regarding the details. The engine nacelles are adapted from the SST design.

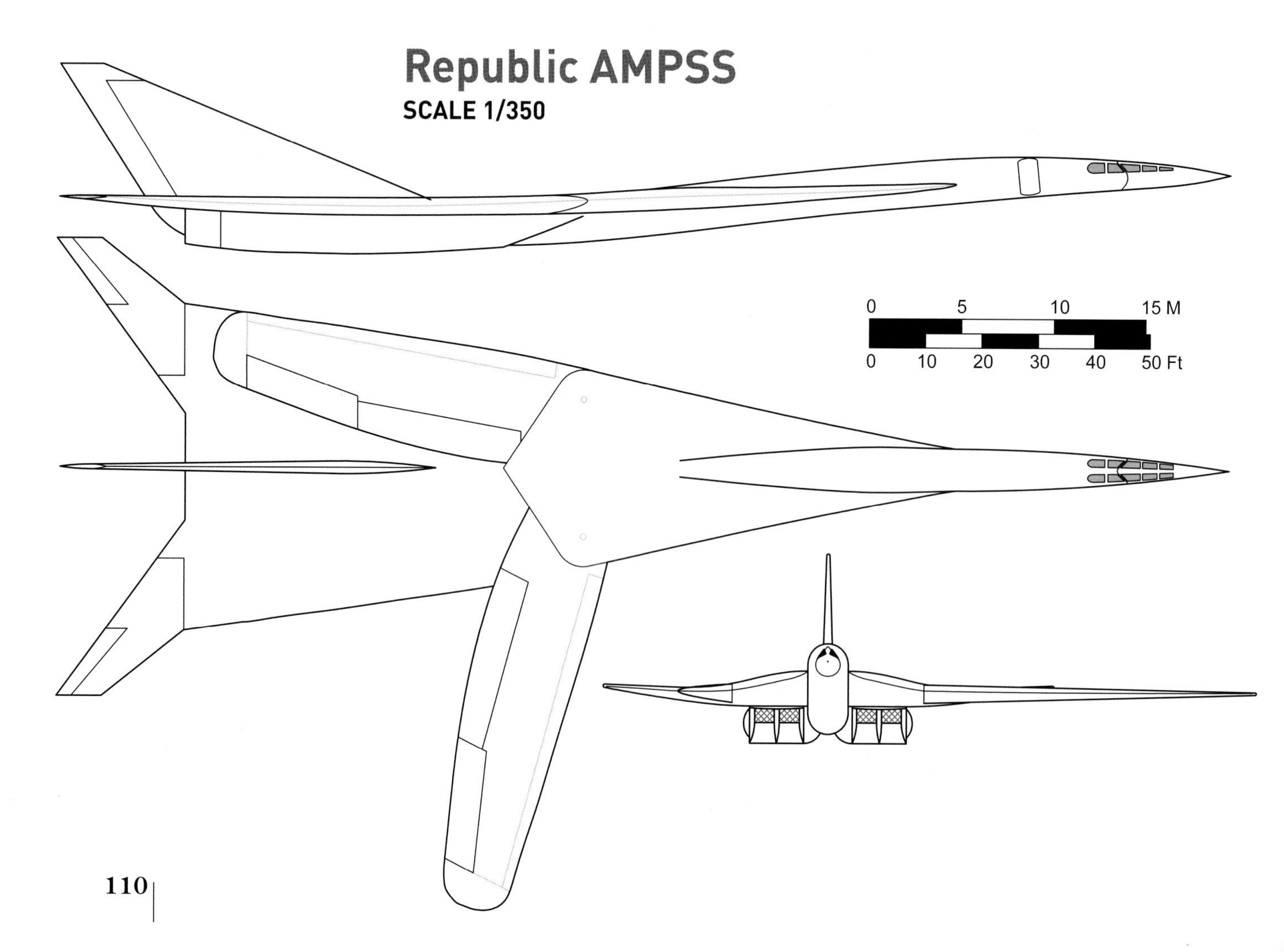

Boeing AMPSS

So far, only a few scattered bits have come out about the Boeing AMPSS proposal. Specifically, two top-view diagrams: one depicting a three-engine design, another with four engines. Both are what at first appears to be a conventional variable geometry design… but, rather inexplicably, the horizontal stabilizers are also variable geometry. What conceivable advantage this could confer, this author cannot conceive. One of the diagrams fortunately includes partial dimensions.

Also available are photos of a pair of display models of a quite similar, though not identical, configuration that is thought to depict somewhat later AMSA configurations. The models differ from the diagrams in all details, but most importantly they show the aircraft with utterly normal non-variable horizontal stabilizers.

The diagram here is accurate in top view, and is somewhat provisional in front and side views. Those were created using the display models as references, and cannot be claimed to be certain. Overall the aircraft appears to be fairly conservative in aerodynamics. Nothing is currently available regarding weights or performance.

NAA High Performance Penetrator

Dating from November 1963, the North American Aviation High Performance Penetrator was a new bomber design meant to fulfill the role of the Advanced Manned Precision Strike System (AMPSS). Known solely from a single drawing and a number of display model photos (which show a slightly differing version of the design, especially in the cockpit area), weight and performance data are unavailable.

The crew of three sat tandem – pilot, recon-nav officer, weapons officer, in B-70-style ejection capsules. The nose gear was located somewhat well aft, behind the weapons officer position. A single narrow cylindrical weapons bay, about 24ft long, was just aft

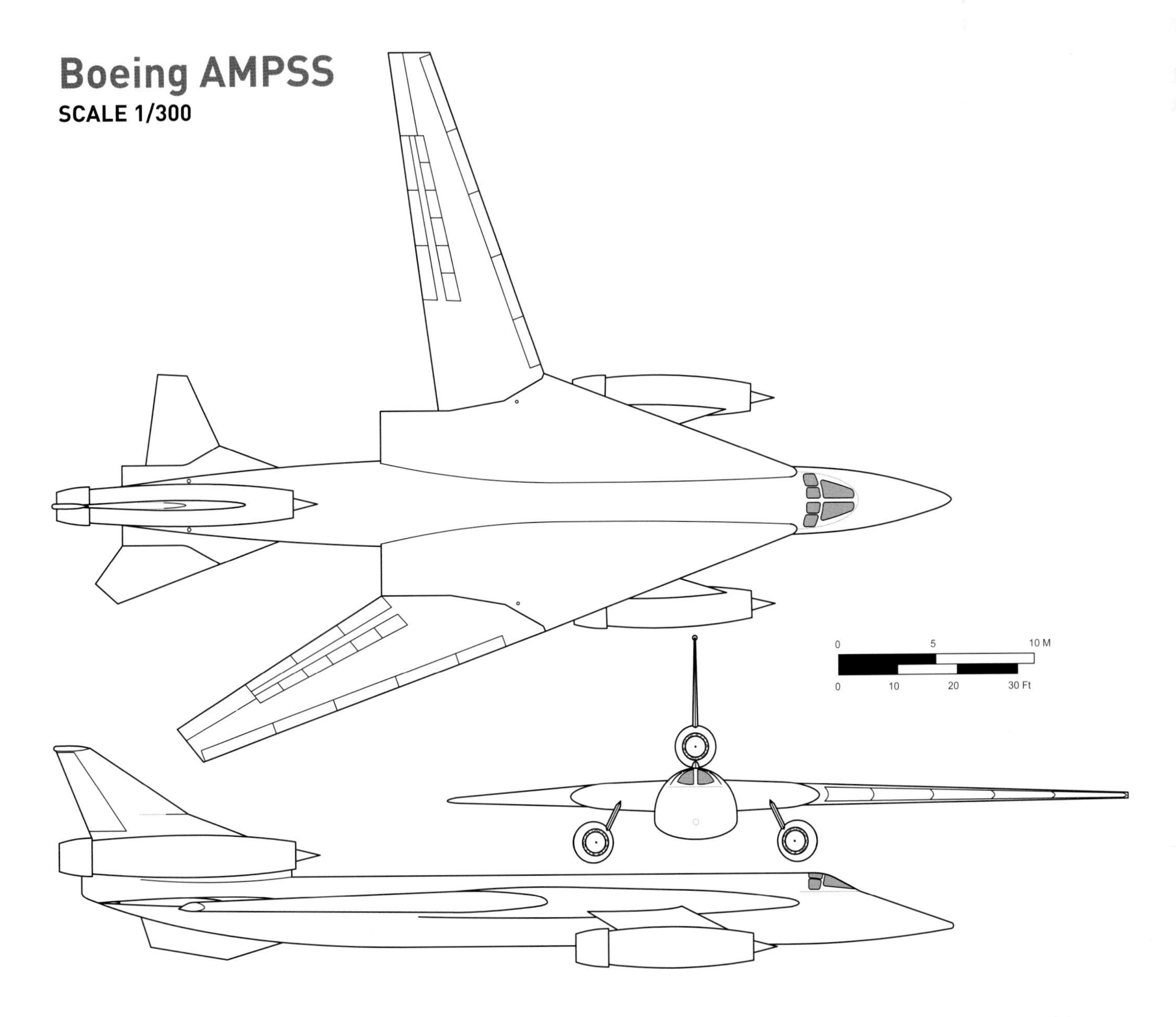

NAA High Performance Penetrator

SCALE 1/250

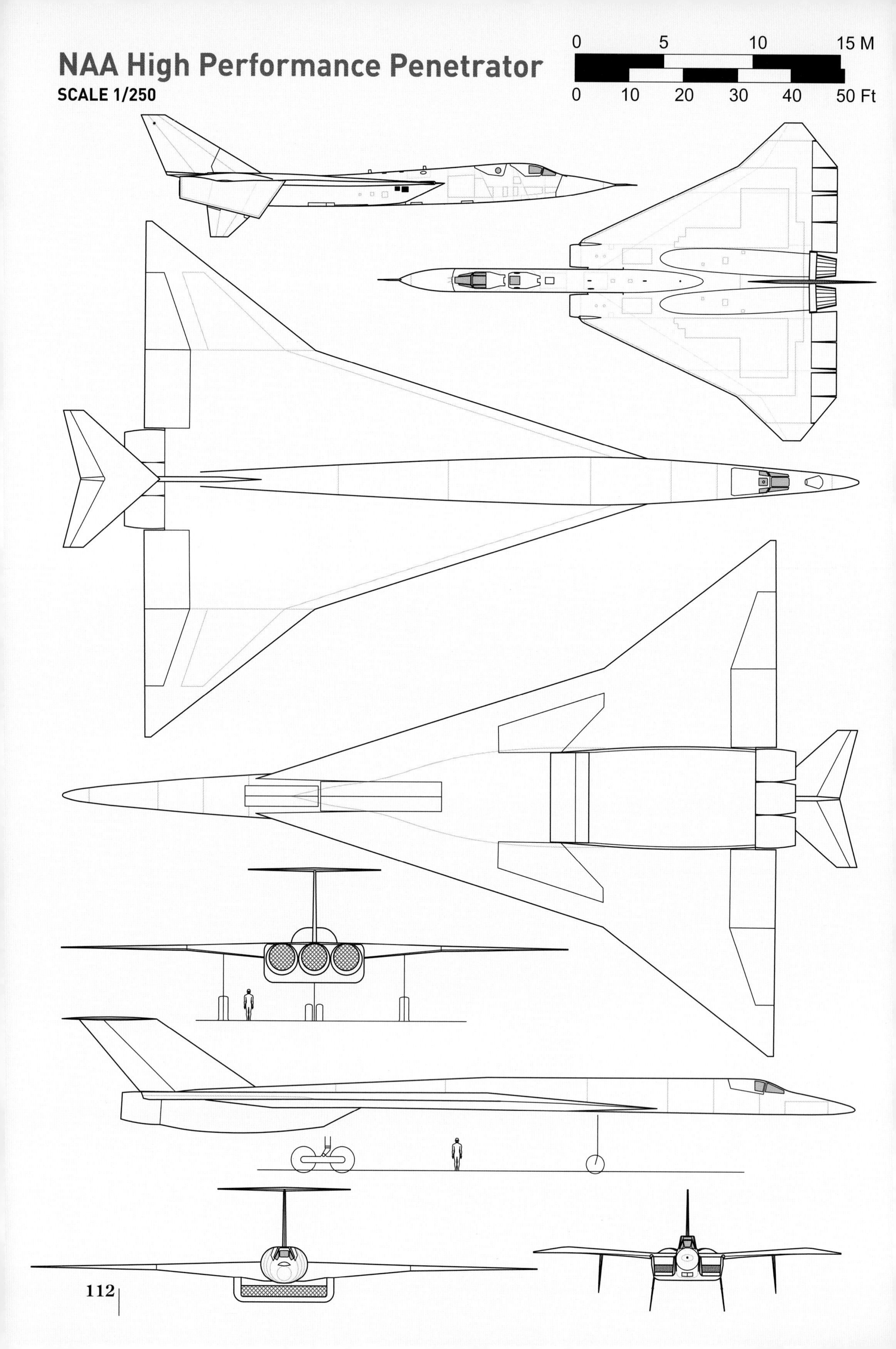

of the nose gear. An inflight refuelling receptacle was on the nose ahead of the cockpit.

The wings were a fixed geometry double delta, rather different from the swing-wings which would dominate the quest to build the eventual B-1. The fuselage was long and slim, terminating in a T-tail empennage. At the nose was a terrain avoidance radar; flanking the nose were a pair of side-looking radar units. While performance data is not available, it was clear that this aircraft was meant to fly low and fast, probably in the area of Mach 1.5 at around 500ft. The radar would be essential to prevent the aircraft from becoming one with the terrain.

Propulsion was provided by three turbojets (80% scaled STF188Bs) laid side-by-side in a module under the centre of the trailing edge of the wing, and fed by a single wide 2D ramp inlet. Only dimensional data is known. The diagram here is shown with the North American XF-108 to scale, showing some faint similarity of design.

North American 1495-25 PAMSS

Many of the AMPSS designs were extremely advanced and would have required a considerable development effort. If a prototype could be put together from existing hardware, then in principle a great deal of time and expense could be saved.

By 1964, there were two XB-70 airframes available for use. The XB-70 programme had been cancelled in 1961, but the two completed aircraft continued to fly for a number of years in a research capacity. In 1964, someone at North American Aviation had the idea to tear at least one of the XB-70s apart and rebuild it in the approximate image of one of the new aircraft under study, in this case the High Performance Penetrator. This idea became the NAA 1495-25 Prototype Advanced Manned Strike System (PAMSS) of March, 1964. It would presumably demonstrate the proposed flight characteristics of the North American AMPSS by flying at high speed and low altitude, utilizing a similar configuration.

The PAMSS was noticeably smaller than the XB-70 it would have been built from. It had four General Electric YJ93 turbojets rather than the XB-70's six; these engines were put into a narrower pack, with a broader and shallower inlet on the underside. This narrowed the fuselage as a whole, and brought the wings in, reducing span. Additionally, the inlet duct was much shorter, allowing the fuselage to also be much shorter. The downward-folding wingtip feature of the XB-70 was deleted and a fairing built over the now-fixed hinge. The canards and twin vertical tails were deleted and replaced with a single vertical tail with a horizontal stabilizer (231sq ft).

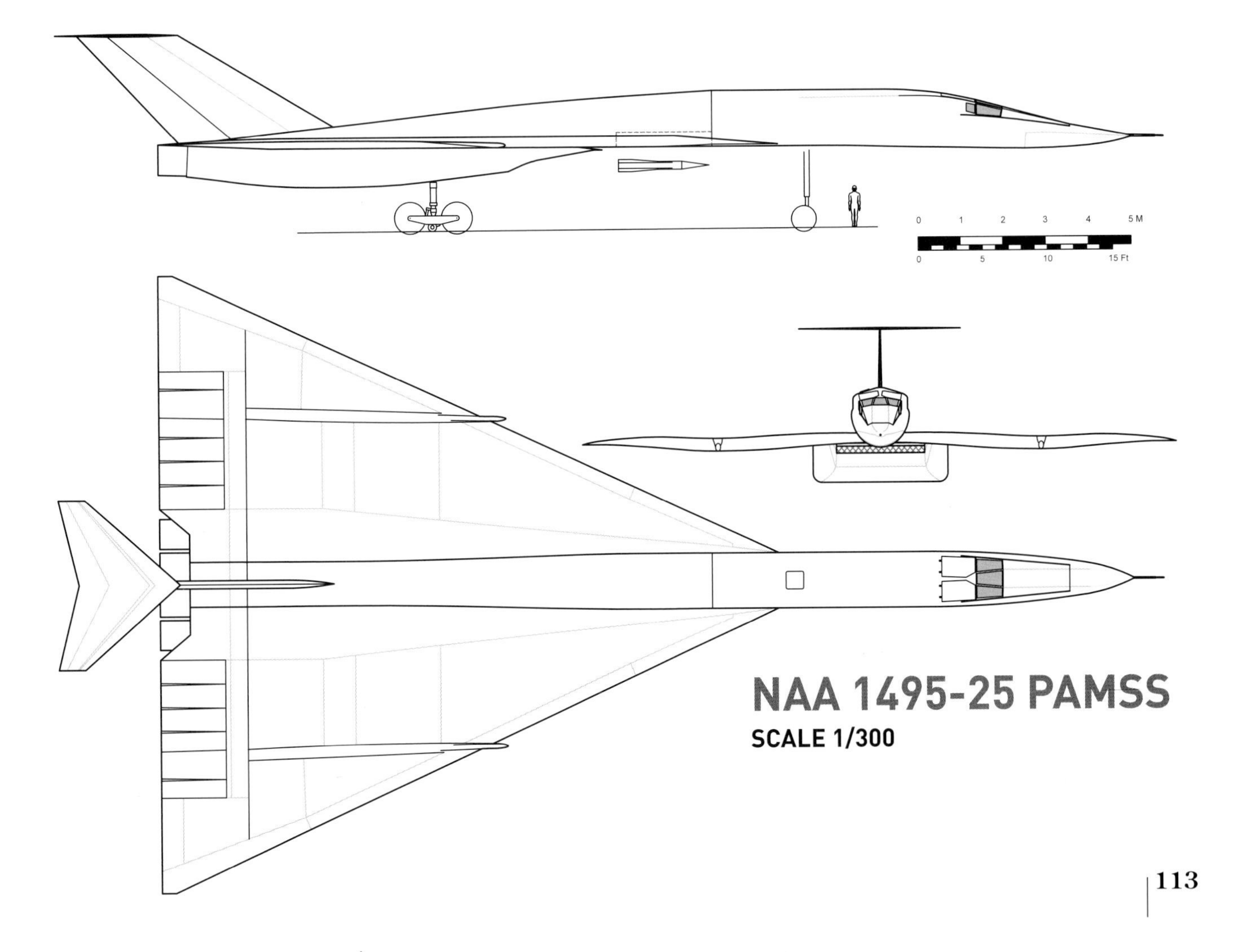

While a prototype aircraft, the PAMSS did have a single relatively small weapons bay where it could carry a single missile of undefined type, possibly an AIM-47 Falcon nuclear air-to-air missile. This, presumably, would be for supersonic stores ejection testing. Landing gear would be all-new, with the nose gear relocated from the XB-70's engine pack to the forward fuselage of the PAMSS. The cockpit would remain, providing for a crew of two. As nothing came of the High Performance Penetrator, there seemed to be no need for a Prototype Advanced Manned Strike System.

General Dynamics Configuration 2120 AMPSS

General Dynamics produced Configuration 2120 in June 1964 as a part of the AMPSS programme. Descended from Configuration 2110 of the LAMP phase, it is one of the relatively few early B-1-related designs which is reasonably well documented. It was a swing-wing design with a clear family relationship to the General Dynamics F-111, looking much like the F-111's older and better-fed brother.

It had a shoulder-mounted variable geometry wing similar to the F-111's; a tail not unlike the F-111's (though with substantial dihedral on the horizontal stabilizers to clear them from the jet engine exhaust); and a nose similar to the F-111's, including an F-111-style escape pod. The wings would extend to 16° sweep for takeoff and landing, and sweep back to 72.5° for supersonic flight.

Unlike the F-111, Configuration 2120 had four 42.6% scale Pratt & Whitney STF200C-35.1 turbofans in four discrete nacelles. Each had its own translating double cone external compression inlet. Their arrangement was unusual in that there were two pairs attached to the sides of the rear fuselage on stubby pylons, with the outboard nacelles moved somewhat aft of the inboard nacelles to reduce supersonic drag.

Configuration 2120 included two separate weapons bays. Illustrations show the aft bay fitted with a single Mk-53 thermonuclear bomb (nine megaton yield), while the forward bay was filled with nine SRAM-like missiles (200 kilotons yield each). The missiles were stacked within the bay in a three by three grid and were of a different configuration than the eventual SRAM; it's unknown if these were generic placeholders or if they reflected a General Dynamics missile design of the time. The B-1 bomber would eventually be fitted with rotary launchers each carrying eight SRAM missiles, a notably different arrangement than depicted here.

The standard mission load would use only the forward bay with nine missiles; the aft weapons bay would have another fuel tank installed, containing 18,000lb of JP-4. At takeoff the tank would have 10,000lb of fuel; after takeoff the plane would rendezvous with a tanker and load up to a gross weight of 403,000lb.

For missions utilizing the Mk-53 in the rear bay, it would be the primary weapon and delivery of that weapon would be the aircraft's primary mission. The bomb would be delivered at low altitude, using a parachute to slow descent. This was more to ensure that the bomb was not destroyed on impact than to give the aircraft time to escape; the Mk-53 would be used in a 'laydown' role where, as the name implies, it would lay down on the ground for a pre-programmed length of time.

This delay was what gave the bomber time to escape, and would provide the locals who witnessed the impact time to contemplate the life choices that had brought them – briefly – to that point. The missiles would most likely be used to 'plough the road' ahead of the bomber by taking out known anti-aircraft missile sites or interceptor airfields and other targets of opportunity. As an alternative to the single Mk-53 the aft bay could carry four Mk-43 nuclear bombs or four CLAMPs... 'Chemical Low Altitude Missile Puny', early jet-powered missile concepts that would evolve into cruise missiles.

The wing centre section box, pivot assemblies and landing gear would be made from heat treated D6ac steel; most of the rest of the aircraft would be made from aluminium (7079-T851 for bulkheads, frames and longerons; 2024-T81 for pretty much everything else). Within a decade, titanium would become a major structural material for aircraft such as this, especially the wing pivot; but in 1964 titanium was still hard to come by. The wings had full-span leading edge slats for low speed lift and sizable spoilers for control.

Non refuelled mission total range was 6,300 nautical miles, with a 2,000 nautical mile dash at Mach 0.85 and a cruise speed of Mach 2.2. Dash speed was indeed lower than cruise; dash occurred at sea level, cruise at 44,400ft. Specific fuel consumption was almost twice as high at Mach 0.85/sea level than it was at Mach 2.2/44,400ft. While it could maintain extended periods at Mach 0.9 at sea level, it could only manage five minutes at Mach 1.2 at sea level. An inflight refuelling receptacle was built into the upper fuselage just aft of the escape capsule. The capsule, interesting, does not extend to the leading edge of the wings as the F-111's did.

The configuration was examined to see what could be done to reduce infrared and radar signatures. Details are sparse, but it appears that General Dynamics concluded that it could be made meaningfully stealthy, but at the cost of considerable redesign. The section detailing the configuration changes contemplated for reduced radar cross section has unfortunately not been released.

USAF AMSA

A design had been known for many years of an AMSA configuration designed in-house by the Air

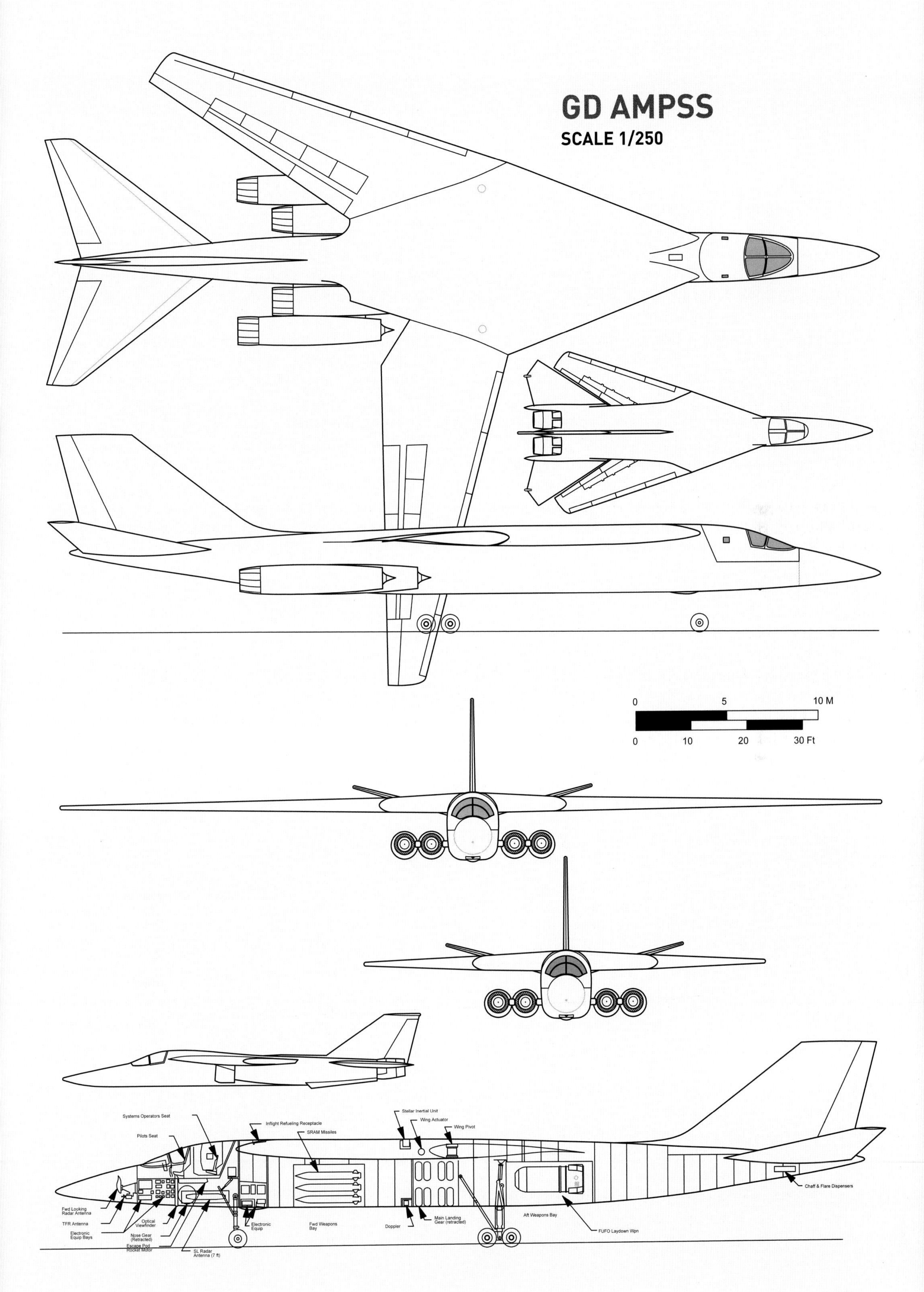
GD AMPSS
SCALE 1/250
0
5
10 M
0
10
20
30 Ft
Systems Operators Seat
Pilots Seat
Inflight Refueling Receptacle
SRAM Missiles
Stellar Inertial Unit
Wing Actuator
Wing Pivot
Chaff & Flare Dispensers
Fwd Looking Radar Antenna
TFR Antenna
Electronic Equip Bays
Optical Viewfinder
Nose Gear (Retracted)
Escape Pod Rocket Motor
SL Radar Antenna (7 ft)
Electronic Equip
Fwd Weapons Bay
Doppler
Main Landing Gear (retracted)
Aft Weapons Bay
FUFO Laydown Wpn

Force Design Branch. The overall configuration is not unlike the early General Dynamics AMPSS work, but somewhat more brutalist in execution. Sadly, while a decent three-view diagram has been publicly available for decades, no data whatsoever seems to have come forth describing any aspect of it.

The USAF AMSA was a swing-wing design of generally conventional layout, somewhat similar to the General Dynamics Configuration 2120. Instead of the engines being placed in Siamese nacelles on the sides of the rear fuselage, the USAF AMSA hung one turbojet engine – type unknown – beneath each wing root, and placed two more side by side in the tail of the fuselage, fed by a bifurcated inlet atop the fuselage. The fuselage itself was long and slim with a rectangular cross section. The diagram shows via dotted lines the outlines of two weapons bays in the rear fuselage; there may have been a third bay further forward, but it is not shown. The rough scale of the aircraft has been estimated based on the assumption that those bays are the same basic size as those of the Configuration 2020.

In addition to the weapons carried internally, each wing was to have four pivoting hardpoints. A display model of the USAF AMSA depicts each hardpoint fitted with a pylon, each pylon carrying six conventional unguided bombs.

North American D436-21

The North American designs for AMSA were reported on in 1967. Like the General Dynamics Configuration 2120, a few of these have the benefit of available documentation. Task S-7 was a Design Characteristics Study intended to look at how new and refined systems requirements affected design criteria and to adjust point design configurations. A Phase I and Phase II are known. The North American Task S-7 Phase I point design was the D436-21.

While the preceding designs are not currently known, they were said to be similar, though the -21 was revised for new requirements. This included enlarging the nose to accommodate a larger antenna for the forward-look radar, 60in wide by 40in high, but then reduced to 20in high. A rear-looking radar was installed in a fairing

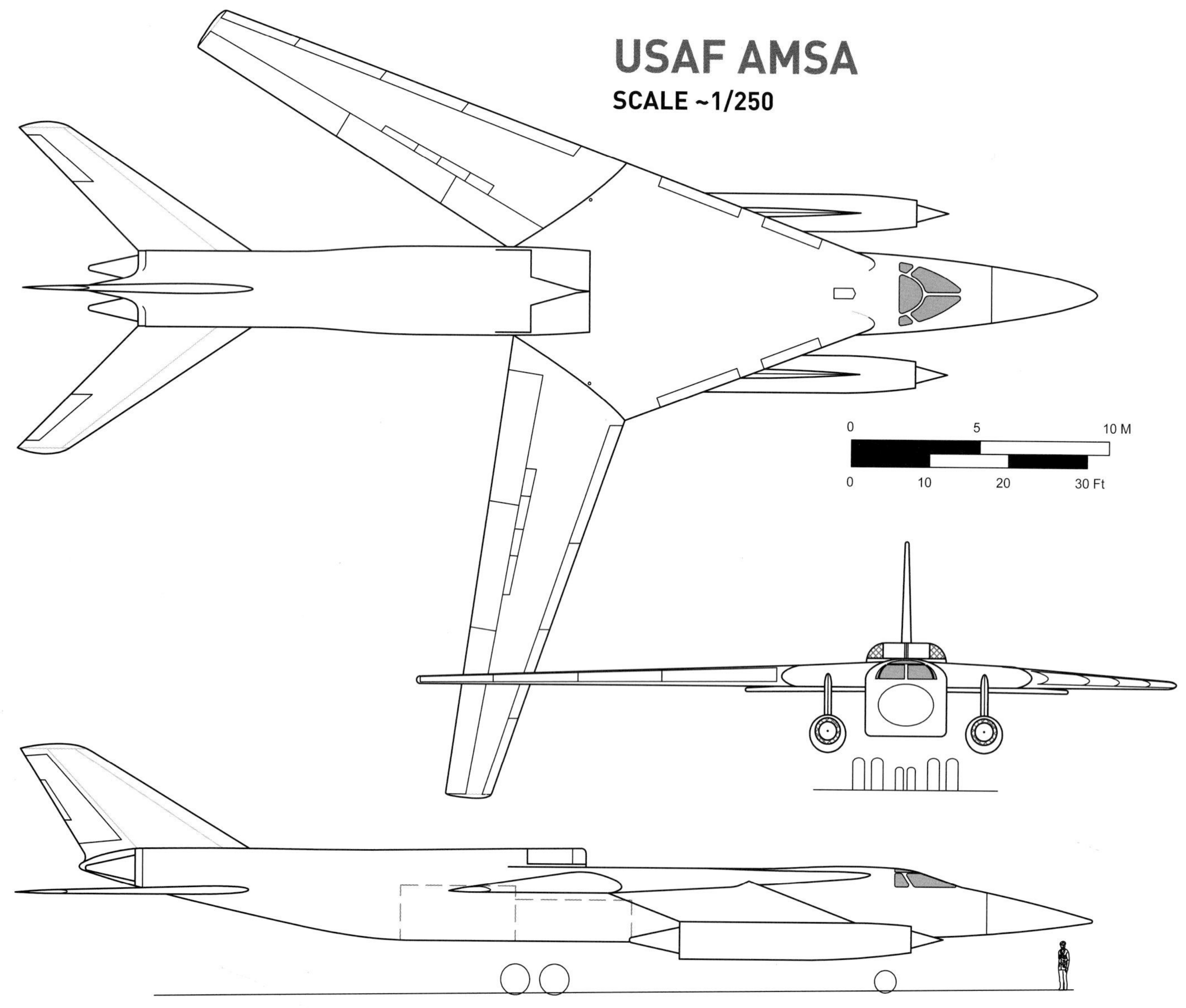

near the top of the vertical stabilizer. The cockpit was an ejectable escape capsule and included a substantial aft extension.

The shoulder-mounted wings of the D436-21 were, like several of the early TFX designs, capable of being folded back more than 90° to 105.5°, stowing onto the back of the fuselage. This provided for a stable high-speed, low altitude platform. For low speed the wings would be swept to 20°, and to 75° for normal high speed operations. The aircraft was designed to maintain a Mach 1.2 cruise at sea level thanks to the reduced wing area with full sweepback. Somewhat unusually, the wings did not have fairings that covered the leading edge of the pivots, but were instead fully exposed. This might have made the aerodynamics a bit more complicated, but it would have probably simplified maintenance and design issues. The underside of the fuselage featured widely spaced long-chord ventral fins to improve lateral stability.

Payload would be carried in two bays, the forward measuring 96in high by 86in wide and 360in long, the aft measuring 96in high by 86in wide and 215in long. The basic load of 25,000lb was 18 SRAMs; 104,000lb of conventional weapon could be carried internally, with another 40,000lb potentially carried under external hardpoints.

Takeoff distance over a 50ft obstacle was to be 6,000ft. The basic subsonic mission had a range of 5,000 nautical miles, of which 2,000 would be at Mach 0.85 at sea level. An alternate supersonic mission carrying the same basic payload would have a range of only 2,500 nautical miles cruising at altitude and at Mach 2.2, but 1,500 of those would be at Mach 1.2 at sea level. Range and duration could be extended via inflight refuelling from a KC-135.

Four 92.5% scale GE1/9F2F afterburning turbofan engines were laid out side-by-side near the rear of the aircraft, separated by the fuselage. The left and right pairs of engines were each fed by a single 2D ramp inlet alongside the fuselage below the wing, well aft of the leading edges. Instead of 'turkey feather' exhausts, the engines were each fitted with variable skirted plug nozzles. Above Mach 1.4 performance would be maximized with a retractable shroud.

North American D458-13D

The Task S-7 Phase II point design was the D458-13D, a swing-wing design capable of Mach 2+ performance.

The D458-13D had three weapons bays, each of which was a wide, low rectangular box, 56in high by 110in wide by 195in long. One bay was located aft of the wing pivot and two forward; the two forward bays were joined together and could serve as a single larger bay. They could each hold eight AGM-69A SRAM missiles, two layers of four missiles side-by-side. Additionally, one Mk-53 hydrogen bomb could be carried in the aft

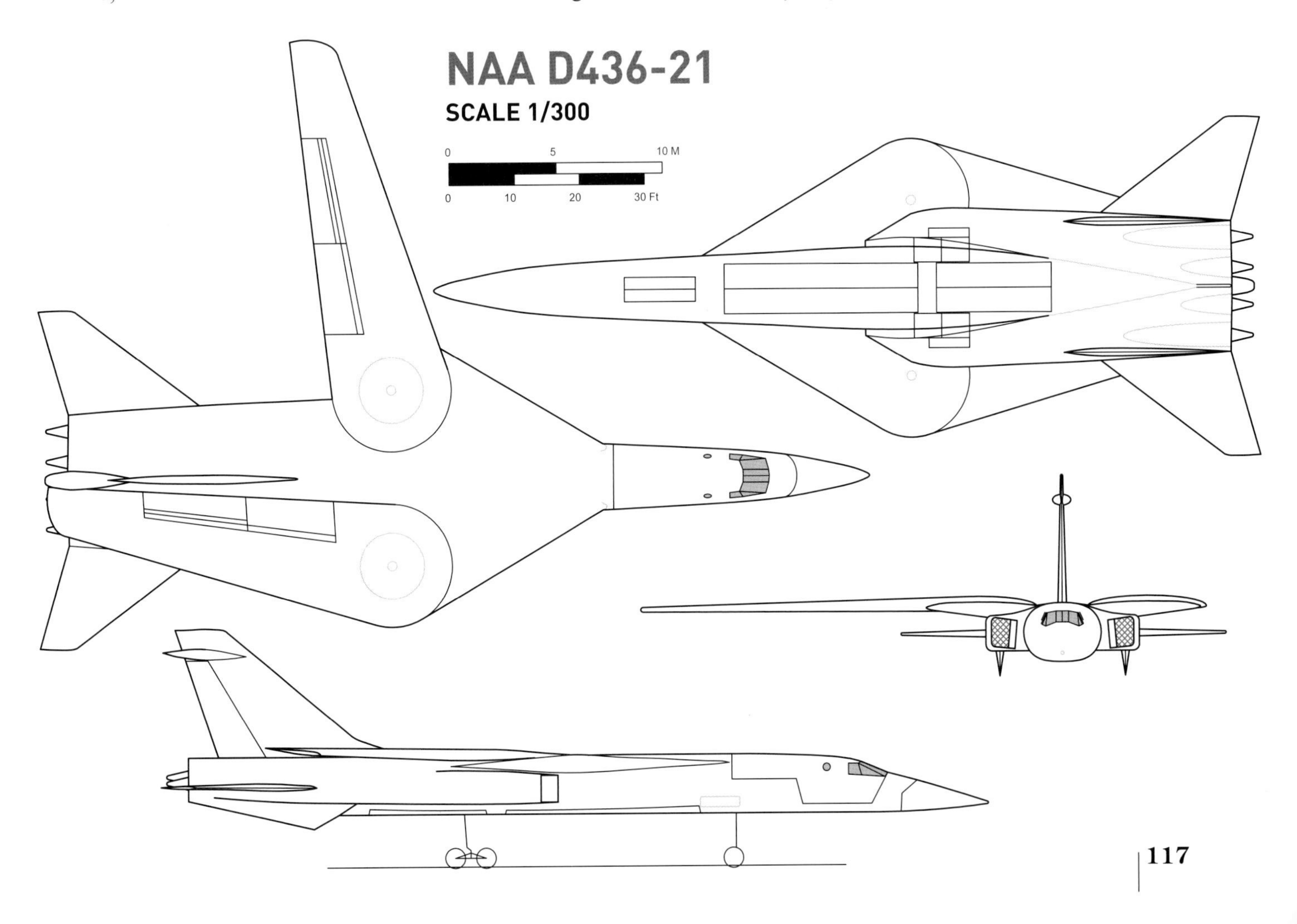

bay, and an additional one in the forward bay. Each fixed wing root held six launch tubes, side-by-side, containing undefined decoy rockets. A stellar inertial platform was located in the upper surface of the port wing root.

The design mission had a payload of 50,000lb and a range of 6,100 nautical miles, utilizing inflight refuelling. A sea level penetration range of 2,000 nautical miles would be carried out at Mach 0.85. An alternate supersonic mission would have a range of 2,500 nautical miles; 1,500 of those would be carried out at altitude and subsonic speed, but 1,000 would occur at greater than 50,000ft and at Mach 2.2.

The pivoting wing panels were distinctly triangular, coming almost to points at the wingtips. The wings were fitted with leading edge Krueger flaps, double slotted flaps along the trailing edges and spoilers on the upper surface. For subsonic cruise the wings would extend to a leading edge sweep of 20°; for high speed dash they would sweep back to 75°.

The nose of the D458-13D was somewhat unusual in profile, being essentially a horizontal straight line all the way to the nose on the underside with a long, straight line on the upper side leading to a well-raised cockpit. This resulted in the cockpit sitting fairly high and having a decent forward view for landing without need for a drooping nose.

The cockpit had provisions for a crew of four plus an additional two instructors, and included a rest area to permit missions of up to 36 hours in length. Entrance into the crew cabin was through a folding ladder from the underside of the fuselage. The cockpit was of course an emergency ejection capsule, capable of safe ejection at all likely conditions. The upper surface of the fuselage aft of the capsule would eject with it, as would portions of the fuselage sides to serve as stabilizing fins. Parachutes and air bags would provide for a reasonably safe landing on any surface.

Four 105% scale GE1/9F7B-34 afterburning turbofan engines were laid out side-by-side near the rear of the aircraft, separated by the fuselage.

North American Rockwell 1968 AMSA

North American Rockwell (North American was acquired and renamed by Rockwell Standard in September 1967) greatly revamped its AMSA design again in 1968. Unfortunately not much documentation is currently available on this version. Payload was increased to 32 AGM-69A SRAMs, and the fuselage stretched considerably.

North American D458-13D

SCALE 1/300

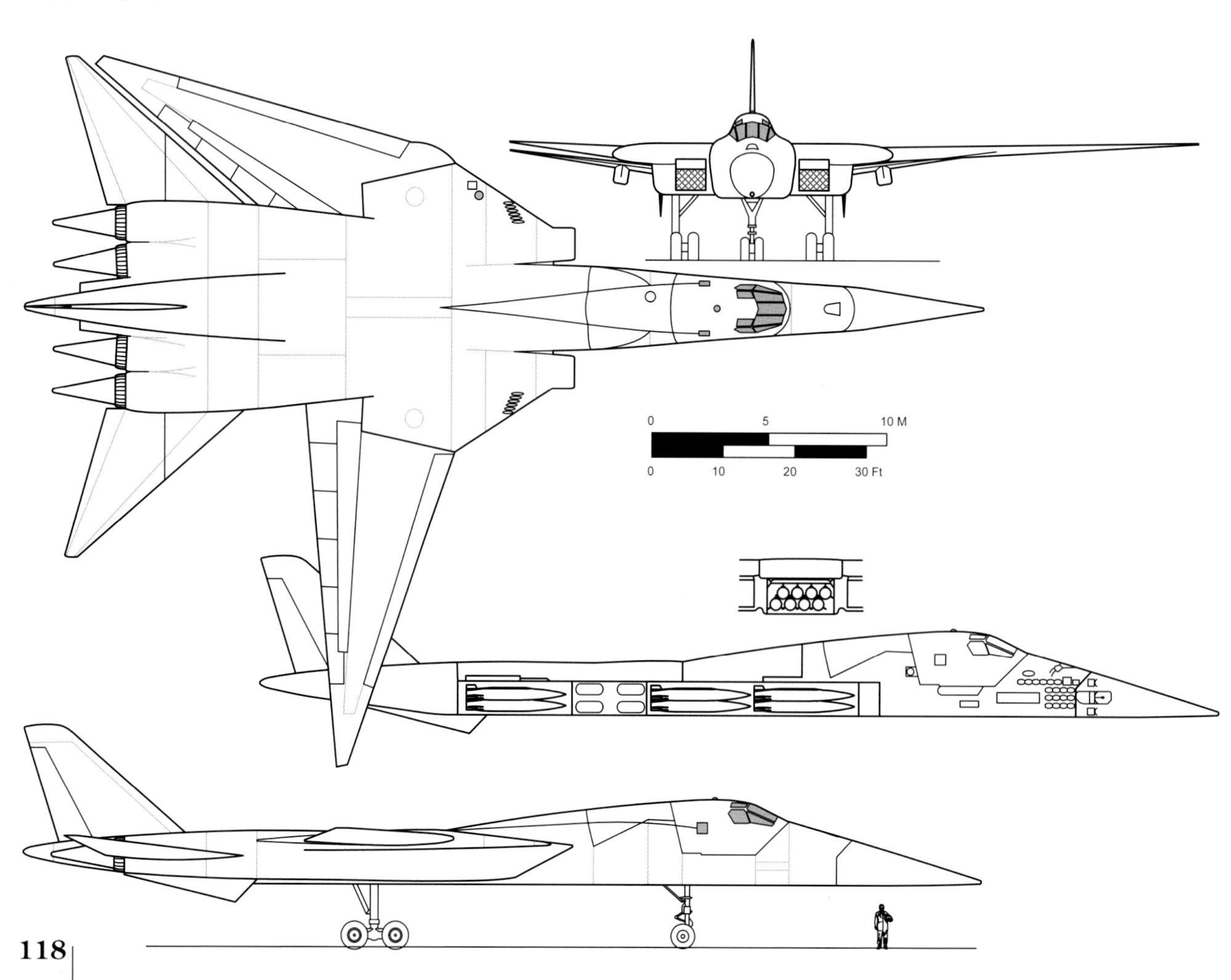

The 1967 design is faintly recognizable in the 1968 version, but basically everything changed. The curiously triangular wings had given way to wings with a curved leading edge; the wings came to a definite point, but had a broader chord throughout much of their span. They continued to have full-span leading edge slats, flaps along the trailing edge and spoilers for lateral control.

The horizontal stabilizers were now well separated from the wings. The engine nacelles were moved below the fuselage, though the inlets reached upwards to sit alongside the fuselage. The nose and cockpit were definitely reminiscent of the earlier design, but the cockpit did not sit quite so distinctly high on the fuselage.

The aircraft had an escape capsule with seating for six (a four man crew was standard, but two additional crew could be onboard for training), but no available diagrams, models or artwork illustrate the capsule configuration.

Boeing Model 975-046

This is likely a design from near the end of the B-1 proposal phase. It has fixed geometry wings, probably to lower cost. No information is available on it apart from display models. While the models are of a specific scale, and thus the full scale dimensions can be reasonably closely approximated, the models that this author has seen have been painted an overall white with no surface details; thus the configurations of cockpit canopies, ejection capsule and control surfaces is speculative.

As with other AMSA and B-1 designs it had four turbojets, this time in four separate nacelles integrated into the underside of the wing; countering the idea that this was meant to be a lower cost design was the fact that the wing was a 'gull wing', a feature that would doubtless have made the wing structure heavier and more difficult.

The design is presumed to be supersonic, though it may have been optimized for high subsonic cruise at low altitude.

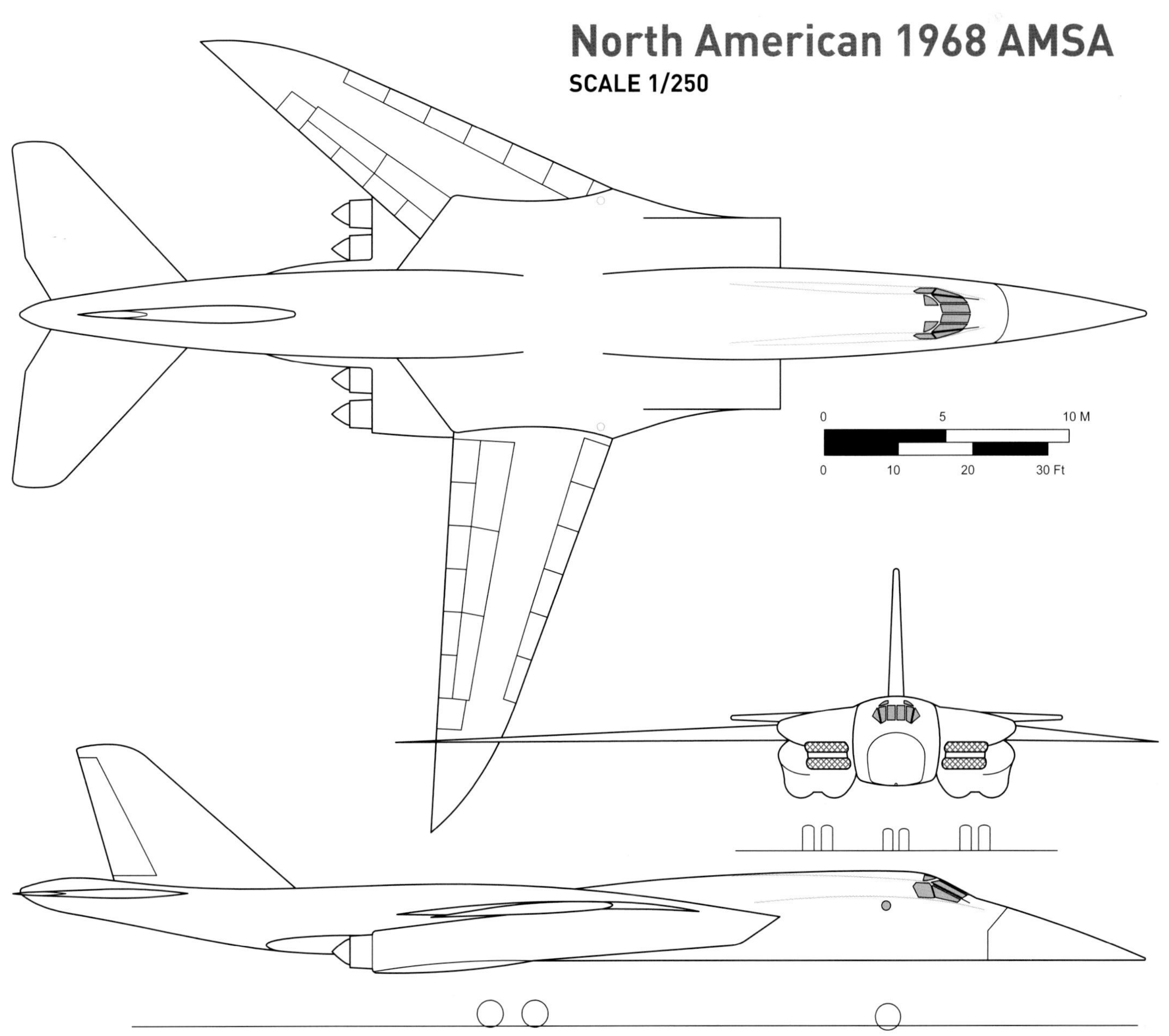

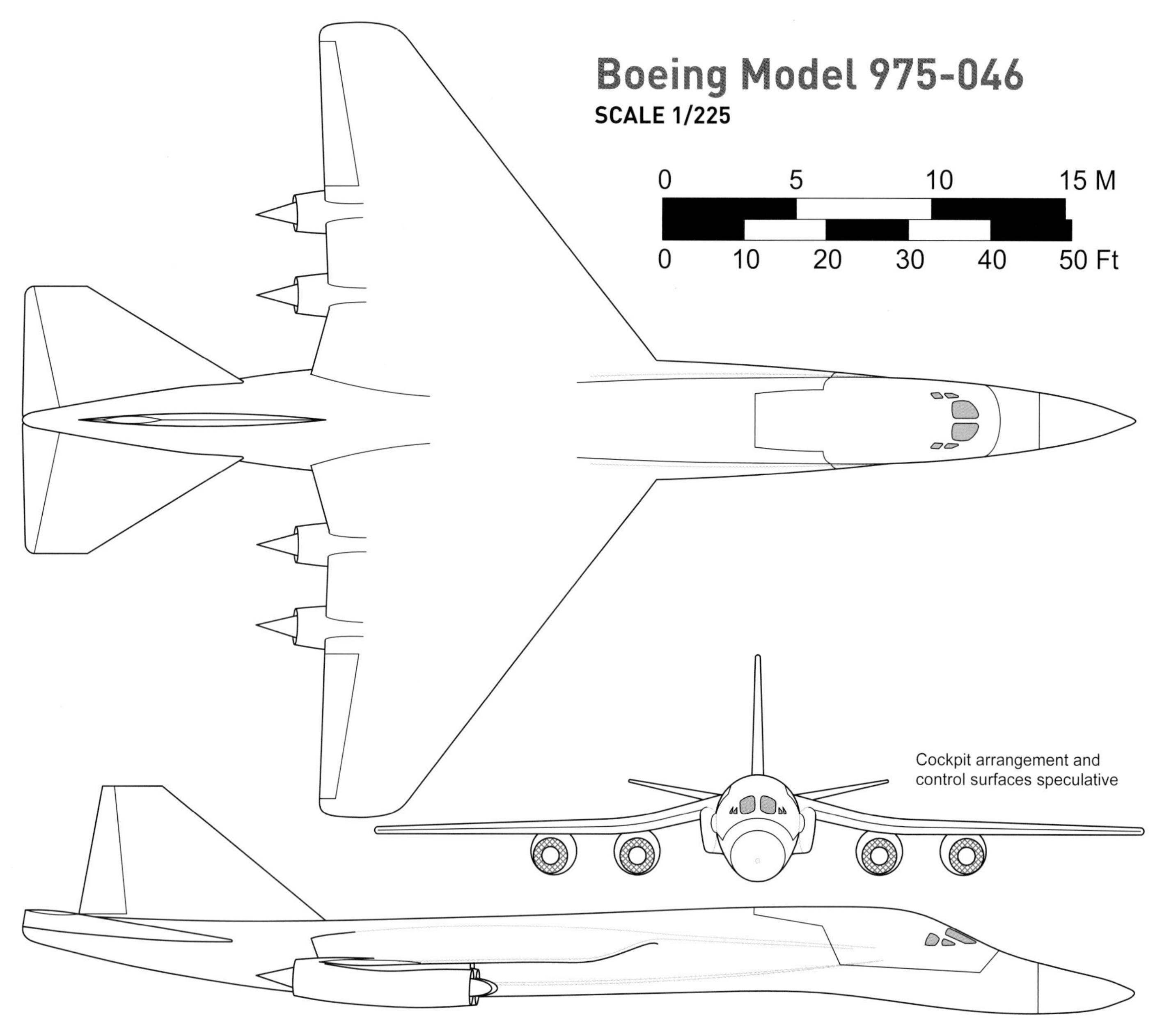

Lockheed 1968 AMSA

Known from a single diagram devoid of data, this Lockheed design for a three-engined AMSA was clearly derived from prior work on supersonic transports. Some family resemblance is apparent between this AMSA design and the Skunk Works A-11, a predecessor design to the SR-71 (See: *Lockheed SR-71 Blackbird: Origins and Evolution*). This aircraft, designed much earlier in 1959, seems similar in appearance, particularly around the cockpit. The likelihood that the AMSA actually shared much lineage with the A-11 is of course low; it may be a case of convergent evolution… and it may have shared some designers, as both designs were created not just by Lockheed, but by the Lockheed Skunk Works.

The 1968 Lockheed AMSA has a three-engined layout with the third engine in much the same position as the Boeing AMPSS, a distinct nacelle near the base of the vertical stabilizer. All three engines featured circular inlets with translating spikes.

Without data, the size of the aircraft can only be estimated. The available diagram shows the outline of two weapons bays; the diagram reconstructed here is scaled using those bays, assuming the same size as the weapons bays on the Rockwell B-1. This is doubtless reasonable, but scale could definitely be off somewhat.

Lockheed 1969 AMSA

As with the Lockheed 1968 AMSA configuration, there are no data to go with the available diagram of the Skunk Works follow-up concept from 1969. Scale here is conjectural, based on the presumption of using much the same wing as the prior design.

While being somewhat further in time from the L-2000 than the 1968 AMSA, the 1969 AMSA more closely resembled the SST. It had four engines in much the same location and a generally similar planform and profile, though with a less elegant and organic appearance. While the SST's nacelles were toed-in, the nacelles of the AMSA are aligned straight; the fuselage of the L-2000 flowed for aerodynamic purposes, while the AMSA fuselage was simple and straight.

The bombers, while similar in configuration to the L-2000, were notably smaller in dimensions. It also worth noting that neither used drooping noses to reduce drag/improve landing visibility. The 1968 and 1969 designs used very different configurations for the canopy; the 1969 design was set up better for side-by-side seating of the pilot and co-pilot, while the 1968 design appears to depicted tandem seating, an unlikely development for a strategic bomber like this. The 1968 canopy is, however, reasonably wide so it may have been meant to have side-by-side seating for the crew.

Boeing B-1 proposal

Very little is known to have survived on the Boeing competitor for the B-1 apart from a single mockup photo and a few pieces of art. No performance data, weights or even dimensions are known. The art fortunately includes orthographic representations of the design along with interior views, allowing a diagram to be re-created. Dimensions are estimated based on the SRAM loading, and are probably accurate to within a few percent.

The Boeing B-1 design was similar to Rockwell's in broad strokes, but with numerous substantial differences. Primary among these was that the engines were in the rear of the fuselage, not in underslung pods; the inlets were thus built into the leading edges of the wings and given variable geometry 2D ramps. The overall effect is an aircraft that bears a striking similarity to the Tupolev Tu-22M Backfire bomber. Performance would likely have been similar to the Rockwell B-1.

Like the Rockwell design, the Boeing B-1 had three bomb bays, each of which could be fitted with a rotary launcher holding eight AGM-69A Short Range Attack Missiles. And like the Rockwell B-1A, the Boeing B-1 design featured an ejection capsule composed of the entire cockpit and a rearward stabilizing extension. This aircraft doubtless had a crew of four but cutaway artwork depicts six crew stations, almost certainly for training missions. Unlike the Rockwell design, the nose of the Boeing design 'drooped' somewhat.

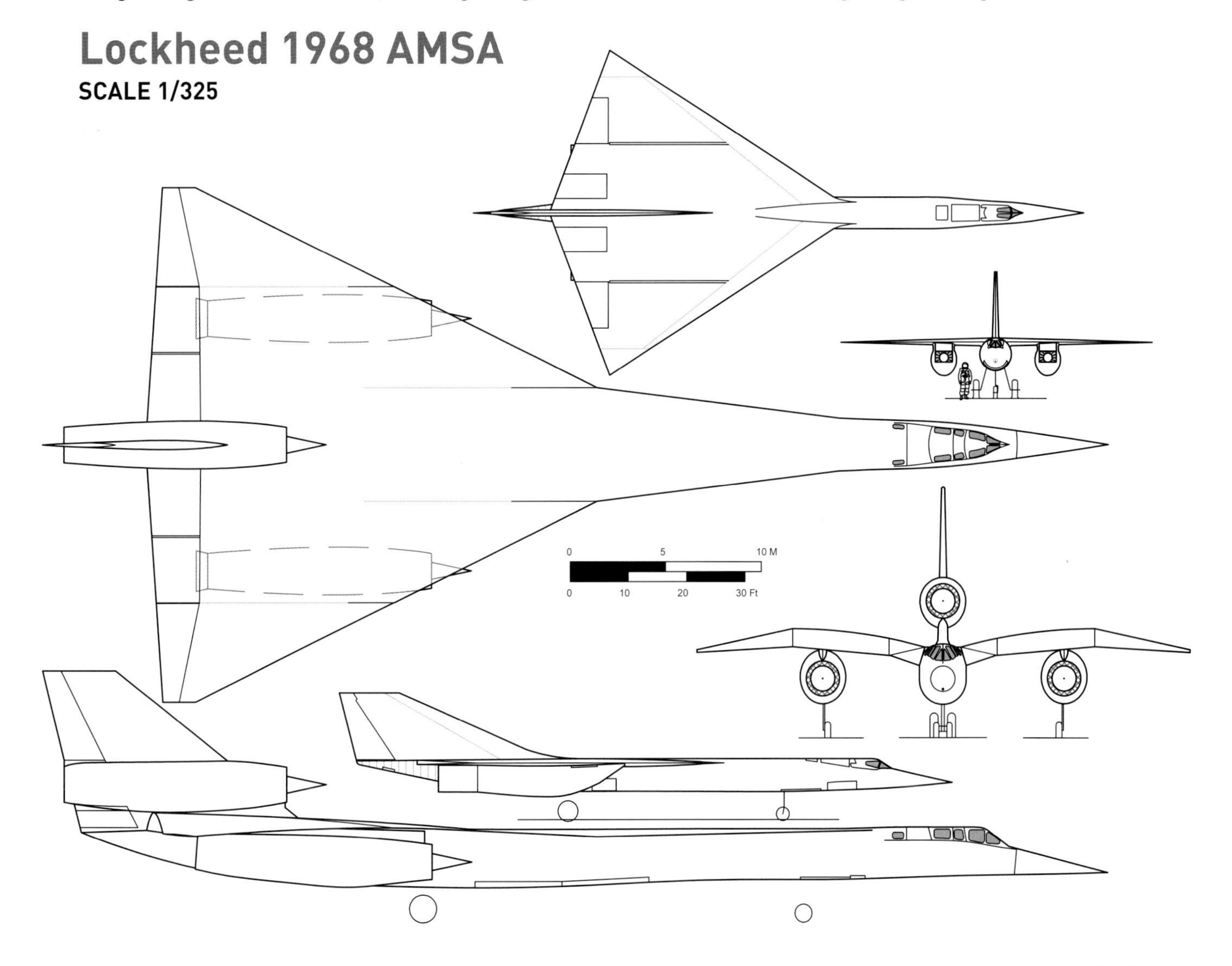

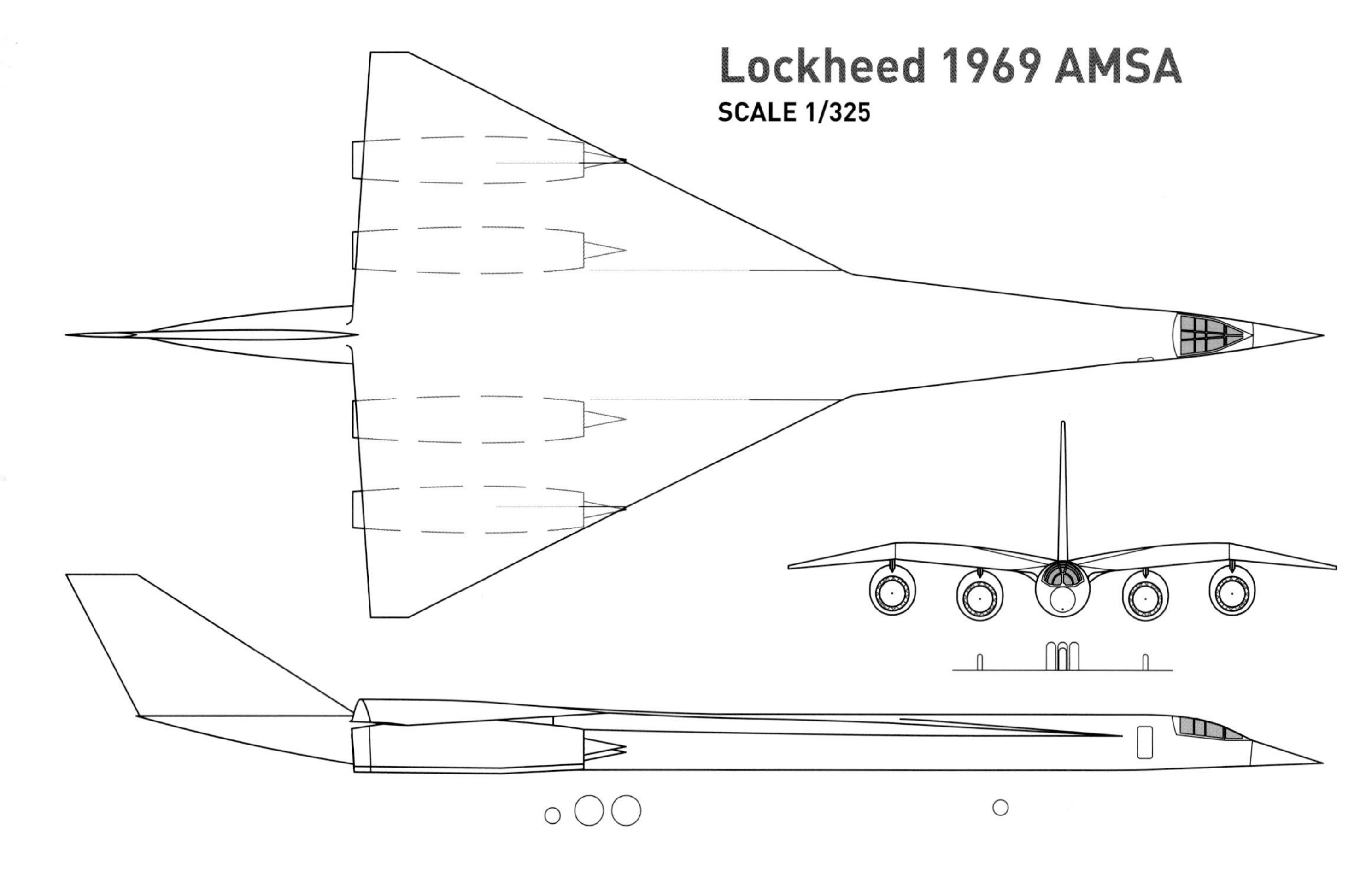

It also did not have the ride control vanes that helped make the Rockwell design distinctive, though it had an inflight refuelling receptacle on the nose in much the same location as on the Rockwell design.

A full scale mockup of the nose of the aircraft including the cockpit was built; so far only a single photograph of it seems to have come to light. It was reported that the B-1 design was a massive effort on Boeing's part, and on the day of the announcement there was confidence that they, not North American Rockwell, would win the programme.

After Boeing's failure, the whole effort seems to have been stuffed down the memory hole. If it was true that Boeing management and staff fully expected to win the contract, the loss must have been a major blow, both financially and psychologically. Throwing everything away thus likely made sense at the time, though it is of course to be hoped that important documentation was saved somewhere.

That this is all there really is to say about the design which almost became the B-1 is historically tragic.

Rockwell B-1 proposal

Unfortunately the Rockwell B-1 proposal documents are not available. However, the configuration that was proposed – and won – is available, though thin on details. This is probably Model D481-39.

The B-1 proposal was generally similar to the B-1A that was actually built, but it did have a number of clear differences. Primary of these were the leading edges of the main wing roots and the layout of the horizontal stabilizers. The wing root leading edge was distinctly concave in planform, giving a clear discontinuity at the pivot point.

The horizontal stabilizers on the proposal aircraft connected to the sides of the rear fuselage; on the actual B-1 they were moved up onto the vertical stabilizer. Additionally, the horizontal stabilizers on the proposal had a higher aspect ratio than those that were built, along with a curved leading edge. The ride control vanes stick straight out the sides and are of a different shape from the final product. Not surprisingly, the overall impression is of a cruder take on the shape of the B-1.

Rockwell B-1A

After North American Rockwell won the B-1A competition in June 1970, it set about refining the design and preparing it for construction. The B-1A programme came at a time of economic downturn and budget cuts; getting the design right early on was therefore essential as the flight test programme, along with the number of bombers to be produced, was cut to save money.

This involved tens of thousands of hours of wind tunnel study, refining contours and horizontal stabilizer

Boeing B-1

SCALE 1/200

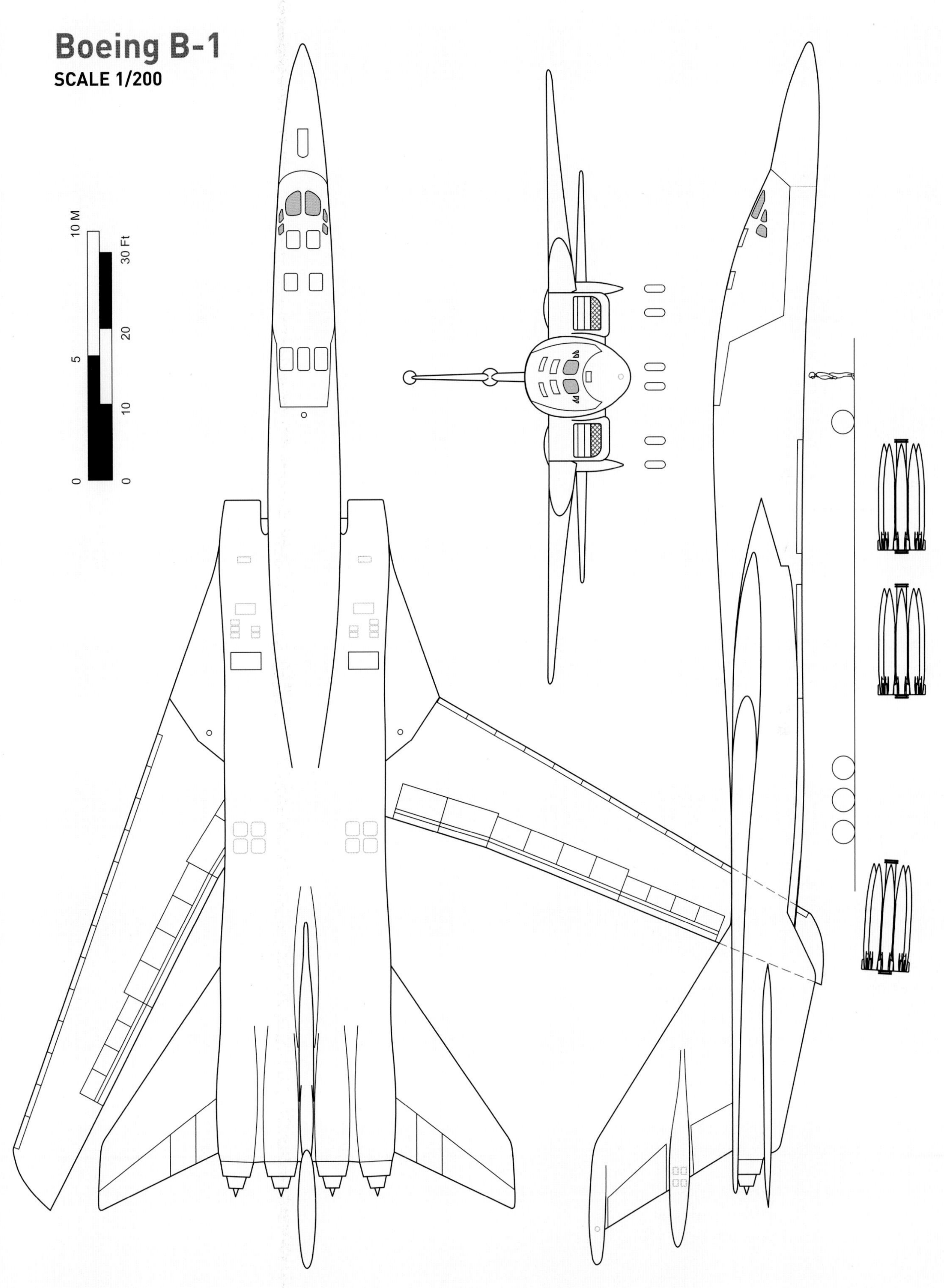

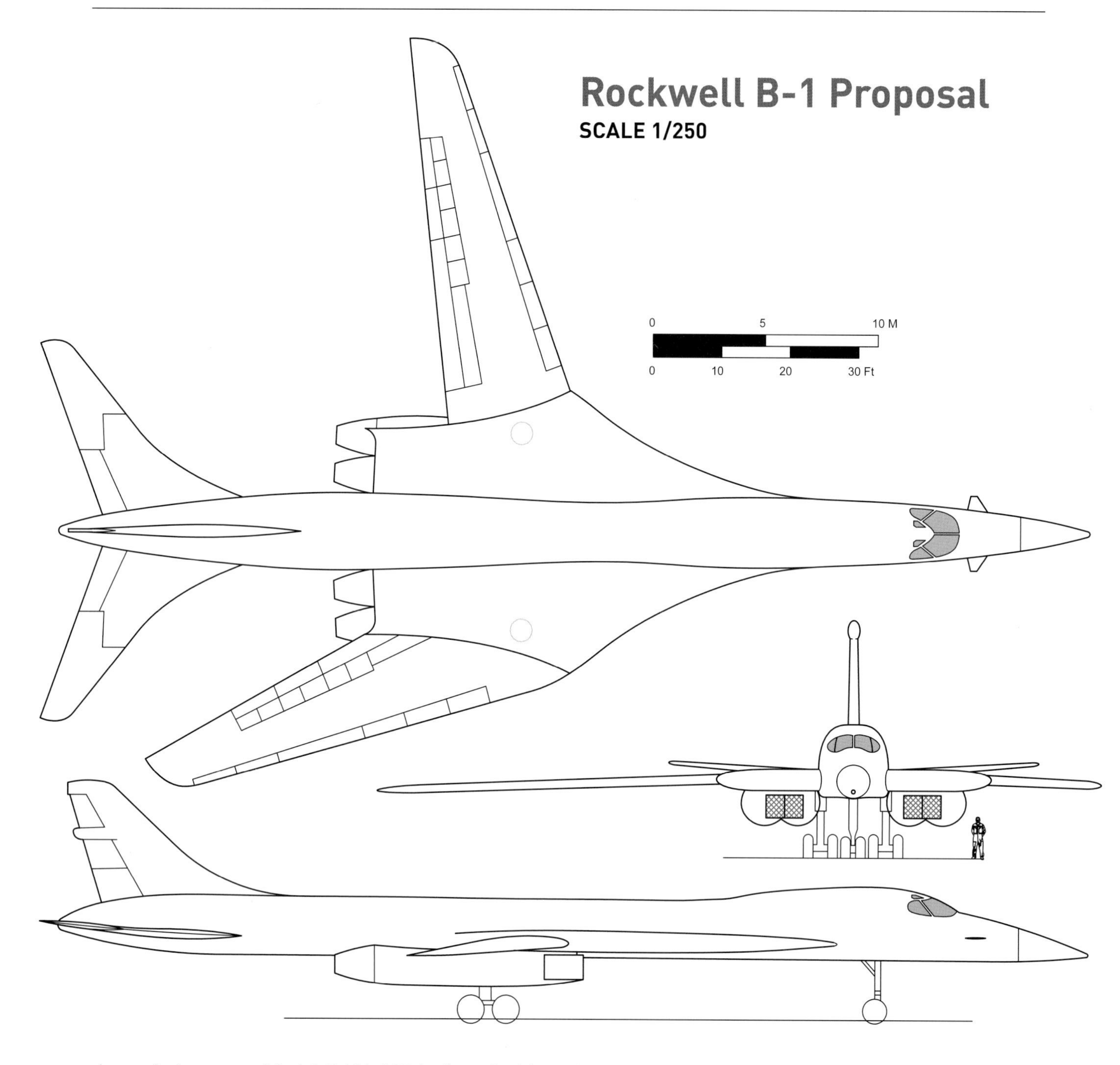

size and placement. Model D481-55B had reached its approximate final form by summer 1971, with detailed diagrams showing only minor differences from the B-1A as it would actually be built.

The design was exemplified by elegant organic curves and contours, with variable sweep wings that could extend out to a leading edge sweepback of 15°at full 'stretch', and back to 67.5° for high speed. Ride control vanes on the forward fuselage were an important feature. These were not canards in the usual sense, but rather an innovation that would have been impossible not many years earlier.

The B-1A was intended to fly at high speed and treetop level, hugging the terrain to avoid enemy radar. Even in clear, still air this would make for a rough ride, but throw in turbulence and the aircraft could have been shaken apart… never mind what the chaotic high-g shaking would do to the crew. But advances in computerization came to the rescue.

The vanes were part of the structural mode control system and would be in a constant state of motion, responding not to input from the pilot but from the computer. The onboard computer systems would use a network of accelerometers throughout the airframe to detect gusts and turbulence and in real time adjust the vanes (and the lower segment of the rudder) to counter those motions. The ride quality would be dampened to safe and acceptable levels. The precise shape of the vanes changed during the development process, but always remained fairly small. The final versions were well-swept (60°) little winglets, angled 30° downwards to provide both vertical and lateral inputs. The whole

Rockwell B-1A

SCALE 1/200

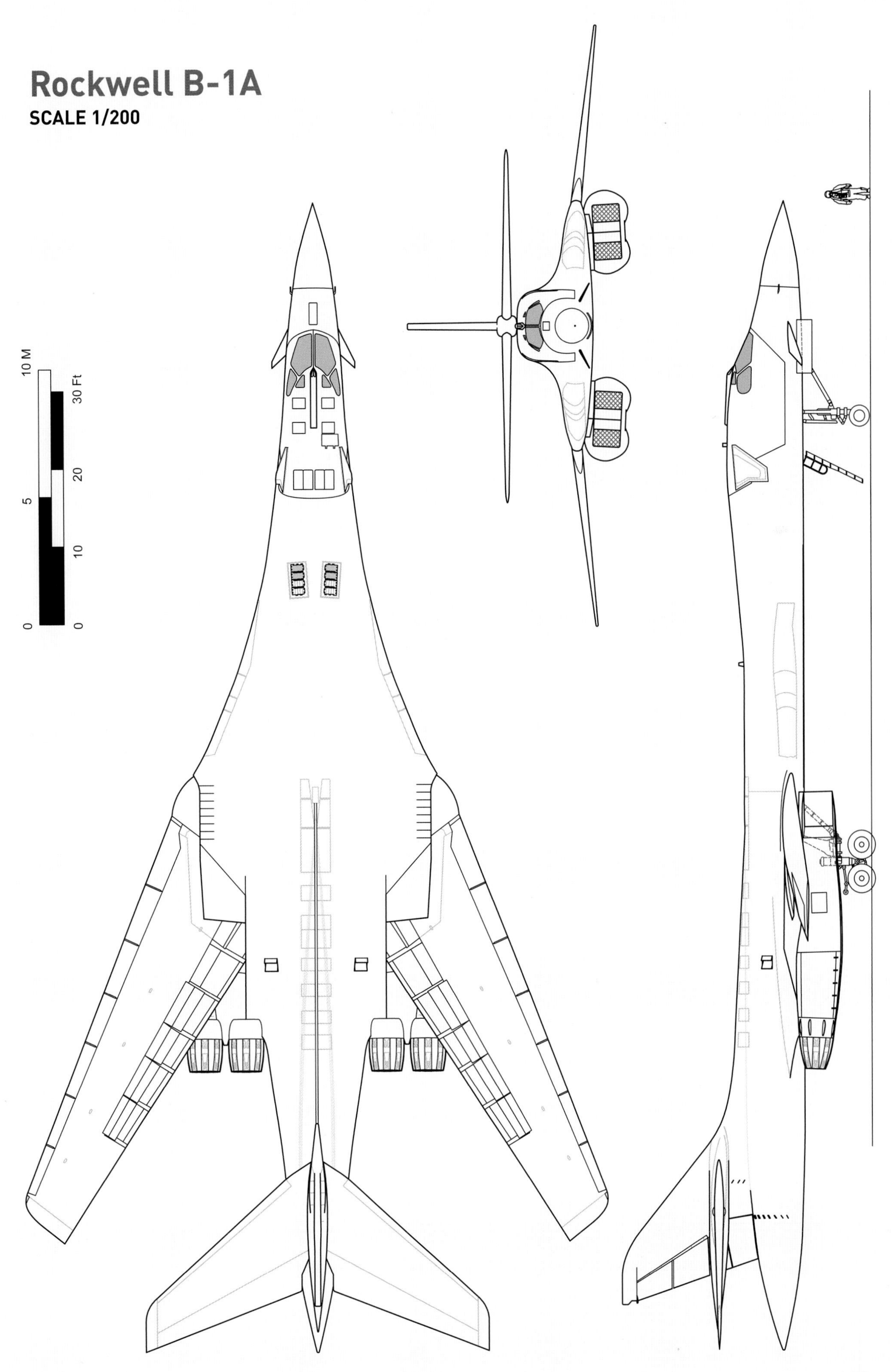

system added around 400lb to the weight of the aircraft; strengthening the structures enough to make do without the vanes would have added 9,800lb. The main wings would be fully aft-swept when flying low in order to reduce wing area.

The leading edges of the wing roots remained concave in plan view, but somewhat less dramatically so than in the proposal design. The wing roots were also fully blended into the fuselage, with no clear demarcation from where one ended and the other began; the blended wing-body arrangement aided both aerodynamics and radar return. The all-moving horizontal stabilizers grew in size, straightened the leading edge and moved up from the fuselage onto the vertical stabilizer. The horizontal stabilizers could tilt up and down together to control pitch, or differentially for roll control when the wings were swept. The vertical stabilizer had a three-segment rudder, the lowest of which was part of the structural mode control system.

Two distinct nacelles were mounted underneath the rear fuselage, each contained two side-by-side afterburning turbofans. Unlike many earlier designs, the nacelles were not integrated into the aircraft structure, but were essentially separate bolt-on components. This simplified both maintenance in the field as well as the design process of the aircraft itself, as ongoing changes in the engines, inlets or other systems did not necessarily impact the design of the airframe.

The nacelles were fitted with mirrored vertical 2D variable ramp inlets that permitted airflow almost directly into the engines, as required by the need to exceed Mach 2. The supersonic diffuser 'wedge' within the inlet would adjust its geometry to fit the current airspeed, creating three oblique shocks and one normal shock forward of the inlet 'lip'. The geometry was adjustable by having a series of rigid ramps that could be moved with hydraulically powered rotary actuators; at low speed the ramps would be brought in to maximize flow area; they would be deflected outwards to narrow the inlet based on the Mach speed of the air trying to ram into the inlet.

The second and third movable panels were porous; this allowed the boundary layer to be drawn off and discharged below the nacelles through hinged doors. Bypass doors could open on the sides of the nacelles midway between the inlet and the turbines, allowing air to be spilled from the subsonic diffuser. This would be used to maintain maximum cruise efficiency under all conditions.

The side lips of the inlet could open up at low speed, increasing the capture area of the inlets. Each engine had its own air induction system so that a disturbance in one would not affect the other. The nacelles, including inlet and air induction systems were wind tunnel tested using models ranging from 0.1 to 0.2 to 0.7 to full scale in order to perfect the system prior to flight. This of course also included testing the nozzles; low drag 'turkey feathers' were added to the exterior of the variable geometry nozzles.

The engines were designed to contain fan, compressor and turbine blades in the event of failure; a structural partition between the engines was designed to prevent both engines from being battle damaged. Auxiliary power units were installed that would be able to bring powered-off engines up to idle in 19 seconds as part of the goal of getting bombers off runways at a moment's notice.

The structure and skin were mostly aluminium, with steel, titanium and boron composites used in certain components. While titanium had been used before, only on the Lockheed A-12, YF-12 and SR-71 had it been used extensively. On the General Dynamics F-111 series, the wing pivots and associated structures had been made from steel, but on the B-1 the pivots, wing torque box and centre section box were made from titanium.

Titanium was also used in the high-temperature aft portion of the engine nacelles for the skin and frames. Considerable effort was put into designing the components to be tolerant of damage, both from enemy action and fatigue, by way of fracture mechanics analysis. This sought to stop the propagation of cracks, greatly extending the service life of properly designed components. The first B-1A would end up being, by weight, 41.3% aluminium, 30.8% fibreglass/quartz/'other', 21% titanium, 6.6% steel and 0.3% composites.

Three weapons bays were installed, two adjoining bays ahead of the wing and one aft. These were identical in size, each intended to contain a single rotary launcher with a standard load of eight AGM-69A SRAMs.

The two forward bays were separated by a bulkhead that could be moved or outright removed, resulting in a weapons bay potentially twice as long; alternatively the bulkhead could be moved to cut the forward bay in half, making the second bay 1.5 times normal length. An alternate weapons load of 28 conventional Mk-82 bombs could be carried in each bay with a clip-in module. It would attach to the same fittings as the rotary launcher, but would not itself rotate. A cylindrical fuel tank could be installed within the 1.5x longer second bay for increased range or duration.

Along with the swing-wings, one distinctive feature that the first three B-1As shared with the FB-111A was the use of an ejection capsule. This encompassed the entire manned volume and, unlike the FB-111 capsule, used flip-out stabilizing fins. These were folded against the side of the fuselage while the capsule was still attached to the aircraft, forming raised fairings on each side of the upper fuselage. Additional spoilers were stowed under the capsule.

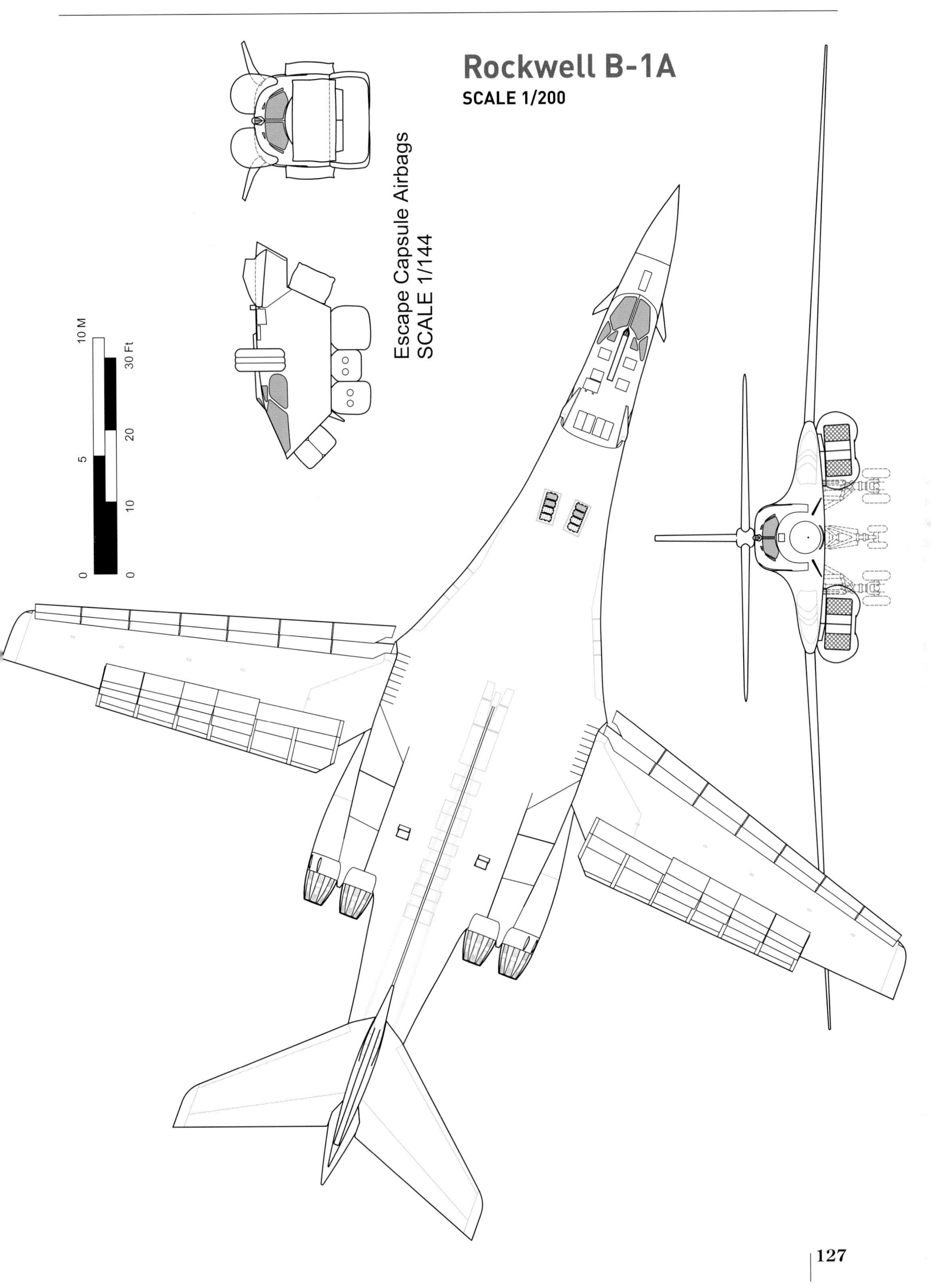
Rockwell B-1A
SCALE 1/200
Escape Capsule Airbags
SCALE 1/144
10 M
5
0
30 Ft
20
10
0

Upon initiation of ejection, shaped charges and explosive bolts would sever the capsule from the aircraft and a solid rocket motor would fire, pushing the capsule forward and up. The side-spoilers would deploy within 0.4 seconds of the ejection handle being pulled; the stabilizing fins and chin spoiler within 0.7 seconds. A drogue line would be fully stretched by that point, and the rocket would burn out in 1.9 seconds. The drogue chute, having pulled out a pair of pilot chutes, would disconnect at 2.5 seconds, and the main chute lines would be stretched by 4.5 seconds.

The main chutes, being dragged behind the capsule, would be fully deployed by about 10.6 seconds and would begin to reposition so that the capsule wound hang horizontally below the chutes. By about 13.5 seconds the capsule would, assuming ejection from the runway, be ready for landing on a set of cushioning airbags. The capsule would reach an apogee of a little below 400ft above the ejection point, and would go downrange about 2,200ft. Escape from the capsule was through either a single hatch on the upper surface or through the removable side windows.

The capsule doubtless seemed a good idea at the time, but it had definite limits. Under level flight conditions it was recommended to eject at least 2,000ft above terrain… a definite challenge given that the B-1 was intended to fly at near treetop level. If the aircraft was spinning or diving, the minimum altitude above terrain was 15,000ft, certainly a major issue.

What's more, ejection at high speed was considered to be virtually assured of fatality: above 500 to 600 knots indicated air speed, the fins and spoilers could simply rip off, sending the capsule into an unsurvivable tumble. This is certainly an issue for an aircraft meant to fly at more than Mach 2. And ejection on the ground below 50 knots carried with it a high risk of injury; forward airspeed was required to attain full parachute deployment.

The cockpit had seating for five. Four were the standard crew (pilot, co-pilot, defensive system operator and offensive system operator) and one was a seat for an avionics instructor.

The ejection capsule was deleted from the fourth B-1A. For that aircraft the four crew were each given ejector seats; the avionics instructor would, if he was lucky, bail out through hatches in the underside. This seems to have been a dubious way to go; he would fall between the engine nacelles, assuming the boundary layer didn't bounce him against the underside of the fuselage. This particular means of escape was never tested in a real-life emergency, fortunately.

Entry to the cockpit was through a ladder that would drop from the underside of the fuselage just aft of the nose gear. Separate emergency escape hatches were located above each of the four crew positions on the fourth B-1A, to be used either during ejection or a more sedate escape from the ground or water.

A distinctive feature that did not last was a fairing over the cockpit for a Low Light Level Television camera system. This appeared as standard on early depictions, in diagrams and art, and on the mockup. However, it did not appear on the actual aircraft; instead, a retractable FLIR turret was installed on the underside, behind the nose landing gear doors.

The mockup was reviewed in late October, 1971, at the North American Rockwell Los Angeles Division. It was full size and depicted the entire left side of the aircraft; the right side was partial and depicted 'skinless' to show interior structure and components. Reportedly, a demonstration of engine replacement was performed on the mockup by trained Rockwell personnel, but their performance was quickly beaten by an Air Force ground team.

North American Rockwell merged with Rockwell Manufacturing and became Rockwell International in February 1973. Thus the era of North American ended while the company was hard at work on two major aerospace programmes, the B-1A and the Space Shuttle Orbiter. This did not stop either programme however, and the first B-1A was rolled out of the Rockwell plant in Palmdale, California, on October 26, 1974. Its first flight occurred on December 23, 1974, and first broke the sound barrier on April 21, 1975.

Throughout 1975, B-1A AV/1 gradually built up demonstrations of nearly all important aspects of the aircraft flight performance… supersonic flight, sustained supersonic flight, full range of wing sweep, low altitude/high speed flight, inflight refuelling. B-1A AV/3 first flew on April 1, 1976, beating the second into the air due to AV/2 undergoing months of static testing. The latter finally flew for the first time on June 14, 1976.The fourth B-1A, built without the ejectable cockpit, debuted in the air on February 14, 1979. But it did not do so while the B-1A programme was still alive.

President Jimmy Carter, elected in 1976, gained control of a country in the midst of economic chaos, with recession, inflation, unemployment and oil crises running rampant. The B-1A programme was very expensive, and, it seemed to the new Administration, something of a political liability. The B-52, which the B-1A was supposed to replace, could be turned into a cruise missile truck at relatively low cost. And the Air Force was already at work on the Advanced Technology Bomber – soon to be known as the 'Stealth Bomber' (B-2).

The ATB would be invisible to detection, while the B-1A was certainly visible on radar and infrared. And not inconsequentially, President Carter wanted the Soviets to sign on to the SALT II strategic arms limitation treaty, and sacrificing the B-1A might be a way to appease them. So on June 30, 1977, Carter summarily cancelled the B-1A.

Many in positions of authority and power in the military and political branches saw this coming. But that was of little comfort to the many thousands of aerospace workers around the country, particularly in California, who suddenly found themselves unemployed in the midst of Carter's 'Malaise'.

Fortunately for the B-1 programme, sufficient funds were retained to allow the flight test programme to continue. And in February of 1978 funds were made available to complete the fourth B-1A airframe, then already well underway. That was handy for the programme, but did little to endear President Carter to thousands of aerospace workers. On the other hand, candidate Reagan promised them that he would restore the B-1 programme. And perhaps surprisingly, it was a promise made by a politician that was then kept.

Rockwell B-1A wind tunnel modifications

The end of the B-1A programme did not mean the end of its utility. In 1979, NASA-Langley reported on a series of wind tunnel tests performed on a modified 0.06 scale B-1A model. The modifications – some of which may have been made as early as 1975, others as late as 1979 – were done in order to improve the aerodynamics of the B-1A across all flight regimes.

These tests were likely the result of internal NASA interest, rather than designs coming from Rockwell, and thus would fall more along the lines of 'pure science' than as an attempt to substantially improve a product line. Still, had the tests shown substantial improvement – and had the B-1A been revived – it's possible that they might have been incorporated to some degree.

Three of the modifications are reproduced here. One idea was to add 'pods' above and behind the engine nacelles. These were to smooth out the cross-sectional area distribution of the aircraft... a solution to 'area ruling' equivalent to the anti-shock bodies added to the wings of the Convair 990 jetliner. Additional studies, not reproduced here, added thickness to the underside and/or side of the forward fuselage, again to adjust the area-rule curve of the configuration. And as with the Convair 990, the added volume could have been used for other purposes; fuel within the pods seems obvious enough, but as the fairings added to the forward fuselage would have been relatively thin, putting meaningful volumes of fuel in them seems unlikely. Sensors or countermeasures – flares and chaff – seem possible. However, testing showed that the pods actually increased drag, negating their value.

Another idea studied was to extend aft the nozzle of the inboard engine on each nacelle. Staggering the nozzles in that fashion was shown to reduce drag; the region of the side-by-side nozzles had proven to be aerodynamically unfortunate, with high levels of drag caused by the sudden step at the end of the glove. Staggering the nozzles essentially stretched the blunt tail end of the nacelle. Drag could be further reduced by extending both nozzles. But doing so risked that extended nozzle(s) scraping the runway at rotation.

Shown, but not well described, was partial modification of the tail of the nacelle to accommodate 2D nozzles. The details of the nozzles were sadly lacking (the important bits of the vectoring nozzles do not seem to have been included in the testing, only their sides), but they doubtless would have allowed for pitch up/down vectoring, potentially useful for nap-of-the-Earth flying. Tests showed that these sorts of nozzles resulted in reduced drag compared to the baseline design.

Nothing came of these studies.

Rockwell B-1B

The B-1A flight test programme ceased at the end of April 1981, upon which the four B-1As were put into storage. In June of that year the Air Force presented a report to Congress and the president explaining that a B-52 replacement was needed, and that between a General Dynamics proposal for a stretched F-111 (the FB-111H, previously described) and a Rockwell concept for a cheaper, stealthier B-1 known as the Long Range Combat Aircraft (LRCA), the Rockwell concept was preferred. The LRCA was not quite the aircraft the B-1A would have been, but it was much larger and longer-legged than the FB-111H; it was a true strategic bomber.

The arguments in favour of the LRCA worked. In October 1981 Reagan announced that 100 B-1Bs would be manufactured; a dead aircraft programme had been revived.

The mission of the B-1B was different from that of the B-1A. It remained a long range strategic bomber, but it was now intended to spend much more of its time down at very low altitude; it had little need to blitz along at high altitude and Mach 2.2. In fact, it was expected that it would rarely go supersonic at all. Speed was not how the aircraft would defend itself. It would survive by going unnoticed.

As the B-1B programme was coming to life, the ATB stealth bomber's development continued. The Northrop B-2 would devote every ounce and square inch to being utterly invisible to radar... but it was going to take some years to perfect and field, and was expected to be expensive. At the time, the ATB programme was estimated to cost $36.6 billion in 1981 dollars for 132 B-2s... nobody quite expected that it would end up costing two billion dollars per plane. The B-1B would take the B-1A airframe and do what it could to make it reasonably stealthy, if not truly invisible.

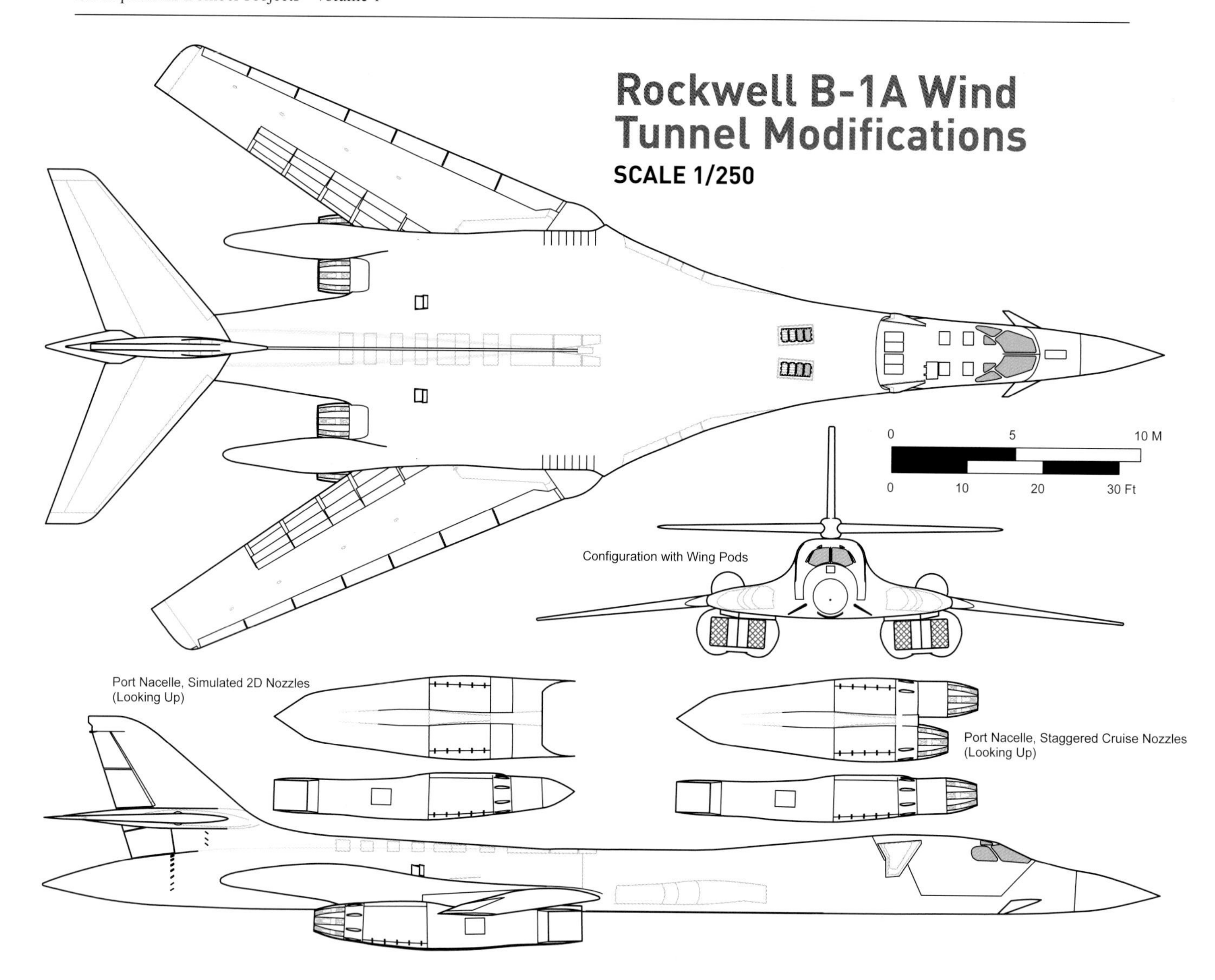

Perhaps the most important functional change was a greatly revised inlet system. On the B-1A, the turbine faces could be seen from directly ahead; the complex variable geometry throat just inside of the inlet did little to actually block radar from shooting straight in and then straight back out. That air induction system was just what was needed for efficient Mach 2+ flight at high altitude, but the B-1B did not need that. So the inlet was simplified, getting rid of the variable geometry throat; long, sinuous and radar-absorbing vanes were added to the inlet ducts, blocking the turbines from view. This greatly reduced the radar cross section of the aircraft as seen from the front, while effectively preventing Mach 2 flight.

The shape of the inlet was also changed. Where the B-1A had an inlet central splitter leading edge that was straight up and down when seen from the side, on the B-1B it was swept aft. Ironically, the nacelles of the B-1B looked faster than those of the B-1A. The F101-GE-100 turbofans used on the B-1A were replaced with improved F101-GE-102 engines with simplified (and cheaper) exhaust nozzles.

The B-1B looked very much like the B-1A and shared about 85% parts commonality, but in many ways was quite different. Most visibly different was the lack of an escape capsule. Instead, each crewman was given an ACES II ejection seat and a separate overhead escape hatch. The cockpit transparencies were different in configuration; the side windows no longer needed to serve as escape hatches, given the new, larger ones overhead. The nose contours were subtly changed, becoming somewhat blunter. The nose contained a new synthetic aperture planar array radar that was tilted down 30° in order to not reflect enemy radar directly back. Coupled with the changes in the inlet and other refinements, the B-1B's radar cross section was one tenth that of the B-1A and only 1% that of the B-52.

The B-1B was structurally improved over the B-1A, adding strength and weight. This was done in order to better survive low altitude, high subsonic flight, where the aircraft was now expected to spend the bulk of its flight time. This meant structural strengthening of the landing gear to deal with the heavier aircraft. The over-wing fairings were changed in outline and to use inflatable seals. As the aircraft was now largely subsonic, the option was made to add a large number of external pylons for the carriage of air launched cruise missiles.

The B-1B critical design review was held in January 1983, at which point the design was frozen and production began. August 1984 saw the crash of B-1A AV/2, which had been modified with some B-1B systems; the ejection capsule separated but the airbags failed to adequately cushion the impact, leading to one death and two serious injuries. The first B-1B rolled out of the Palmdale plant on September 4, 1984, and flew for the first time on October 18. The 100th and final B-1B was delivered on May 2, 1988.

The first operational B-1B, the second built, was delivered to the Strategic Air Command on June 27, 1985... the 30th anniversary of the delivery of the first operational B-52. Initial operational capability occurred on October 1, 1986, with B-1Bs at Dyess Air Force Base in Texas going on alert for the first time. But even though it was officially operational, development continued, with the first launch of an AGM-86A SRAM occurring on January 16, 1987. This was performed from the first B-1B, at a speed of Mach 0.9 and an altitude of only 500ft.

The B-1B tested the low level delivery of a number of weapons, including the B83 thermonuclear bomb. This bomb was designed for ground burst and penetration; immediately upon dropping from a low level B-1B it would deploy a chute that would slow the admittedly short descent. This would limit the impact forces and grant the bomber a few extra moments to clear the blast range.

The B-1B ended up being capable of carrying a large number of a wide variety of weapons, nuclear and conventional. Initial planning included carrying weapons both within the bays and under external hardpoints, including pivoting hardpoints under the wings.

It was not equipped with missiles or guns for defence against missiles trying to take it down. For defence it relied upon a mix of low radar cross section, low altitude flight, high speed, electronic countermeasures, chaff and flares. The latter two were stored within and deployed from dispensers.

The Gulf War of 1991 passed without the involvement of the B-1B. At the time it was the premier nuclear strike aircraft, and was held in reserve for that role; the job of bomb truck fell to the B-52. Given the complete devastation of the Iraqi air force and anti-aircraft capability, the bigger, slower, more visible B-52 was perfectly adequate for that job. But after the fall of the Soviet Union and the general decline of the perceived need of an American nuclear offensive capability, the B-1B ceased to be a strategic bomber in 1995. The ability to carry and deploy nuclear weapons – bombs or cruise missiles – was eliminated in part to fulfill provisions of the New START treaty. At that point, the B-1B became a carrier of conventional weapons only, a role it continues with to this day.

Unlike in the first Gulf War, the B-1B found itself carrying out offensive operations when war returned to a world that had briefly deluded itself that peace had finally come. It carried out conventional bombing missions over Iraq in 1998 and Kosovo in 1999. After 9/11, the B-1B was used in earnest. Mere days after the attacks in New York and Washington, D.C., B-1Bs started arriving on the British island of Diego Garcia in the Indian Ocean. B-52s and B-1Bs out of Diego Garcia, along with aircraft from aircraft carriers, began bombing Afghanistan in October 2001.

The role of the B-1B in combat was quite different from what had originally been envisioned. Instead of blitzing along at treetop level just below the speed of sound to drop or launch nuclear weapons at a near-peer enemy, the B-1B would often loiter at high altitude, dropping a single conventional bomb. With targets often selected and pointed out in real time by observers on the ground, a lone bomb would fall out of the sky and land with pinpoint precision, guided by GPS. With little need to fear anti-aircraft missiles, the B-1B would loiter with wings outstretched high in the sky for hours on end, casually dropping bombs on whatever target was foolish enough to make itself known.

War did not so much return to the skies of Iraq in 2003 as pick up pace. The B-1B was there for that, dropping GPS guided JDAM bombs on both planned targets and targets of opportunity. Early in the war, though, the B-1B was faced with an enemy with the theoretical ability to shoot it out of the sky. Onboard ECM, flares and chaff proved up to the task of keeping surface-to-air missiles from hitting their marks.

The B-1B proved a capable and popular close air support platform, a fact that doubtless would have proven rather surprising to the initial designers back in the AMSA days. But its capabilities were somewhat limited due to the use of GPS guided munitions.

Static targets such as buildings, emplacements, even cavern entrances could be easily targeted via GPS if there were intelligence assets on the ground, but that was not always practical. So from 2006 to 2008 the Sniper targeting pod was tested on the B-1B. This pod, suspended below the forward fuselage, provides not only high resolution electro-optical vision of ground targets for the crew but also a laser for illuminating ground targets, as well as the ability to generate GPS co-ordinates for ground targets. The GPS data is then automatically loaded into the JDAM bomb, allowing it to be quickly dropped without the weapons system officer having to manually enter the data.

Starting in 2008, the B-1B began dropping 500lb JDAM bombs that made use of the aircraft-generated GPS targeting co-ordinates; not long after, laser guidance was added to some of the JDAM bombs, allowing the B-1B to hit ground targets that were on the move.

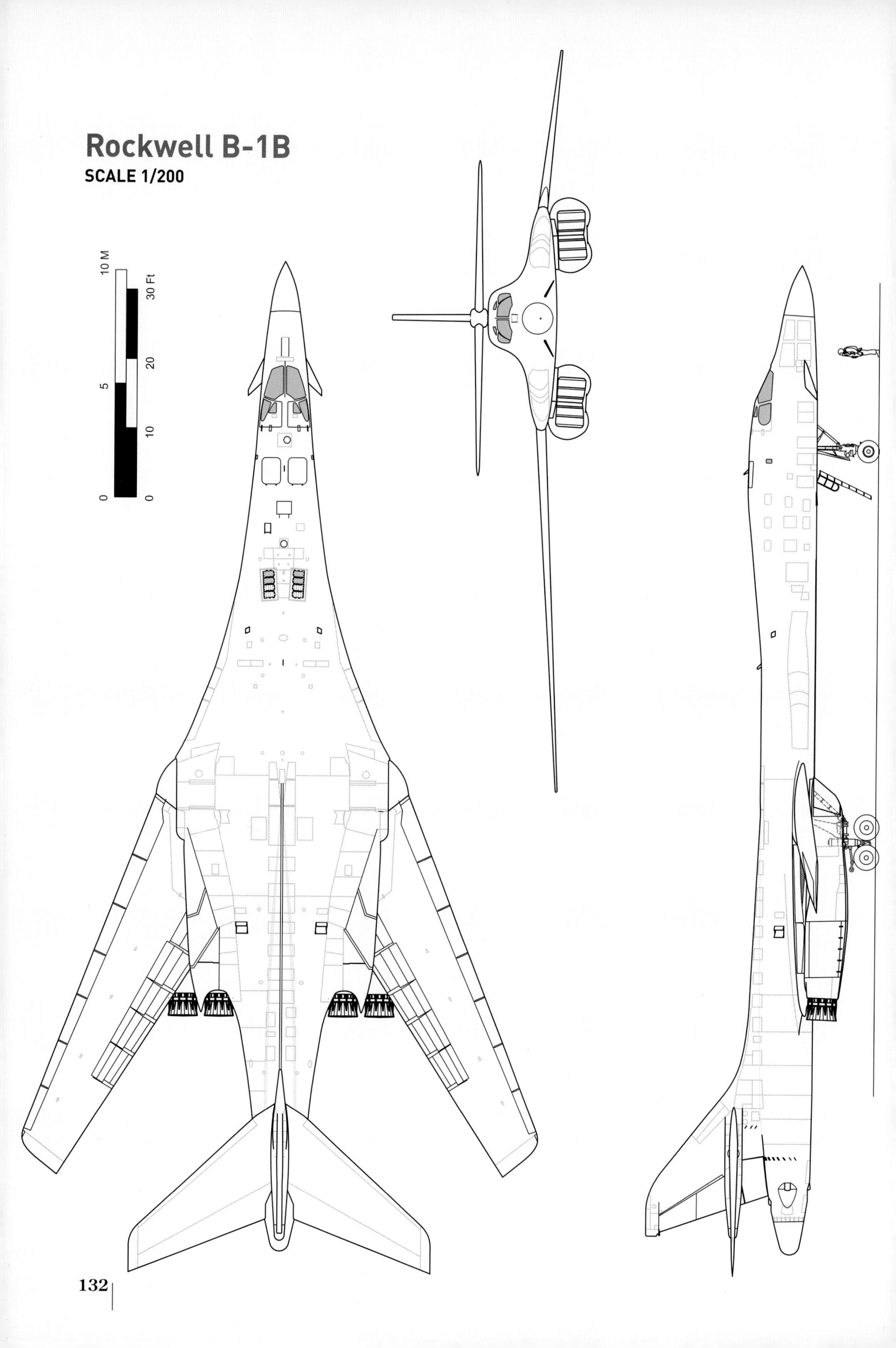
Rockwell B-1B
SCALE 1/200
10 M
5
0
30 Ft
20
10
0

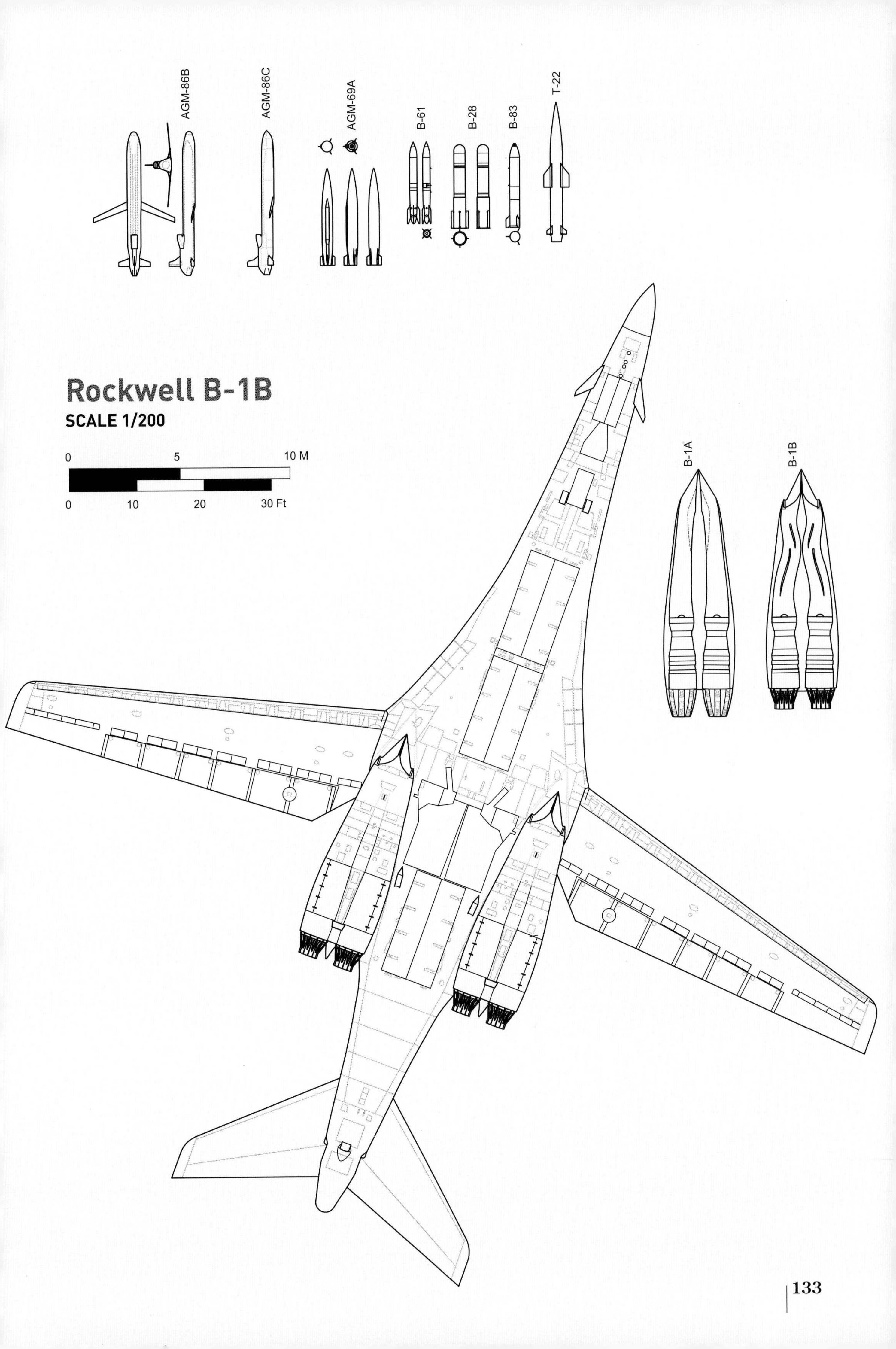
AGM-86B
AGM-86C
AGM-69A
B-61
B-28
B-83
T-22
Rockwell B-1B
SCALE 1/200
0
5
10 M
0
10
20
30 Ft
B-1A
B-1B

The B-1B is the last American supersonic bomber in operation, and will likely remain flying into the 2030s. Its replacement will probably be the B-21 Raider, which, as of this writing, has not yet been revealed. However, the B-21 is fairly reliably understood to be a flying wing platform somewhat like the B-2 in configuration, and incapable of supersonic flight. In early 2021 the USAF announced that 17 of the existing fleet of 62 B-1Bs would soon be retired to make way for the B-21. The era of the supersonic dedicated bomber seems to be over.

Few derivatives of the B-1B have come to light over the years, and those few that have not involved any major changes to the configuration of the aircraft.

B-1R

As operations were ramping up in Iraq and Afghanistan in 2004, the Air Force realized that its bomber capabilities were stretched thin. In many ways the Northrop B-2 was the perfect bomber for many roles... nigh on invisible (and thus indestructible), able to haul vast amounts of ordnance, with the precision to drop surprise packages onto the heads of enemies with great precision. But there were only 21 B-2s and they were too expensive to risk.

So the Air Force and the American aerospace industry began looking at alternatives that could be produced in fairly short order... modifications of the F-22, cargo planes filled to overflowing with bombs or hypersonic missiles, clean-sheet bomber designs.

Boeing suggested modifying the existing B-1B into the so-called 'B-1R', with 'R' standing for 'Regional'. The B-1R would have updated electronics and radar systems; be capable of carrying air-to-air missiles (AIM-120 AMRAAMs) for self defence, have the external hardpoints made fully functional, and swap out the F101-GE-102 turbofans for Pratt & Whitney F119s, used on the Lockheed F-22. The F119 is longer (203in vs 181in), narrower (46in diameter vs 55in) and lighter (3,900lb vs 4,400lb) than the F101, but produces more thrust in afterburner (35,000lb-ft vs 30,800lb-ft) and, importantly, much more thrust 'dry' (26,000lb-ft vs 17,400lb-ft).

Importantly, the newer engine is more fuel efficient with a lower parts count, theoretically easier and cheaper to maintain. The claim was that the B-1R would be capable of reaching Mach 2.2. This would presumably involve removing the radar-defeating vanes within the inlet ducts and returning to a B-1A style inlet.

Range would be reduced 20% compared to the B-1B (again, presumably, because the B-1R would cruise supersonically rather than subsonically), and doubtless radar cross section would suffer from below and ahead... but the ability to operate more quickly across the Middle East and central Asia from bases hundreds of miles away would benefit from the speed increase. This maximum speed would seem to apply to the B-1R in 'clean' configuration, without tons of ordnance hanging from under-fuselage pylons.

At the time, the B-1R was seen to have an initial operational capability of before 2015. But if any serious design work was carried out, it does not seem to have come to light; it's known only from a few bare-bones descriptions. It also does not seem to have lasted very long; no serious effort to turn B-1Bs into something resembling the B-1R has been attempted.

B-1B gunships

This, perhaps, may be a bit of a stretch. In 2016 Boeing applied for, and in 2018 received, a patent covering various approaches towards turning the B-1B into a 'gunship'. The gun in question seems to have been something akin to the 30mm 'chain gun' used by the AH-64 Apache attack helicopter, though depicted at various sizes, sometimes two differently sized cannon being shown side-by-side. The purpose of this armament would be precision attack of ground targets; something like taking out specific individuals, perhaps, or close support of troops on the ground.

Given the altitude that the B-1B tended to loiter at, though, a relatively small cannon round, no matter how well aimed, would be lucky to hit its target. Of course, progress has been made in recent years on guided projectiles as small as .50 calibre, so it's possible that a single shot fired from miles above could be placed onto the head of a specific rather unfortunate individual.

The patent illustrations show concepts such as turrets that would deploy from opened B-1B weapons bays, or guns attached to new full-width bomb bay doors. When opened, the guns would fire 'sideways' in the manner well known from the AC-130 gunship. In this case, the gun would doubtless be fired fully automatically and at a higher rate of fire. A B-1B gunship would have less damage potential than the AC-130, which is armed with everything up to and include a 105mm howitzer; but the B-1B gunship would have the advantage of being much faster, able to get rounds on target much sooner.

Little beyond the patent has come out on this concept. Presumably the system would be a plug-in module, not a permanent modification to the aircraft, and the B-1B could continue to carry a substantial load of laser or GPS guided bombs in the other two weapons bays. The B-1B has also from time to time been proposed as a carrier for a laser weapon system to be used to attack ground targets, low-flying aircraft and missiles, and ballistic missile in boost phase. However, this idea also seems to have produced no actual hardware.

References

Chapter 1: Convair B-58

'Escape and Survive,' Stanley Aviation Corporation, Denver, CO, date unknown
'Memorandum Report on Super Hustler Capabilities,' MR-A-1166, General Dynamics Corporation, 26 May 1958
'Super Hustler,' FZM-843, General Dynamics Corporation, 10 February 1958
'Drag at Model Trim Lift of a 1/15-Scale Convair B-58 Supersonic Bomber,' RM SL56G23, NACA-Langley Aeronautical Laboratory, July 1956
'Transonic Aerodynamics Characteristics of a 1/15-Scale Model of the Convair B-58 Airplane,' RM SL56J22, NACA-Langley Aeronautical Laboratory, October 1956
'Drag Near Zero Lift of a 1/7-Scale Model of the Convair B-58 External Store as Measured in Free Flight Between Mach Numbers of 0.8 and 2.45,' RM SL55G22a, NACA-Langley Aeronautical Laboratory, July 1955
'Transonic Aerodynamic and Trim Characteristics of 1/15-Scale Models of the Convair MX-1964 Airplane with indented Fuselage,' RM SL54B14a, NACA-Langley Aeronautical Laboratory, April 1954
'Characteristics Summary – Bomber (Non Refueled) B/RB-58A,' 10 July 1959
'Standard Aircraft Characteristics B/RB-58A,' 10 July 1959
'Technical Manual Structural Repair Instructions Aircraft and Pod, USAF Series YB/B-58A and B/RB-58A Aircraft,' T.O. 1B-58A-3, General Dynamics/Fort Worth, 9 September 1959
'Technical Manual Organizational Maintenance General Airplane USAF Series B-58A and TB-58A Aircraft,' T.O. 1B-58A-2-1, General Dynamics/Fort Worth, 3 February 1961
'Technical Manual Location and Application Exterior Stencils B-58A Aircraft,' T.O. 1B-58-8, General Dynamics/Fort Worth, 10 January 1964
'Technical Manual Illustrated Parts Breakdown Two Component Pod USAF Series BLU-2/B,' T.O. 1B-58A-4-2, General Dynamics/Fort Worth, 20 January 1967
'Technical Manual Organizational Maintenance Free-Fall Bomb Pod USAF Series B-58A and TB-58A Aircraft,' T.O. 1B-58A-2-18, 31 March 1961
'B-58 as a Missile Launcher,' General Dynamics, 21 March 1962
'Additional Studies of B-58 Missile Launch Capabilities,' FZM-2612, General Dynamics, 14 May 1962
'History of the Development of the B-58 Bomber,' Historical Division, Information Office, Aeronautical Systems Division, Air Force Systems Command, November 1965

Chapter 2: Boeing B-59

'Boeing MX-1712,' Boeing Aircraft Company, D-12006, July, 1951
Final Report – Project MX-1965,' Boeing Aircraft Company, D-11905-7, July 1, 1953

Chapter 3: Martin B-68

'Investigation of the Aerodynamic Characteristics of a Model of a Supersonic Bomber Configuration with a Swept and Unswept Wing at Mach Numbers from 1.79 to 2.67,' RM L58C27, NACA-Langley Aeronautical Laboratory, July 21, 1958
'Effect of Several tail Configurations on the Stability Characteristics of a Midwing Supersonic-Bomber Model at Mach Numbers of 1.60, 1.90, 2.20 and 2.50,' Technical Memorandum X-279, NASA Langley Research Center, January 14, 1960

Chapter 4: North American A3J-1

'Characteristics Summary – Attack A-5B (A3J-2),' NAVWEPS 00-110A-2, 15 November 1962
'Standard Aircraft Characteristics A3J-1 (J79-GE-8 Engine) Vigilante,' North American Aviation, Inc., 15 April 1961
'Standard Aircraft Characteristics Navy Model A-5A Aircraft,' NAVAIR 00-110AA5-1, 1 July 1967
'Standard Aircraft Characteristics A-5C (A3J-2),' North American Aviation, Inc., 15 August 1963
'Stability and Control Characteristics at a Mach Number of 1.97 of an Airplane Configuration Having Two Types of Variable-Sweep Wings,' TM X-323, NASA-Langley Research Center, August 1960
'Stability and Control Characteristics at Low Subsonic Speeds of an Airplane Configuration having Two Types of Variable-Sweep Wings,' TM X-303, NASA-Langley Research Center, August 1960
'Subsonic and Supersonic Aerodynamic Characteristics of an Airplane Configuration Utilizing Double-Pivot Variable-Sweep Wings,' TM X-743, September 1962
'Subsonic Aerodynamic Characteristics of an Airplane Configuration Utilizing a Variable-Sweep Wing Having a Free-Floating Apex,' TM X-1126, NASA-Langley Research Center, May 1965

Chapter 5: North American B-70

'Standard Aircraft Characteristics B-70 Valkyrie,' 1 December 1959
'Standard Aircraft Characteristics B-70 Valkyrie,' 8 June 1960
'Standard Aircraft Characteristics XB-70 Valkyrie,' 1 September 1961
'Standard Aircraft Characteristics XB-70B Valkyrie,' 1 May 1963
'Standard Aircraft Characteristics XB-70A Valkyrie,' November 1965
'Standard Aircraft Characteristics XB-70A Valkyrie,' January 1972
'Characteristics Summary Bomber (Supersonic) B-70,' 1 December 1959
'Characteristics Summary Bomber (Supersonic) XB-70,' 20 December 1960
'Characteristics Summary Bomber (Supersonic) XB-70 Air Vehicle Nr 1,' 11 May 1964
'Characteristics Summary Bomber (Supersonic) XB-70 Air Vehicle Nr 1,' February 1965
'Characteristics Summary Bomber (Supersonic) XB-70 Air Vehicle Nr 1,' April 1967
'Characteristics Summary Bomber (Supersonic) XB-70 Air Vehicle Nr 2,' 11 May 1964
'Characteristics Summary Bomber (Supersonic) XB-70 Air Vehicle Nr 2,' February 1965
'Characteristics Summary Bomber (Supersonic) XB-70 Air Vehicle Nr 2,' October 1965
'Characteristics Summary Bomber (Supersonic) XB-70 Air Vehicle Nr 2,' April 1967
'Characteristics Summary Bomber (Supersonic) XB-70 Air Vehicle Nr 3,' 20 December 1961
'Characteristics Summary Bomber (Supersonic) XB-70 Air Vehicle Nr 3,' 18 April 1962
'Characteristics Summary Bomber (Supersonic) XB-70 Air Vehicle Nr 3,' 9 May 1963
'Characteristics Summary Bomber (Supersonic) YB-70,' March 1961
'History – Boeing Weapon System 110A,' D2-2371, Boeing airplane Company, December 1957
'High Altitude heavy Bomber Study,' D-14822, Boeing Airplane Company, January 8, 1954
'Boeing Model 724-15 & 724-16 Characteristics Charts,' D2-1097, Boeing Airplane Company, July 24, 1956
'NAA B-70 Valkyrie Variants,' HQ AFMC History Office, 2020

Chapter 6: General Dynamics F-111

'TFX Weapon System 324A Proposal – Presentation,' FZM-65-073, General Dynamics – Fort Worth, December, 1961
'Aerodynamics Characteristics at transonic Speeds of an Airplane configuration with An 83.5° Delta Wing Having Auxiliary Variable-Sweep Wing Panels,' TM-X-704, NASA-Langley Research Center, February 1963
'Low Speed Lateral Stability Characteristics of an 83.5° Delta Wing Having Auxiliary Variable-Sweep Wing Panels and Various Vertical-Tail Arrangements,' TM-X-741, NASA-Langley Research Center, March 1963
'Low-Speed Longitudinal Aerodynamic Characteristics of an 83.5° Delta-Wing Airplane Model Having Auxiliary Variable-Sweep Wing Panels,' TM-X-729, NASA-Langley Research Center, February 1963
'Effects of Twin-Vertical-Tail Arrangement on the Aerodynamic Characteristics at a Mach Number of 2.20 of a Model of an 83.5° Delta-Wing Airplane Having Auxiliary Variable-Sweep Wing Panels,' TM-X-709, NASA-Langley Research Center, February 1963
Choo, B., Craig, D., Dupuy, B., King, D., Verani, M. 'F-111 Case Study,' Massachusetts Institute of Technology, December 9, 2003
'Summary of NACA/NASA Variable-Sweep Research and Development Leading to the F-111 (TFX),' LWP-285, NASA-Langley Research Center, December 22, 1966
'Stability Characteristics at Mach 2.20 of a Variable-sweep Configuration Having Pylon-Mounted Nacelles with Conical Inlets,' TM X-1058, NASA-Langley Research Center, February, 1965

'Transonic Longitudinal Aerodynamic Characteristics of a Variable-Sweep Fighter Model Having Body-Mounted Having Body-Mounted Nacelles,' TM X-916, NASA-Langley Research Center, May, 1964
'Summary of NASA Support of the F-111 Development Program, Part I – December 1962 – December 1965,' LWP-246, NASA-Langley Research Center, October 10, 1966
'WS-324A Proposal Summary,' D3-70455, The Boeing Company, 26 October 1962
'Structural Description Report F-111A, FB-111A, F-111E,' FZM-12-4144B Volume II, General Dynamics, February 28, 1970
'F-111/FB-111 Structural Breakdowns,' FZM-12-6282, General Dynamics, 1 September 1969
'The F-111 Crew Module,' FZM-12-4094C, General Dynamics, 15 September 1969
'Aerodynamic Characteristics at a Mach Number of 2.20 of a Variable-sweep Fighter Model with Wing Sweeps of 50°, 60°m and 75°,' TM X-1041, NASA-Langley Research Center, December 1964
'A Summary of Research on Variable-Sweep Fighter Airplanes,' TM X-1185, NASA-Langley Research Center, December 1965
'Stability and Control Characteristics at a Mach Number of 1.41 of a Variable-sweep Airplane Configuration Capable of Low-Level Supersonic Attack - Outer Wing Swept 75° and 108°,' TM X-320, NASA-Langley Research Center, August 1960
'The Transonic Aerodynamic Characteristics of Two Variable-Sweep Airplane Configurations Capable of Low-Level Supersonic Attack,' TM X-304, NASA-Langley Research Center, August 1960
'Transonic Aerodynamic Characteristics of a Variable-Sweep Airplane Configuration Having a 12-Percent-Thick Wing and an Inboard Pivot Location,' TM X-429, NASA-Langley Research Center, December 1960
'Effects of Twin-Vertical-Tail Arrangement on the Aerodynamic Characteristics at a Mach Number of 2.20 of a Model of an 83.5 Degree Delta-Wing Airplane Having Auxiliary Variable-Sweep Wing Panels,' NASA TM X-709, Langley Research Center, February 1963

Chapter 7: Rockwell B-1

'Advanced Manned Precision Strike System, Task I Baseline AMPSS Configuration, Task II Additional Studies,' FZM-4176-I, General Dynamics – Fort Worth, 30 June 1964
'Advanced Manned Strategic Aircraft (WS-139A) Final Technical Report, Systems Studies, Design Characteristics Study' NA-67-436, Part 1, North American Aviation, Inc., 30 June 1967
'NASTRAN Model of a Large Flexible Swing-Wing Bomber,' NASA Contractor Report 170392, 5 Volumes, Rockwell International, 1982
'B-1B Fact Book,' NA 95-1210, Rockwell International, 20 July 1995
'Standard Aircraft Characteristics B-1A,' December 1986
'Characteristics Summary Bomber B-1A,' November 1971
'Characteristics Summary Bomber B-1A,' January 1976
'Standard Aircraft Characteristics B-1,' January 1972
'Effect of Several Airframe/Nozzle Modifications on the Drag of a Variable-Sweep Bomber Configuration,' NASA Technical Memorandum 80129, NASA Langley Research Center, October 1979
Hibma, R., Wegner, D. 'The Evolution of a Strategic Bomber,' AIAA81-0919, Rockwell International, May 1981.
Schoenheit, A., Karger, W., 'Aerodynamic Integration of Externally Mounted Engines on a Long-Range Bomber,' AIAA81-1693, Rockwell International, August 1981.
McMullen, Colonel T., 'Evolution of the B-1 Escape System,' AIAA73-440, Rockwell International, May 1973
Wykes, J., Mori, A. 'B-1 Structural Mode Control System,' AIAA72-772, Rockwell International, August 1972
Christensen, L. 'Propulsion System Configuration Development for the B-1 Strategic Bomber,' AIAA75-1040, Rockwell International, August 1975
Haagenson, W., Randall, L. 'Inlet Development for the B-1 Strategic Bomber,' AIAA74-1064, Rockwell International, October 1974
Sargent, J., Gunter, J. 'Nozzle/Afterbody Configuration Development for the B-1Strategic Bomber,' AIAA74-1102, Rockwell International, October 1974
Patton, R., 'The B-1 Bomber – Concept to Hardware,' in 'Aircraft Design and Integration,' Advisory Group for Aerospace Research and Development, AD-783 307, June 1974
Magiawala, K. 'The B-1B Bomber: A Program History,' Massachusetts Institute of Technology, February 1988
'B-1B Systems Familiarization, Course No. 002A, Student Handout,' Rockwell International, December 1982
'B-1 Flight Manual,' AF74-0158A, NA-73-296, Rockwell International, 7 December 1976
'B-1 Flight Manual,' AF76-0174, NA-77-400, Rockwell International, 15 January 1979
Chattopadhyay, A. US Patent 9,963,231 "System and Method for deployment of an Aircraft Weapons System," The Boeing Company, May 8, 2018

Bibliography

Knaack, Marcelle, *Encyclopedia of US Air Force Aircraft and Missile Systems, Volume 1, Post-World War II Fighters, 1945-1973*, Office of Air Force History, 1978
Knaack, Marcelle, *Encyclopedia of US Air Force Aircraft and Missile Systems, Volume 2, Post-World War II Bombers, 1945-1973*, Office of Air Force History, 1978
Buttler, T., *American Secret Projects 4: Bombers, Attack and Anti-Submarine Aircraft 1944-1974*, Crecy Publishing Ltd., 2021
Slade, S., *United States Strategic Bombers 1945-2012*, Defense Lion Publications, 2012
Zichek, J., *Secret Aerospace Projects of the U.S. Navy: The Incredible Attack Aircraft of the USS United States – 1948-1949*, Schiffer Publishing Ltd., 2009
Jones, L., *U.S. Bombers 1928 to 1980s*, Aero Publishers Inc., 1980
Peacock, L., *Convair B-58 Hustler and Variants*, Alan W. Hall Publications Ltd., 1978
Miller, J., *Convair B-58 Hustler*, Aerofax, Inc., 1997
Doyle, D., *B-58 Hustler In Action*, Squadron/Signal Publications, 2015
Robinson, D., *The B-58 Hustler*, Aero Publishing Company, Inc., 1967
Holder, B., *Convair B-58 Hustler*, Schiffer Publishing Ltd., 2001
Doyle, D., *B-58 Hustler Convair's Cold War Mach 2 Bomber*, Schiffer Publishing Ltd., 2021
Yenne, B., *Convair Deltas From SeaDart to Hustler*, Crecy Publishing Ltd., 2009
Pace, S., *Valkyrie North American XB-70*, TAB books, 1990
Jenkins, D., Landis, T., *North American XB-70A Valkyrie*, Warbird Tech Series Vol 34, Specialty Press Publishers, 2002
Jenkins, D., Landis, T., *Valkyrie North American's Mach 3 Superbomber*, Specialty Press, 2004
Ginter, S., *North American A-5A RA-5C Vigilante*, 2005
Grove, M., Miller, J., *North American Rockwell A3J/A-5 Vigilante*, Aerofax Minigraph 9, Aerofax, Inc., 1989
Stafrace, C., *North American RA-5C Vigilante*, Warpaint Series No. 97, Warpaint Books Ltd., 2014
Gunston, B., *F-111*, Charles Scribner's Sons, 1978
Drendel, L., *F-111 in Action*, Squadron/Signal Publications, 1978
Logan, D., *General Dynamics F-111 Aardvark*, Schiffer Military History, 1998
Miska, K., *Aircraft Profile General Dynamics F-111A to F & FB111A*, Profile Publications Ltd., 1973
Kinzey, B., *F-111 Aardvark*, Aero Publishers Inc., 1982
Miller, J., *General Dynamics F-111 'Aardvark'*, Aero Publishers Inc., 1982
Thornborough, A., *General Dynamics F-111: A Comprehensive Guide*, SAM Publications Ltd., 2013
Gourley, J., *F-111 Aardvark*: General Dynamics' Variable-Swept-Wing Attack Aircraft, Schiffer Publishing, Ltd., 2021
Wachsmuth, W., *B-1 Lancer in Detail & Scale*, Detail & Scale Inc., 1990
Holder, W., *The B-1 Bomber*, TAB Books Inc., 1988
Peacock, L., *B-1B Bomber*, Osprey Publishing Ltd., 1987
Miller, J., Logan, D., *Rockwell International B-1A/B, aerograph Minigraph 24*, Aerofax, Inc. 1986
Pace, S., *Boeing North American B-1 Lancer, Warbird Tech Series Vol. 19*, Specialty Press Publishers, 1998
Katz, K., *The Supersonic BONE*, Pen & Sword Aviation, 2022

General data table

Aircraft	Source Grade		Span	Wing area (sq ft)	Length	Engines	Dry weight (lbs)	Design Fuel (lb)	Design Payload (lbs)	Max Payload (lbs)	Gross weight (lb)	Range (n.mi.)	Cruise speed	Max speed	Ceiling (ft)
B-58 evolution															
Convair Class VA/GEBO	4	2	45' 7"	900	43' 4" (return) 78' 3" (composite)	4 Westinghouse XJ40-WE-10	35,510 (composite) 18,700 (return)	50,000	10,000		96,260 (composite)	1,700 (radius)		Mach 1.6 @ 40,000 ft	
Douglas Model 1186A	4	2	42' 6" (expendable) 19' 3" (escape)	600 (expend) 125 (escape)	~128' (overall) 54' 5" (escape)	4 Westinghouse XJ40-10 (expend) 1 Westinghouse X24C-10 (escape)	53,253 (expend) 7,652 (escape)		10,000		100,000 (expend) 9,500 (escape)	459 (radius)		1149 kts @ 54,600 ft	
Convair GEBO II	3	2	~47.25'		~81.5'	4 Turbojets									
Convair MX-1626	3	2	567.73"	1200	800" (aircraft) 972.67" (overall)	3 GE J53-X25 Turbojets, non-afterburning	38,529 lbs		6,000		107,250	3610		Mach 1.7	50,500
Convair MX-1964	3	3	56.9'		92.9'	4 XJ79-GE-1	46,914	15,614 gal		7,000	160,000	2,300 (radius)	549 knots	1150 knots	61,900
Convair Early XB-58	4	3	56.8'	1542.5	96.8'	4 J79-GE-5A									
Convair B-58	4	3	56.8'	1542.5	96.8'	4 J79-GE-5A	51,061		6230		158,000	2,250 (radius)	544 knots	1147 knots @ 64,000 ft	64,000
B-58B	3														
Convair B/J-58 B-58C	3	3	53' 3.2"	1746.7	104' 9.2"									Mach 2.0	
B-58/Minuteman	3														
B-58C1	5	2	56' 10.3"		101' 2.7"	2 P&W J58						5,200		Mach 2.4+	
B-58 tactical bomber	4														
B-58MI	4	4	64' 1"	1581	104' 9"	4 GE J-79 X-207	61,108	116,789			186,627	7,300 radius		Mach 2.2	~65,000
Super Hustler	4	2	23' 4" (booster) 18' 9" (manned)	242.5 (booster) 278 (manned)	48' 9" (booster) 46' 7" (manned) 74' 4" (overall)	2 38.6-in RJ59 ramjets (booster) 1 38.6-in. RJ59 ramjet (manned) 1 GE J85 turbojet (manned)	10,813 (booster) 9740 (manned)				25,713 (booster) 20,190 (manned) 45,903 (overall)			Mach 4	
B-59 evolution															
Boeing Model 484-2-2	4	3	87' 6"	2190	129' 8"	4 Wright Aero J-67-W-1 Turbojets	86,500	100,630	10,000		200,000	4,021	523 kts	Mach 1.3	
Boeing Model 484-415	4	3	91' 3"		130' 1"	4 XP-57-P-5 turbojets w/A.B.		17,920 gal			200,000				
Boeing model 701-238	4	3	87' 6"	2190	140' 7"	4 afterburning turbojets					200,000				
Boeing XB-59	4	3	81' 4"	1650	123' 4"	4 GE J73-X24A turbojets w/A.B.	63,200	10,533 gal	7,700	14,200	148,300	2,380 (radius)		1,080 knots	51,000
B-68 Evolution															
Douglas Model 1364	3	2	40.3'	660	118.1'										
Boeing Model 721	3	2	49' 5.5"	700	87' 10"	2 GE J79			8,500		65,900			Mach 2	
NAA WS-302A	2	2	46'		88'	2 GE J79 w/AB			7,200		76,294			Mach 2 @ 50 kft	
Martin model 281-5	4	3	96' 11"	840	49' 11.1"	4 scaled J73		28,600			73,500			719 kts sea level	
Martin Model 316	5	2	53' 8" (centers of tip pods)	900	105' 9"	2 Wright J-67 w/A.B.					96,600			Mach 2+	
Martin XB-68	4	2	53' 0"	875	109.8'	2 P&W J75 (JT4B-21) w/A.B.		40,500	3,500	8,500	100,000	598 (rad ss mission)		1380 knots	45,400
B-68 wind Tunnel tail mod	4	2	~53.75'		~118.9' - 125.9'										
B-70 Evolution															
Boeing MX-2145	3	6	155'	6,000	192'	8 turbojets		368,500			600,000	5,000 radius		~Mach 3	
Boeing Model 713-1-101	3	4	116'	3636	170	4 GE X-84 turbojets		257,500	7,500		400,000		582 kts @ 21 kft	1150 kts @ 55 kft	55,000
Boeing Model 713 w/tip tanks	4		241' 0"	3793	207' 0"	4 BAC turbofans					624,500				
NAA WS-110A	3	4	189' 6"		163'	G GE X279A turbojets			10,000		700,000			Mach 3	
Boeing Model 724-13	4	4	232' 6"	4500	156' 8"	4 GE 275 Turbojets	106,710		10,000		460,000			Mach 3	
Boeing Model 724-15	4	4	275' 2"	5360	156.7'	4 scaled GE X-275A Turbojets	197,000	435,700	10,000	25,000	580,000	4,660 radius	489 knots	1725 knots	63,000
Boeing Model 724-16	4	4	275' 2"		170' 10"	4 GE X-278A turbojets	211,000	446,250	10,000	25,000	605,000	4,660 radius	489 knots	1725 knots	65,700
Convair 110 water based tip tank	3		219' 0"	4800		4 PW JT9 dry or GE 275B or 276B dry					710,000		Mach 0.95	Mach 3	
Convair WS-110 TUG-TOW: tug	3		185' 0"	4000	176.5'	4 P&W JT-9A w/A.B.	162,900	284,000			450,000	3260 (radius)			
Convair WS-110 TUG-TOW: Dash	3		59' 6"	1200	125' 3"	3 Allison 701C w/A.B.	64,930	68,500			158,810			Mach 3	75,000
Boeing Model 804-1	4	4	94' 5"	5625	208' 8"	6 GE X279E				24,200	487,800				
Boeing Model 804-4	4	4	94' 5"	5625	206' 1"	6 GE X279J	169,910	55,500 gal	20,000	25,000	542,000	6420	1725 knots	1725 knots	82,450
Early NAA B-70 Wind tunnel	3		~108.75'		~184.25'										
NAA XB-70	4	2	105' 0"	6297	185.8'	6 GE YJ93-GE-3 w/A.B.	231,215	43,646 gal			534,792	2969	1089 kts @ 35 kft	1721 knots	75,500
RSB-70	4	4	105' 0"	6297	185.8'	6 GE J93-GE-3 w/A.B.	188,326	51,897 gal	25,000	25,000	554,609	5309	1089 kts @ 35 kft	1721 kts @ 72,700 f	83,500
B-70 w/GPM	2	4	105' 0"	6297	185.8'	6 GE J93-GE-3 w/A.B.									

Aircraft	Source Grade		Span	Wing area (sq ft)	Length	Engines	Dry weight (lbs)	Design Fuel (lb)	Design Payload (lbs)	Max Payload (lbs)	Gross weight (lb)	Range (n.mi.)	Cruise speed	Max speed	Ceiling (ft)
A-5 Vigilante															
A-5 Mockup/wind tunnel model	2	2	52.92'		68.75' (1 tail)										
NAA A-5	4	2	53.02'	700	75.862'	2 GE J79-8 w/A.B.	32,714	19,074	1885		62,953	1758	487	1147 knots	52,100
Retaliator	2	2	~53.02'	~700	~75.9'										
A-5 NASA VG Config 1	3	2	~35.7' / ~61.4'		~75.55'										
A-5 NASA VG Config 2	3	2	~34.3' / ~52.7'		~75.55'										
A-5 NASA VG Config 3	3	2	~24.8 / ~60.7'		~75.55'										
A-5 NASA VG Config 3 Alt.	3	2	~35.7' / ~61'		~75.55'										
A-5 NASA VG Config 4	3	2	~37.5' / ~58.3'		~75.55'										
A-5 NASA VG floating apex	3	2	~37' / ~58.9		~75.55'										
F-111															
Super Hustler TAC	3	2	27' 6.4"	600	70' 10"	2 JT8	31,095		1 TX-43	60,000					
Super Hustler TAC Modified	3	2	35' 8"	600	72' 6"	2 JT8	31,335		1 TX-43	60,000					
Super Hustler TAC Diamond wing	3	2	~50.1'	600	73' 6"	2 JT8	31,625		1 TX-43	60,000					
Super Hustler TAC Variable sweep	3	2	22' 8" - 55' 10"	600	76' 2"	2 JT8			1 TX-43						
WADD 46	3	2	70'	500	73.0'	2 TF-30 (JTF10A-20)	33,083	3700 gal	2000		60,000	800 (radius)	Mach 1.2 @ 500 ft	Mach 2.5 @ 40 kft	60,000
TFX competition															
Lockheed CL-590	3	2	29' 8" - 60' 0"		67' 5"	2 GE MF-295A Turbofans	33,746				78,270				
MAC Model 156	3	2	~20.3' - ~46.4'		~84.7'										
NAA 326-49	4	2	~26' - ~51.9'	475.84	76.3'	2 AR-168-18A turbofans									
Repubic TFX "A"	3	2	25.3' - 49.74'		80.9'										
Repubic TFX "B"	3	2	29.7' - ~46.3'		74.64'										
Boeing 818-192	3	2	33' - 67'		98'	2 TF-30 turbofans	43,700				78,000				
Boeing 818-193	3	2	27' 6" - 57' 0"		~95.4'	2 TF-30 turbofans					60,000				
Boeing 818 - USAF	3	2	38.9' - 70'	574.22	73'	2 TF-30 turbofans	35,410	30,250	2,330		69,000	800 (radius)	Mach 072	Mach 2.5 @ 45 kft	66,000
GD Config 430	3	2	~15.9' - ~48.6'	361	90' 2"						59,940				
GD Config 1000	3	2	~25.25' - ~48.8'	350	63'						55,749				
GD TFX Dec 1961	4	2	29' - 57' 4"	503	73'	2 P&W JTF 10A-2D	34,525	27,434			61,959				
GD TFX April 1962	4	2	29' 10" - 63' 0"	481		2 P&W JTF 10A-2D	37,302	27,400	4,310		64,702	800 (radius)		Mach 2.5	67,000
F-111 derivatives															
GD FB-111A	4	2	33.96' - 70.0'	550	75.54'	2 P&W TF30-P-7	47,481	9223 gal	8988		110,646	5334	444 knots	1262 kts @ 50 kft	50,263
F-111 BX	3	2	33.96' - 70.0'	550	87' 7"	2 P&W TF30-P-100									
FB-111G	3	2	33.96' - 70.0'	550	88' 3"	2 P&W TF30-P-100		55,271	12,520		124,224				
FB-111H	4	2	44' 10.2" - 70' 0"	550	88' 2.5"	2 F101-GE-100	51,832	64,574			140,000	2,600+ (radius)		Mach 2.5	
B-1															
AMSA															
Lockheed CL-820-8	3	2(?)	76' 0" - 123' 0"		203'	4 afterburning turbojets								~Mach 3	
Republic AMPSS	3		80' - 153'		210'										
Boeing VG tail AMPSS	2		~82.5' - ~145'		~150'	3 afterburning turbojets									
NAA High performance penetrator	4	3	94' 0"	4000	~148.9'	3 80% STF188B turbofans									
NAA -1495-25 PAMSS	4		91' 2"	4776	~169'	4 GE YJ93									
GD AMPSS	4	4	69' 2" - 149' 10"	2882	149' 3"	4 42.6%-scale P&W STF200C-35.1 turbofans	134,405		10,000	20,000	395,000	6300	Mach 0.73	Mach 2.2	
USAF AMSA config	3		~69' - ~125.7'		~138.4'	4 afterburning turbofans									
NAA D436-21	4	4	130.7' (20°) 44.2' (105.5°)	3735 (20°) 2441 (105.5°)	1522"	4 GE1-9F2F	123,340		25,000		333,000	5,000		Mach 2.2	
NAA D458-13D	4	4	1493" (20°) 66.6 (75°)	1887 (20°) 1957 (75°)	1615"	105% GE9/F7B	139,250				350,000			Mach 2.2	
North American AMSA 1968	3	4	~70.3' - 133.2'		149.6'	4 afterburning turbofans									
Boeing Model 975-046	3	4	~94.5'		~136.9'	4 afterburning turbofans									
Lockheed AMSA 1968	3	4 (?)	~85.5'		~183.6'	3 afterburning turbofans									
Lockheed AMSA 1969	3	4 (?)	~86.4'		~199'	4 afterburning turbofans									
B-1															
Boeing B-1	4	4 - 6	~79.8' - ~141.7'		~161.3'	4 afterburning turbofans			24 AGM-69						
Rockwell B-1 submission	3	4	71.8' - 140.2'		151.0'	4 afterburning turbofans									
Rockwell B-1A	5	4	77.8' - 136.7'	1946	145.3'	4 GE F101-GE-100	173,000	34,104 gal	50,000		422,000	5685 radius	562 knots	1262 kts @ 53,200 ft	
B-1 Wind Tunnel Mods	4	4	77.8' - 136.7'	1946	145.3'	4 GE F101-GE-100									
Rockwell B-1B	5	4	78.2' - 136.68'	1950	145.76'	4 GE F101-GE-102	180,500		75,000	125,000	477,000	7,455	Mach .92 @ 500 ft	Mach 1.25 @ 50 kft	60,000